MOSFET & GaN FET Application Handbook

A Power Design Engineer's Guide

Nexperia

Manchester, United Kingdom

MOSFET & GaN FET Application Handbook.
A Power Design Engineer's Guide
Copyright © Nexperia
www.Nexperia.com
ISBN: 978-0-9934854-7-3

Contributors

Andy Berry
Adam Brown
Dilder Chowdhury
Phil Ellis
Mark Fang
Tony Friel
Jim Honea
Burkhard Laue
Wayne Lawson
Sami Ould-Ahmed
Kilian Ong
Jim Parkin
Martin Pilaski
Christitian Radici
Eleonora Terrugi
Andrew Thomson
Andrei Velcescu
Barry Wynne
Mike Zeng

Power MOSFETs

Small-signal MOSFETs

Power GaN FETs

Introduction

Welcome to the Nexperia MOSFET and GaN FET Application Handbook, the second edition of our successful design guide. Written by engineers for engineers, this unique collection of technical materials and application notes provides essential and up-to-date information for anybody tasked with integrating MOSFETs and GaN FETs into real-world systems. In the following pages we share expertise and learnings that Nexperia's engineering teams have built up over many years of helping customers in a variety of sectors take their applications from initial concept, through prototyping and on into final production.

The knowledge contained in this guide could not be more relevant or timely. Never before has there been such pressure on engineers to create products and systems that not only deliver high levels of performance and functionality but do so within increasingly restrictive size and power constraints. What's more, the requirement for cost-effective and efficient power conversion and electrification is only going to intensify as society looks to reduce energy costs, drive down greenhouse gas emissions and make the most of renewable resources while meeting the increased demands of a growing population and an explosion in the number of applications reliant on electricity.

From consumer products to automotive electronics, data centres to industrial automation, and communication infrastructure to medical equipment, no application area is untouched by the need for components that switch, convert and manage power and engineers who know how to deploy those components to optimal effect.

At the lower end of the power spectrum, IoT, consumer and other mobile electronic devices rely on high-efficiency configurations to support the best possible user experience in tandem with minimizing form factor and maximizing time between charge or battery replacement. Reliance on electronics for safety, comfort and infotainment combined with a shift to autonomous, connected vehicles and hybrid and fully electric powertrains makes power design a critical factor in the automotive sector. For data centres significant cost and environmental benefits can be realized by even small efficiency gains when extrapolated across millions of servers. In modern factory automation systems where output in kilowatts for motor drives is now common, effective use of power is the cornerstone of efficient and accurate motion control. And when it comes to communications infrastructure, 5G roll-out is set to generate major demand for technologies that deliver high-density, ultra-efficient, ultra-reliable power use.

What is clear is that, irrespective of the application, no longer can power be seen as an afterthought, something to be addressed only after the design and prototyping of a product or system's core functionality. What's more, with efficient and effective power management at or near the very top of the design agenda, not only is the role of the power engineer more relevant than ever before but other engineers are having to broaden their skillset to address power and efficiency challenges. Which means gaining an understanding of discrete semiconductor technologies such as power MOSFETs, small-signal MOSFETs and GaN FETs and knowing how best to use these devices to both meet demanding product specification and performance requirements and deliver the efficiencies expected by customers and legislators.

For mains- and battery-powered applications, advances in power MOSFET structures and packaging continue to drive forward system efficiency and performance. In addition to fast and efficient switching for power supplies, many power MOSFETs are now designed with particular applications in mind. Such application-specific MOSFETS (ASFETs) may include, for example, optimised parameters to address soft-start, live insertion, short-circuit resilience, avalanche ruggedness and advanced thermal management.

Today's low-current, small-signal MOSFETs are deployed in applications that range from DC-DC conversion and load switching to level shifting in bi-directional bus systems. Among the trends for these devices are high-speed switching and advanced packaging that supports the performance, power density and miniaturization needs of high-component-density applications such as mobile battery-powered electronics and wearables.

More recent additions to the portfolio of power discretes include those fabricated from wide bandgap (WBG) materials such as gallium nitride, which have already achieved great success in RF power. Now, thanks to a combination of ultra-low $R_{DS(on)}$ at high voltages, excellent switching FOM (figure of merit), thermal stability, high-frequency operation and reducing price points they are becoming important for a growing number of high-power, high-density, ultra-high-speed switching applications – including hard-switched topologies where silicon super-junction FETs cannot be used. Offering options for automotive, telecommunications, computing and industrial market sectors, the power GaN technology covered in this Handbook targets the needs of AC-DC and DC-DC conversion, power factor correction (PFC), automotive on-board charging and electric drive applications.

It is interesting to note that the patent for the first field effect transistor was filed by Polish-American physicist Julius E. Lilienfeld in 1926 and the first super-junction FET was patented back in 1984. Although FET technology has clearly moved on significantly in the last few decades (not least in terms of switching speeds - some of the latest MOSFETs switch in the time it takes light to move just 3 m), many of the key issues that engineers must consider remain the same. Understanding the impact of switching, conduction and avalanche losses on system efficiency, for example, is critical in most designs, as are techniques for ensuring EMC compliance, optimised thermal management and reliability. A range of other factors will need to be taken into account for applications based on emerging GaN FET technology.

Furthermore, as product choice grows, so too does the challenge of narrowing down the plethora of FET options to those that are most likely to match the requirements of a given use case, comparing those devices on a 'like-for-like' basis and then deciding which will deliver the 'real-world' performance demanded by the target application. This challenge is not made any easier by a lack of consistency between suppliers regarding the conditions used for rating key parameters.

This Application Handbook provides useful guidance on all of these topics and many other issues that the design engineer is likely to encounter when working with MOSFETs and GaN FETs. By providing insight into their sometimes confusing and complex behaviour – including information necessary to solve common problems and avoid potential pitfalls – Nexperia's belief is that the Handbook will become a 'go-to' reference for anybody tasked with delivering optimised power and small-signal switching, power conversion and power management.

To supplement the handbook, further product information and the most up-to-date application notes can be found at www.nexperia.com

Contents

Chapter 1
Understanding power MOSFET data sheet parameters
Application Note: AN11158

Chapter 2

Designing in MOSFETs for safe and reliable gate-drive operation

Application Note: AN90001

Chapter 3

Using power MOSFETs in parellel

Application Note: AN11599

Chapter 4

Power MOSFET single-shot and repetitive avalance ruggedness rating

Application Note: AN10273

Chapter 5

Using RC Thermal models

Application Note: AN11261

Chapter 6

Designing RC snubbers

Application Note: AN11160

Chapter 7

Half-bridge MOSFET switching and its impact on EMC

Application Note: AN90011

Chapter 8

Failure signature of electrical overstress on power MOSFETs

Application Note: AN11243

Chapter 9
LFPAK MOSFET thermal design guide
Application Note: AN90003

Chapter 10

Maximum continuous currents in Nexperia LFPAK power MOSFETs

Application Note: AN90016

Chapter 11

LFPAK MOSFET thermal resistance - simulation, test and optimization of PCB layout

Application Note: AN90019

Chapter 12

H-bridge motor controller design using Nexperia discrete semiconductors and logic ICs

Application Note: TN90002

Chapter 13
Power and small-signal MOSFET frequently asked questions and answers
Technical Note: TN00008

Chapter 14
Leakage of small-signal MOSFETs
Application Note: AN90009

Chapter 18

Understanding Power GaN FET data sheet parameters

Application Note: AN90005

Chapter 19

An insight into Nexperia Power GaN technology – Applications, quality, reliability and scalability

Application Note: TN90004

Chapter 20

Power GaN technology: the need for efficient power conversion
Application Note: AN90021

Chapter 21

Circuit design and PCB layout recommendations for GaN FET half bridges
Application Note: AN90006

Chapter 22
Probing considerations for fast switching applications
Application Note: AN90004

Chapter 1

Understanding power MOSFET data sheet parameters

Application Note: AN11158

1 Introduction

This chapter describes the content of power MOSFET data sheet parameters. The goal is to help an engineer decide what device is most suitable for a particular application.

It is important to pay attention to the conditions for which the parameters are listed, as they can vary between suppliers. These conditions can affect the values of the parameters making it difficult to choose between different suppliers.

Throughout this document, the data sheet for BUK7Y3R5-40H is used as an example. BUK7Y3R5-40H is an automotive-qualified part in a SOT669 (LFPAK56) package, with a voltage rating of 40 V.

The layout of this data sheet is representative of the general arrangement of Nexperia power MOSFET data sheets.

Nexperia Power MOSFETs are designed with particular applications in mind. For example, switching charge is minimized where switching losses dominate, whereas on-resistance is minimized where conductive losses dominate.
- General description, describing the technology used, the package and relevant qualifications, e.g. AEC-Q101
- Features and benefits, listing important features of the MOSFET and the benefit they offer.
- Applications, listing the applications for which the MOSFET is particularity suited.

The product overview is followed by these technical sections:
- Quick reference data
- Pinning information
- Ordering information
- Limiting values
- Thermal characteristics
- Electrical characteristics
- Package outline

2 Data sheet technical sections

Nexperia power MOSFET data sheets begin with an overview of the device, giving the designer the key information regarding device suitability. The overview consists of:
- General description, describing the technology used, the package and relevant qualifications, e.g. AEC-Q101

- Features and benefits, listing important features of the MOSFET and the benefit they offer.
- Applications, listing the applications for which the MOSFET is particularity suited.

The product overview is followed by these technical sections:
- Quick reference data
- Pinning information
- Ordering information
- Limiting values
- Thermal characteristics
- Electrical characteristics
- Package outline

2.1 Quick reference data

The quick reference data table contains more detailed information and the key parameters for the intended application. An example of a quick reference data table is shown in Table 1 "Quick reference data".

Table 1: Quick reference data

Symbol	Parameter	Conditions	Min	Typ	Max	Unit
V_{DS}	drain-source voltage	25 °C ≤ T_j ≤ 175 °C	-	-	40	V
I_D	drain current	V_{GS} = 10 V; T_{mb} = 25 °C; Figure 1 [1]	-	-	120	A
P_{tot}	total power dissipation	T_{mb} = 25 °C; Figure 2	-	-	115	W
Static characteristics						
$R_{DS(on)}$	drain-source on-state resistance	V_{GS} = 10 V; I_D = 20 A; T_j = 25 °C	2	2.9	3.5	mΩ
Dynamic characteristics						
Q_{GD}	gate-drain charge	I_D = 20 A; V_{DS} = 44 V; V_{GS} = 10 V	-	6	15	nC
Source-drain diode						
Q_r	recovered charge	I_S = 25 A; dI_S/dt = -100 A/μs; V_{GS} = 0 V; V_{DS} = 20 V	-	16	-	nC

[1] 120 A continuous current has been successfully demonstrated during application tests. Practically the current will be limited by PCB, thermal design and operating temperature.

Understanding power MOSFET data sheet parameters

The general format for describing a parameter is to provide the official symbol and then the correct parameter name. Any relevant conditions and information are listed after the parameter names. The values and units of the values are entered in the remaining columns. Generally, measurement methods are as described in IEC 60747-8.

The quick reference data parameters are described in more detail in the characteristics section of the data sheet. The following list is an introduction to some of the key symbols together with a description of the parameter each represents:

- **V_{DS}** - the maximum voltage between drain and source that the device is guaranteed to block in the off state. This section of the data sheet deals with the most commonly used temperature range, as opposed to the full temperature range of the device.
- **I_D** - the maximum continuous current the device can carry with the mounting base held continuously at 25 °C with the device fully on. In the example provided in Table 1, I_D requires a V_{GS} of 10 V.
- **P_{tot}** - the maximum continuous power the device can dissipate with the mounting base held continuously at 25 °C.
- **$R_{DS(on)}$** (drain-source on state resistance) - the typical and maximum resistance of the device in the on-state under the conditions described. $R_{DS(on)}$ varies greatly with both T_j and the gate-source voltage (V_{GS}). Graphs are provided in the data sheet to assist in determining $R_{DS(on)}$ under various conditions.
- **Q_{GD}** (gate-drain charge) - an important switching parameter that relates to switching loss, along with Q_{GS} and $Q_{G(tot)}$. Q_{GD} is inversely proportional to $R_{DS(on)}$, therefore choosing an appropriate balance between $R_{DS(on)}$ and Q_{GD} is critical for optimal circuit performance.
- **Q_r** (recovered charge) – the total amount of charge recovered from the anti-parallel diode when it is switched from its conducting state to its reverse biased state under controlled conditions. Q_r is an important factor involved in voltage spiking when interacting with external inductances and an important consideration when investigating EMC and efficiency. Generally the higher the Q_r value the larger the voltage and current spikes at switch off leading to longer damping times. Nexperia includes stored charge Q_s as well as output charge Q_{oss} in its stated value for Q_r such that $Q_r = Q_s + Q_{oss}$.

2.2 Pinning information

This section describes the internal connections and general layout of the device. Note that the symbol is for an enhancement mode n-channel MOSFET with the source and body tied together, and a parallel diode between the source and drain. The parallel diode is known as the body diode and is inherent in power MOSFETs. N-channel power MOSFETs have the body diode between drain and source, as shown in Table 2.

Table 2: Pinning Information

Pin	Symbol	Description	Simplified outline	Graphic symbol
1	S	source		
2	S	source		
3	S	source		
4	G	gate		
mb	D	mounting base; connected to drain	LFPAK56; Power-SO8 (SOT669)	

2.3 Ordering information

The ordering section provides information on how to order the device. The package version and decription are given as well as any commonly used package name.

2.3.1 Marking

Depending on the device package, the data sheet may include a marking section. This provides the marking code which is printed onto the device during manufacter, (else the device name will be printed).

2.4 Limiting values

The limiting values table provides the range of operating conditions allowed for the MOSFET. The conditions are defined in accordance with the absolute maximum rating system (IEC 60134). Operation outside of these conditions is not guaranteed, so it is recommended that these values are not exceeded. Doing so runs the risk of immediate device failure or reduced lifetime of the MOSFET. The avalanche ruggedness conditions, when given, describe the limited conditions for which the V_{DS} rating can be exceeded.

To calculate how the limiting values change with temperature, they are read together with the derating curves provided.

The limiting values table for the BUK7Y3R5-40H is given as an example of a standard limiting values table, in Table 3.

Table 3: Limiting values
In accordance with the Absolute Maximum Rating System (IEC 60134).

Symbol	Parameter	Conditions		Min	Max	Unit
V_{DS}	drain-source voltage	25 °C ≤ T_j ≤ 175 °C		-	40	V
V_{GS}	gate-source voltage			-10	20	V
P_{tot}	total power dissipation	T_{mb} = 25 °C;		-	115	W
I_D	drain current	V_{GS} = 10 V; T_{mb} = 25 °C; Figure 1	[1]	-	120	A
		V_{GS} = 10 V; T_{mb} = 100 °C; Figure 2	[1]	-	93	A
I_{DM}	peak drain current	pulsed; t_p ≤ 10 µs; T_{mb} = 25 °C		-	526	A
T_{stg}	storage temperature			-55	175	°C
T_j	junction temperature			-55	175	°C
Source-drain diode						
I_S	source current	T_{mb} = 25 °C	[1]	-	120	A
I_{SM}	peak source current	pulsed; t_p ≤ 10 µs; T_{mb} = 25 °C		-	526	A
Avalanche ruggedness						
$E_{DS(AL)S}$	non-repetitive drain-source avalanche energy	I_D = 120 A; V_{sup} ≤ 40 V; R_{GS} = 50 Ω; V_{GS} = 10 V; $T_{j(init)}$ = 25 °C; unclamped; Figure 3	[2] [3]	-	45	mJ

[1]   120 A continuous current has been successfully demonstrated during application tests. Practically the current will be limited by PCB, thermal design and operating temperature.
[2]   Single-pulse avalanche rating limited by maximum junction temperature of 175 °C.
[3]   Refer to application note AN10273 for further information.

- **V_{DS}** (drain-source voltage) - the maximum voltage the device is guaranteed to block between the drain and source terminals in the off-state for the specified temperature range. For the BUK7Y3R5-40H, the temperature range is from +25 °C to +175 °C. For operation below 25 °C, the V_{DS} rating reduces due to the positive temperature coefficient of avalanche breakdown. This is covered in

Section 2.4.1 of this document.

- **V_{GS}** (gate-source voltage) - the maximum voltage the device is specified to block between the gate and source terminals. Some Nexperia data sheets specify different values for DC and pulsed V_{GS}. In these cases the DC value is a constant gate voltage over the lifetime of the device at the maximum T_j, whilst the higher-value pulsed-rating is for a shorter, specified accumulated pulse duration at the maximum specified T_j.

  Gate-oxide lifetime (refer to AN90001 (chapter 2 of this book) - Designing in MOSFETs for safe and reliable gate-drive operation) reduces with increasing temperature and/or increasing gate voltage. This means that V_{GS} lifetimes or ratings quoted for lower junction temperatures are significantly greater than if specified at higher temperatures. This can be important when comparing data sheet values from different manufacturers.

- **V_{DGR}** (drain-gate voltage) is typically the same value as the V_{DS} rating. This parameter appears in the data sheets of older devices but is not quoted for newer devices such as in the BUK7Y3R5-40H data sheet.

- **I_D** (drain current) - the maximum continuous current the device is allowed to carry under the conditions described. This value can be related to either package construction, or the maximum current that would result in the maximum T_j. As such it depends on an assumed mounting base temperature (T_{mb}), the thermal resistance (R_{th}) of the device, and its $R_{DS(on)}$ at maximum T_j. Note that some suppliers quote the "theoretical" silicon limit, while indicating the package limited value in the characteristic curves.

- **I_{DM}** (peak drain current) is the maximum drain current the device is allowed to carry for a pulse of 10 μs or less.

- **P_{tot}** (total power dissipation) is the maximum allowed continuous power dissipation for a device with a mounting base at 25 °C. The power dissipation is calculated as that which would take the device to the maximum allowed junction temperature while keeping the mounting base at 25 °C. In reality, it is difficult to keep the mounting base at this temperature while dissipating the 105 W that is the calculated power dissipation for the BUK7Y3R5-40H. In other words, P_{tot} indicates how good the thermal conductivity of the device is, and its maximum allowed junction temperature.

  Note that some other semiconductor vendors quote performance when mounted on a copper PCB usually 1 inch square. In practice, this information is rather meaningless as the semiconductor vendor has no control over how the device is cooled. See AN10874 - (chapter 9 of this book) - LFPAK MOSFET thermal design guide. AN10874 describes different techniques that can be used during the design phase to ensure that the PCB layout provides optimum thermal performance.

- **T_{stg}** (storage temperature) is the temperature range in which the device can be stored without affecting its reliability. Long term storage should be in an inert atmosphere to prevent device degradation, for example, by tarnishing of the metal leads.

- **T_j** (junction temperature) is the operational temperature range of the device. Typically, T_j is the same as the storage temperature. Outside of this range, device parameters are outside the range of the data sheet and device lifetime is reduced.

- I_S (source current) - the maximum continuous current of the MOSFET body diode, which is briefly discussed in Section 2.2. The same considerations apply as for I_D.
- I_{SM} (peak source current) - the maximum current pulse that the MOSFET body diode is diode is guaranteed to carry. The same considerations apply as for I_{DM}.
- $E_{DS(AL)S}$ (non-repetitive drain-source avalanche energy) - the maximum allowed single overvoltage energy pulse under the conditions specified. For this example, the conditions are the maximum continuous drain current allowed for a mounting base temperature of 25 °C. The avalanche energy allowed is the energy pulse that would raise the device temperature from 25 °C to its maximum allowed T_j, while the mounting base temperature is held at 25 °C.

  The avalanche energy is specified for the maximum continuous drain current. Some vendors specify the avalanche energy for a different current and higher inductive load, which can increase the apparent avalanche energy for an inferior performance. An example is given with the derating curve as described in Section 2.4.3 of this document.
- $E_{DS(AL)R}$ (repetitive drain-source avalanche energy) - the maximum amount of energy allowed in each avalanche event when more than one avalanche event occurs. The thermal constraints imposed for repeated avalanche operation is given by curve 3 of Figure 3 in Section 2.4.3 of this document. There are also the standard thermal requirements in addition to the energy requirements for repetitive avalanche events. These requirements are assessed with the thermal characteristic curves as described in Section 2.5. Avalanche performance is covered in detail in application note AN10273 (Chapter 4 of this book) - Power MOSFET single-shot and repetitive avalanche ruggedness rating.

  This parameter is only listed on Nexperia data sheets where the repetitive avalanche capability has been assessed. It is not shown in Nexperia data sheets where it has not been assessed, for example non-automotive MOSFETs.

2.4.1 Derating curves

The derating curves are provided immediately after the tabulated limiting value data, and help the designer calculate how the limits change with temperature.

2.4.1.1 Continuous drain current

The following procedure serves as an example to calculate the maximum continuous drain current for the BUK7Y3R5-40H. Assume an application with a mounting base temperature T_{mb} of 75 °C.

Refer to the graph depicted in Figure 1 which depicts the continuous drain current as a function of mounting base temperature.

Figure 1 shows that for a T_{mb} of 75 °C, the maximum continuous drain current has reduced from 120 A, listed at 25 °C, to 105 A, see Equation (1) and Equation (2) below.

The maximum current at any T_{mb}, is the current that increases T_j to the maximum allowed temperature (175 °C). $P = I^2 \times R_{DS(on)}$ represents the power dissipation at T_j, where the $R_{DS(on)}$ used is the maximum value for the maximum T_j. Therefore, the allowed current is proportional to the square root of the allowed power dissipation.

The power dissipation allowed for a given T_{mb} is proportional to the allowed temperature increase. This means that the derating curve shown, is based on the following equations:

$$I_D{}^2(T_{mb}) \propto \frac{T_j - T_{mb}}{T_j - 25°C} \qquad [1]$$

$$I_D(T_{mb}) = I_D(25°C) \times \sqrt{\frac{T_j - T_{mb}}{T_j - 25°C}} \qquad [2]$$

At the maximum allowed junction temperature of 175 °C, this current has decreased to zero

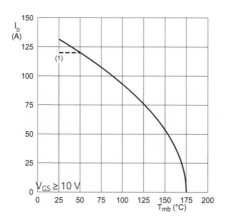

aaa-026228

(1) 120 A continuous current has been successfully demonstrated during application tests. Practically the current will be limited by PCB, thermal design and operating temperature.

Figure 1 | Continuous drain current as a function of mounting base temperature

2.4.2 Power dissipation

Power dissipation varies with different temperatures. However, in this case, the power dissipation curve is normalized. The allowed power is presented as a percentage of the allowed power dissipation at 25 °C, as opposed to an absolute value.

Example:
By observing the curve in Figure 2, the allowed power dissipation for a T_{mb} of 75 °C is approximately 66 % of that allowed at 25 °C. The graphic data in Figure 2, shows the maximum continuous power dissipation (P_{tot}) at 25 °C is 105 W.

This means that the maximum power dissipation allowed at 75 °C, is 66 % of 105 W which is 70 W.

Equation (3) is the equation to calculate power dissipation:

$$P_{tot}\ (T_{mb}) - P_{tot}\ (25°C)\ x\ \frac{T_j - T_{mb}}{T_j - 25°C} \qquad [3]$$

Where $T_j = T_j(max)$, usually 175 °C.

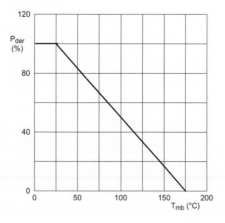

Figure 2 | Normalized total power dissipation as a function of mounting base temperature

The curves provided in Figure 1 and Figure 2 are read in conjunction with the limiting values tables. The information extracted, assists in calculating the maximum current allowed and the power dissipation with respect to temperature.

2.4.3 Avalanche ruggedness

Avalanche ruggedness is covered in detail in AN10273 (chapter 4 of this book) -
Power MOSFET single-shot and repetitive avalanche ruggedness rating.

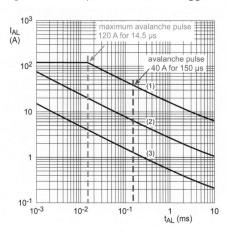

Figure 3 | Avalanche current as a function of avalanche period

A simple example for the BUK7Y3R5-40H, using the information in AN10273, is
extracted from the limiting values Table 3:

With I_D = 120 A, V_{sup} ≤ 40 V, R_{GS} = 50 Ω, V_{GS} = 10 V and $T_{j(init)}$ = 25 °C unclamped, the
maximum $E_{DS(AL)S}$ is 45 mJ.

An avalanche event has a triangular pulse shape, so the average power is calculated
as $(0.5 \times V_{DS} \times I_{DS})$.

AN10273 states that the assumed breakdown voltage is 130 % of the rated
voltage, in the case of the BUK7Y3R5-40H this is 52 V (40 V x 1.3).

Figure 3 shows a maximum current of 120 A at 25 °C (the limiting values Table 3
confirms this value). The time for the maximum avalanche energy can be read from
Figure 3 as 14.5 μs.

This means that the maximum avalanche energy allowed is:
0.5 × (40 V × 1.3) × 120 A × 14.5 μs = 45.24 mJ.

However the limit value quoted in Table 5 of the data sheet is rounded to 45 mJ.
If a competitor quotes avalanche energy at 40 A, the graph shows that the
avalanche time for the BUK7Y3R5-40H has increased to 150 μs. The avalanche
energy is now
0.5 × (40 V × 1.3) × 40 A × 150 μs = 156 mJ, which is much higher than data sheet

1

limiting value. Ruggedness events lie outside the Safe Operating Area (SOA).

2.4.4 Safe Operating Area (SOA)

The Safe Operating Area (SOA) curves are some of the most important on the data sheet.

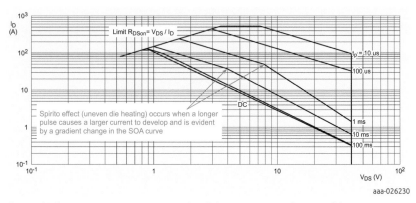

Figure 4 | Safe operating area; continuous and peak drain currents as a function of drain-source voltage

The SOA curves show the voltage allowed, the current and time envelope of operation for the MOSFET. These values are for an initial T_{mb} of 25 °C and a single current pulse. This is a complex subject which is further discussed in the appendix (Section 3.1).

2.5 Thermal characteristics

This section describes the thermal impedance as a function of pulse duration for different duty cycles. This information is required to determine the temperature that the silicon reaches under particular operating conditions, and whether it is within the guaranteed operation envelope.

The thermal characteristics are shown in Table 4. The thermal impedance changes with pulse length because the MOSFET is made from different materials. For shorter durations, the thermal capacity is more important, while for longer pulses, the thermal resistance is more important.

The thermal characteristics are used to check whether particular power loading pulses above the DC limit would take T_j above its safe maximum limit. Repetitive avalanche pulses must be considered in addition to the constraints specific to avalanche and repetitive avalanche events.

Table 4: Thermal characteristics

Symbol	Parameter	Conditions	Min	Typ	Max	Unit
$R_{th(j\text{-}mb)}$	thermal resistance from junction to mounting base	Figure 5	-	1.18	1.3	K/W

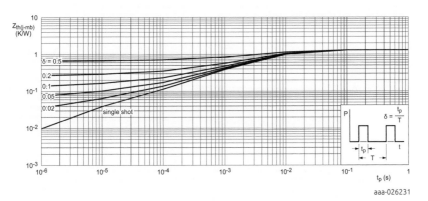

aaa-026231

Figure 5 | Transient thermal impedance from junction to mounting base as a function of pulse duration.

Thermal resistance (R_{th}) and thermal impedance (Z_{th}) are related because the thermal resistance is the steady-state measure of how the device blocks heat flow. Thermal impedance is how the device responds to transient thermal events. It involves different thermal capacities of parts of the device and the thermal resistances between these parts. Under DC conditions, Z_{th} is equal to R_{th}. Equation (4) represents the temperature rise for a particular power dissipation:

$$\Delta T_j = |Z_{th(j\text{-}mb)}| \times Power \qquad [4]$$

A worked example is discussed in the appendix (Section 3.1.2).

2.6 Electrical characteristics

This section is used to determine whether the MOSFET would be suitable in a particular application. This section differs from the previous two sections that are used to determine whether the MOSFET would survive within the application. The examples in this section are taken from the data sheet for the BUK7Y3R5-40H unless otherwise stated.

2.6.1 Static characteristics

The static characteristics are the first set of parameters listed in this section and an example is shown in Table 5:

Table 5: Static characteristics

Symbol	Parameter	Conditions	Min	Typ	Max	Unit
$V_{(BR)DSS}$	drain-source breakdown voltage	I_D = 250 µA; V_{GS} = 0 V; T_j = 25 °C	40	42.7	-	V
		I_D = 250 µA; V_{GS} = 0 V; T_j = -40 °C	-	40.1	-	V
		I_D = 250 µA; V_{GS} = 0 V; T_j = -55 °C	36	39.7	-	V
$V_{GS(th)}$	gate-source threshold voltage	I_D = 1 mA; V_{DS} =V_{GS} ; T_j = 25 °C; Figure 6; Figure	2.4	3	3.6	V
		I_D = 1 mA; V_{DS} =V_{GS} ; T_j = -55 °C; Figure 6	-	-	4.3	V
		I_D = 1 mA; V_{DS} =V_{GS} ; T_{jj} = 175 °C; Figure6	1	-	-	V
I_{DSS}	drain leakage current	V_{DS} = 40 V; V_{GS} = 0 V; T_j = 25 °C	-	0.03	1	µA
		V_{DS} = 16 V; V_{GS} = 0 V; T_j = 125 °C	-	1	10	µA
		V_{DS} = 40 V; V_{GS} = 0 V; T_j = 175 °C	-	37	500	µA
I_{GSS}	gate leakage current	V_{GS} = 20 V; V_{DS} = 0 V; T_j = 25 °C	-	2	100	nA
		V_{GS} = -10 V; V_{DS} = 0 V; T_j = 25 °C	-	2	100	nA
$R_{DS(on)}$	drain-source on-state resistance	V_{GS} = 10 V; I_D = 25 A; T_j = 25 °C	2	2.9	3.5	mΩ
		V_{GS} = 10 V; I_D = 25 A; T_j = 105 °C; Figure9	2.7	4.1	5.2	mΩ
		V_{GS} = 10 V; I_D = 25 A; T_j = 125 °C; Figure9	2.9	4.5	5.6	mΩ
		V_{GS} = 10 V; I_D = 25 A; T_j = 175 °C; Figure9	3.4	5.4	6.7	mΩ
R_G	gate resistance	f = 1 MHz; T_j = 25 °C	0.32	0.8	2	Ω

- **V$_{BR(DSS)}$** (drain-source breakdown voltage) - an expansion of the parameter listed and explained in Section 2.4. This section lists the minimum voltage the device is guaranteed to block between the drain and source terminals in the off-state over the entire MOSFET temperature range. The temperature range is from -55 °C to +175 °C. The current between the drain and the source terminals of the BUK7Y3R5-40H when testing V$_{(BR)DSS}$ is 250 µA at the temperatures stated. V$_{(BR)DSS}$ is 40 V or less if the device is cooler than +25 °C and 40 V if the device is between +25 °C and +175 °C.

The effect of temperature on the off-state characteristics is twofold. The leakage current increases with temperature, turning the device on. Competing against the leakage current increase, the breakdown voltage also increases with temperature.

- **V$_{GS(th)}$** (gate-source threshold voltage) is important for determining the on-state and the off- state of the MOSFET. V$_{GS(th)}$ is defined where V$_{DS}$ = V$_{GS}$, although it is sometimes quoted   for a fixed V$_{DS}$ (e.g. 10 V). Note that the definition of the threshold voltage for a particular current where the gate and drain are shorted together, can differ from examples in textbooks. The parameter in textbooks describes a change in the physical state of the MOSFET and is independent of the MOSFET chip size. The parameter used in the data sheet is for a specified current and is dependent on the chip size, as the current flow is proportional to the chip area.

The threshold voltage in the data sheet is defined in a way that is best for routine measurement, but not how the actual device would typically be used. Consequently, the graphs provided in Figure 6 and Figure 7.

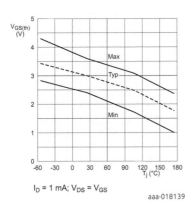

I_D = 1 mA; V$_{DS}$ = V$_{GS}$

aaa-018139

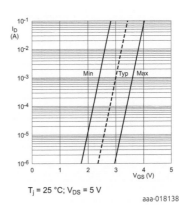

T$_j$ = 25 °C; V$_{DS}$ = 5 V

aaa-018138

Figure 6 | Gate-source threshold voltage as a function of junction temperature

Figure 7 | Subthreshold drain current as a function of gate-source voltage

Figure 6 shows the variation in the threshold voltage for the typical and limit devices over the rated temperature range. All the MOSFETs are guaranteed to have a threshold voltage between the lines.

Consequently, for the BUK7Y3R5-40H at 65 °C, if V_{DS} and V_{GS} are both less than 2 V, all devices carry less than 1 mA. Also, all devices carry more than 1 mA if V_{DS} and V_{GS} are both greater than 4 V. At 175 °C, the lower limit has fallen to 1 V, while the upper limit has fallen to 2.4 V. The lower limit is usually more important as it determines when the device is guaranteed to be turned off, and the gate driver performance an application needs.

Figure 7 shows how the device turns on around this threshold voltage. For the BUK7Y3R5-40H, the current increases 100,000 times for an increase in gate voltage of less than 1 V. An example is given for the situation when the drain-source voltage is fixed at 5 V.

- **I_{DSS}** (drain leakage current) guarantees the maximum leakage current that the device passes at its maximum rated drain-source voltage(40V in this case) during the off-state. It is important to note how much higher I_{DSS} is at high temperature, which is the worst case.
- **I_{GSS}** (gate leakage current) guarantees the maximum leakage current through the gate of the MOSFET. The I_{GSS} is important when calculating how much current is required to keep the device turned on. Because it is a leakage current through an insulator, this current is independent of temperature, unlike I^{DSS}.
- **$R_{DS(on)}$** (drain-source on-state resistance) is one of the most important parameters. The previous parameters guarantee how the device functions when it is off, how it turns off and what leakage currents could be expected. These factors are important when battery capacity is an issue in the application.

$R_{DS(on)}$ is a measure of how good a closed-switch the MOSFET is, when turned-on. It is a key factor in determining the power loss and efficiency of a circuit containing a MOSFET. The on-resistance $R_{DS(on)} \times I_D 2$ gives the power dissipated in the MOSFET when it is turned **fully** on. Power MOSFETs are capable of carrying tens or hundreds of amps in the on-state.

Power dissipated in the MOSFET makes the die temperature rise above that of its mounting base. Also when the MOSFET die temperature increases, its $R_{DS(on)}$ increases proportionally. Maximum recommended junction temperature is 175 °C (for all Nexperia **packaged** MOSFETs).

Using the BUK7Y3R5-40H data sheet as an example:

$R_{th(j-mb)}$ temperature rise per Watt between junction (die) and mounting base = 1.3 K/W (1.3 °C/W).

Maximum power dissipation for temperature rise of 150 K (T_{mb} = 25 °C, T_j = 175 °C) = 150 / 1.3 = 115.38 W, note data sheet P_{tot} is rounded to 115 W.
Maximum $R_{DS(on)}$ at a die temperature (T_j) of 175 °C = 6.7 mΩ.
Therefore, at steady state with T_{mb} = 25 °C and T_j = 175 °C; P = 115.38 W = $I_D 2 \times$

$R_{DS(on)}(175\ °C)$. Therefore:

[5]

$$I_{max} = \sqrt{\frac{P_{(max)}175\ °C}{R_{DS(on)}175\ °C}} = \sqrt{\frac{115.38\ W}{0.0067\ \Omega}}$$

= 131.23 A (rounded down to 120 A in the data sheet).
Note this value appears on the curve for I_D vs T_{mb} in Figure 1 but only 120 A is claimed in the data sheet. Practically, limitations are placed on MOSFET performance due to PCB, thermal design and operating temperature, which will all act together to raise the mounting base temperature.

Figure 8 shows the dependency of $R_{DS(on)}$ on the gate-source voltage for a standard level MOSFET (e.g. BUK7Y12-55B); the red dashed line shows the curve for a hot device and is indicative of how the dependency changes at a high temperature.

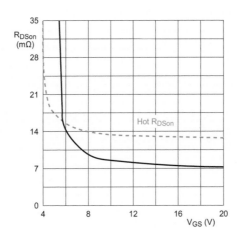

aaa-002470

This diagram is for illustrative purposes only and not to be taken as an indication of hot $R_{DS(on)}$ performance for any device.

Figure 8 | Drain-source on-state resistance as a function of gate-source voltage at 25 °C and high temperature

If an application requires good $R_{DS(on)}$ performance for lower gate-source voltages, then MOSFETs are made with lower threshold voltages, e.g. the BUK9Y12-55B (logic level MOSFET). However, the lower threshold voltage of such a device means that it has a lower headroom for its off-state at high temperature. This lower headroom often means that a device with a higher threshold voltage is needed.

Figure 9 shows how the ratio of $R_{DS(on)}$ to $R_{DS(on)}$ at 25 °C typically varies with junction temperature for BUK7Y3R5-40H.

Understanding power MOSFET data sheet parameters

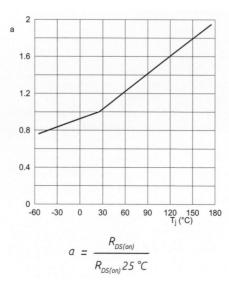

$$a = \frac{R_{DS(on)}}{R_{DS(on)} \, 25\ ^\circ C}$$

aaa-018451

Figure 9 | Normalized drain-source on-state resistance factor as a function of junction temperature

R_G (gate resistance) is the internal series resistance presented to the gate pin. In most applications an external "gate stopper" resistance of a larger value is employed to mitigate gate oscillation and, dependent on value chosen, decrease output slew rate.

2.6.2 Dynamic characteristics

The dynamic characteristics determine the switching performance of the device. Several of these parameters are highly dependent on the measurement conditions. Consequently, understand the dynamic characteristics before comparing data sheets from suppliers with different standard conditions. Table 6 is a sample dynamic characteristics table.

Table 6: Dynamic characteristics
List of constants and limitations relating to the table i.e. voltages, currents and temperatures

Symbol	Parameter	Conditions	Min	Typ	Max	Unit
$Q_{G(tot)}$	total gate charge	I_D = 25 A; V_{DS} = 32 V; V_{GS} = 10 V;	-	31	53	nC
Q_{GS}	gate-source charge		-	10	15	nC
Q_{GD}	gate-drain charge		-	6	15	nC
C_{iss}	input capacitance		-	2294	3441	pF
C_{oss}	output capacitance	V_{DS} = 25 V; V_{GS} = 0 V; f = 1 MHz; T_j = 25 °C;	-	682	954	pF
C_{rss}	reverse transfer capacitance		-	112	247	pF
$t_{d(on)}$	turn-on delay time		-	10	-	ns
t_r	rise time	V_{DS} = 30 V; R_L = 1.2 Ω; V_{GS} = 10 V; $R_{G(ext)}$ = 5 Ω	-	8	-	ns
$t_{d(off)}$	turn-off delay time		-	19	-	ns
t_f	fall time		-	9	-	ns
Source-drain diode						
V_{SD}	source-drain voltage	I_S = 25 A; V_{GS} = 0 V; T_j = 25 °C;	-	0.8	1.2	V
t_{rr}	reverse recovery time	I_S = 25 A; dI_S/dt = -100 V/μs; V_{GS} = 20 V;	-	25	-	ns
Q_r	recovered charge		-	16	-	nC

2.6.2.1 Gate charge

$Q_{G(tot)}$, Q_{GS}, and Q_{GD} are all parameters from the same gate charge curve. They describe how much gate charge the MOSFET requires to switch, for certain conditions. This is particularly important in high frequency switching applications. Much of the power loss occurs during switching, when there are significant voltage and current changes simultaneously between the drain, gate and source. In the blocking state, there are significant voltages but negligible currents. In the full-on state, there are significant currents and small voltages.

The gate charge parameters are dependent on the threshold voltage and the switching dynamics as well as the load that is being switched. There is a difference between a resistive load and an inductive load.

An example of a gate charge curve is shown in Figure 10:

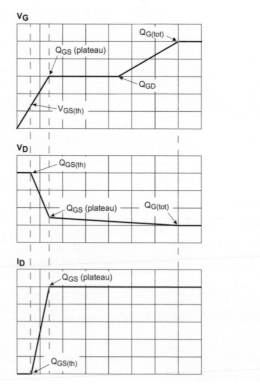

aaa-002471

Figure 10 | Gate charge curve also showing drain-source currents and voltages

Due to capacitance variation with voltage and current, it is better to look at the gate charge data rather than the capacitance data when determining switching performance. This is especially true if the gate-driver circuit for the MOSFET is limited to a particular current, and a rapid switch is required

The gate charge curve describes what happens to a MOSFET which has a drain supply limited to a particular current and voltage. The operation of the test circuit means that during the gate charge curve, the MOSFET is provided with either a constant voltage or a constant current.

During this time, the drain-source voltage begins to fall because the increased charge on the MOSFET allows easier conduction. Consequently, although the gate-source voltage is constant, the drain-gate voltage is falling.

Eventually the capacitance stops increasing and any further increases in gate charge increase the gate-source voltage. This characteristic is sometimes referred to as the "Miller plateau" as it refers to the time during which the so-called Miller capacitance increases. The Miller plateau is also known as the gate-drain charge (Q_{GD}).

During this period, there are significant currents and voltages between the drain and source, so Q_{GD} is important when determining switching losses.

Once the end of the Miller plateau is reached, the gate-source voltage increases again, but with a larger capacitance than before Q_{GS} had been reached. The gradient of the gate charge curve is less above the Miller plateau.

The gate-charge parameters are highly dependent on the measurement conditions. Different suppliers often quote their gate-charge parameters for different conditions, demanding care when comparing gate charge parameters from different sources.

Higher currents lead to higher values of gate-source charge because the plateau voltage is also higher. Higher drain-source voltages, lead to higher values of gate-drain charge and total gate charge, as the plateau increases.

The drain-source currents and voltages during the gate charge switching period are shown in Figure 10.

If the MOSFET starts in the off state ($V_{GS} = 0$ V), an increase in charge on the gate initially leads to an increase in the gate-source voltage. In this mode, a constant voltage (V_{DS}) is supplied between the source and drain.

When the gate-source voltage reaches the threshold voltage for the limiting current at that drain- source voltage, the capacitance of the MOSFET increases and the gate-voltage stays constant. This is known as the plateau voltage and the onset charge is referred to as Q_{GS}. The higher the current is, the higher the plateau voltage (see Figure 11). This relates to the transfer characteristic, see Figure 15. The transfer curve shows the dependency of drain current on gate voltage. The higher the voltage on the gate the higher the charge applied, (Q = C × V), hence making it the easier for the MOSFET to conduct.

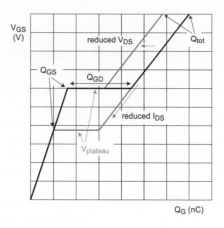

aaa-002472

Figure 11 | Features of gate charge curve

2.6.2.2 Capacitances

Capacitance characteristics are generally less useful than the gate charge parameters, for the reasons already discussed. However, they are still listed on data sheets. The three capacitances that are normally listed are as follows:

- C_{iss} (input capacitance) is the capacitance between the gate and the other two terminals (source and drain).
- C_{oss} (output capacitance) is the capacitance between the drain and the other two terminals (gate and source).
- C_{rss} (reverse transfer capacitance) is the capacitance between the drain and the gate. See Figure 13.

Semiconductor capacitances generally depend on both voltage and the frequency of the capacitance measurement. Although it is difficult to compare capacitances measured under different conditions, many suppliers specify a measurement frequency of 1 MHz. Consequently, the capacitances vary with drain-source voltage (see Figure 12). However, the capacitances also vary with gate-source voltage, which is why the gradients in the gate-charge curve vary for different voltages (see Figure 10).

The relationship between charge, voltage and capacitance in the gate charge curve is: ΔQ = ΔC x ΔV. For different gradients at different gate voltages, the capacitance changes significantly with gate-source voltage.

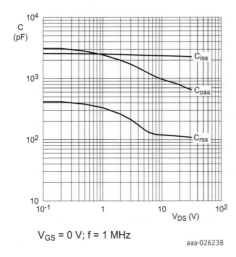

10^4
C
(pF)
C_{iss}
10^3
C_{oss}
10^2
C_{rss}
10
10^{-1}
1
10
10^2
V_{DS} (V)
V_{GS} = 0 V; f = 1 MHz
aaa-026238

Figure 12 | Capacitances as a function of drain source voltage

C_{GD}
NMOS
C_{DS}
C_{GS}
$C_{iss} = C_{GS} + C_{GD}$
$C_{oss} = C_{DS} + C_{GD}$
$C_{rss} = C_{GD}$
aaa-02233

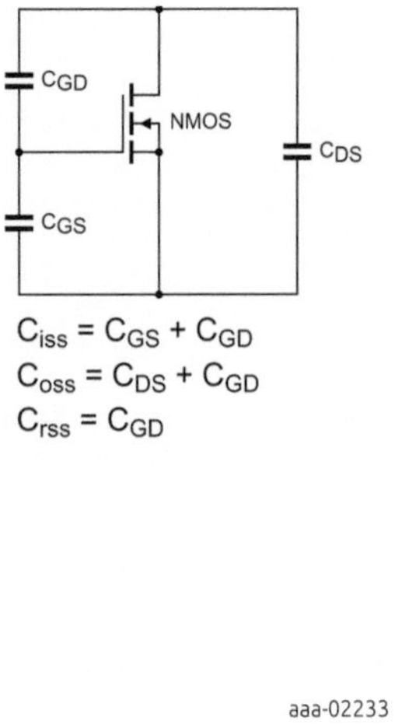

Figure 13 | MOSFET capacitance parameters

2.6.2.3 Switching times

Most manufacturers quote resistive load switching times. However, extreme care is needed when comparing data from different manufacturers, as they are highly dependent on the resistance of the gate drive circuit used for the test and in the case of logic level devices, the gate voltage applied.

In devices for fast switching applications, the gate resistance of the MOSFET is often quoted as capacitive time constants which are equally dependent on resistance and capacitance.

2.6.2.4 Diode characteristics

The diode characteristics are important if the MOSFET is being used in the so-called "third quadrant". The third quadrant is a typical arrangement where the MOSFET replaces a diode to reduce the voltage drop from the inherent diode forward voltage drop. In such a situation, there is always a small time period when the MOSFET parasitic diode is conducting before the MOSFET turns on. For such applications, the diode switching parameters are important. In addition, diode reverse recovery (Figure 14) contributes to the power losses as well as oscillation and voltage spikes, which can cause EMC concerns.

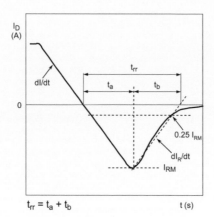

Figure 14 | Reverse recovery waveform definitions

2.6.2.5 Transfer characteristics

Figure 15 shows the transfer characteristics of the MOSFET which indicate the theoretical drain current that can be handled by the device as a result of applied gate to source voltage. The graph shows the temperature dependency of the characteristic. The convergent point indicates where the current is dependent only on gate voltage and not temperature hence the MOSFET's Zero Temperature Coefficient point I_ZTC. Gate charge test current and plateau voltage (refer to Figure 10) can be directly read from the transfer curve.

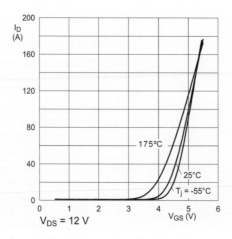

Figure 15 | Transfer characteristics; drain current as a function of gate-source voltage; typical values

3 Appendices

3.1 Safe Operating Area (SOA) curves

To highlight the key features, Figure 16 provides an idealized SOA curve for a hypothetical MOSFET. Data for a hypothetical MOSFET for a single pulse length, is shown to highlight the region where it deviates from the ideal curve.

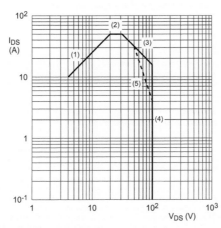

1. $R_{DS(on)}$ limit (V_{DS}/I_{DS} is constant)
2. Maximum pulsed drain current (I_{DS} is constant)
3. Maximum pulsed power dissipation ($V_{DS} \times I_{DS}$ is constant)
4. Maximum allowed voltage (V_{DS} is constant)
5. Linear mode derating - a departure from the ideal behavior shown in (3) due to operation within a regime of positive feedback, and potential thermal runaway

aaa-002473

Figure 16 | Idealized SOA curve at a single time pulse for hypothetical MOSFET

The dashed line (5) is to emphasize where the curve deviates from the ideal. In reality, there is a single curve with a change of gradient where the linear mode derating becomes important.

R$_{DS(on)}$ limit

R$_{DS(on)}$ is region (1) of the graph and Equation [6] represents the limiting line:

$$\frac{V_{DS}}{I_{DS}} \leq R_{DS(on)(max)}\ (175°C) \tag{6}$$

The limit is when the MOSFET is fully on and acting as a closed switch with a resistance that is no greater than the hot R$_{DS(on)}$.

Constant current region

The constant current region is region (2) of the graph. It is the maximum pulsed drain current, which is limited by the device manufacturer (for example, the wire-bonds within the package).

Maximum power dissipation (linear mode) limit

In this region, the MOSFET is acting as a (gate) voltage-controlled current source. This means that there are significant voltages and currents applied simultaneously, leading to significant powerdissipation. Line (3) shows the idealized curve, whereas the dotted line (5) shows where it deviates from the ideal.

The limiting factor for the SOA curve in region (5), is the heating applied during a rectangular current and voltage pulse. Even in the ideal situation, this curve depends on the transient thermal impedance of the MOSFET, which is covered in Section 2.5.

The transient thermal impedance varies with the pulse length. This is due to the different materials in the MOSFET having different thermal resistances and capacities. The differences create a thermal equivalent to an RC network from the junction (where the heat is generated) to the mounting base. Equation (7) is the calculation used to determine the ideal curve in this region.

$$P = I_D \times V_{DS} = \frac{T_{j(max)} - T_{mb}}{Z^{th(j-mb)}} = Constant \tag{7}$$

The ideal situation accurately describes the situation for sufficiently high current densities. However, it is overly optimistic for low current-densities, i.e. towards the bottom right of region (3). Low current densities and high voltages can lead to thermal runaway in the linear mode operation. Thermal runaway is discussed in the following section.

Thermal runaway in linear mode

Power MOSFETs are often considered to be immune to thermal runaway due to the temperature coefficient of resistance, which means that as temperature rises, current falls.

This is only true for MOSFETs that are fully on (i.e. in region 1), but it is not the whole story.

When a MOSFET is turned on, there are two competing effects that determine how its current behaves with increasing temperature. As the temperature rises, the threshold voltage falls. The MOSFET is effectively turned on more strongly, thereby increasing the current. In opposition, the resistance of the silicon increases with increasing temperature, thereby reducing the current. The resultant effect for a constant drain-source voltage, is shown in Figure 17. This situation occurs when the gate-source voltage of a MOSFET is being used to control the current, or when the MOSFET is switched sufficiently slowly.

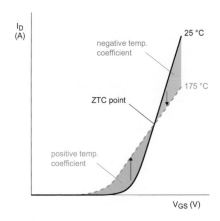

aaa-02474

Figure 17 | Transfer characteristics for a hypothetical MOSFET, showing regions of positive and negative temperature coefficient

The resistance increase dominates at high currents, meaning that localized heating leads to lower currents. The threshold-voltage drop dominates at low currents, meaning that localized heating lowers the threshold voltage. This condition effectively turns on the device more, leading to higher currents and a risk of thermal runaway.

Consequently, for a given V_{DS}, there is a critical current below which there is a positive-feedback regime and a subsequent risk of thermal runaway. Above this critical current, there is negative feedback and thermal stability. This critical current is known as the Zero Temperature Coefficient (ZTC) point.

This effect reduces the SOA performance for low currents and high drain-source voltages. The constant power line must be reduced as shown in region (5). For short switching events, this effect is insignificant. However, as the duration of the switching event becomes longer, for example to reduce electromagnetic interference, the effect becomes more important and potentially hazardous.

Voltage-limited region

The device is limited by its breakdown voltage V_{DS} which is shown in region (4). The quick reference data provides values for V_{DS} at temperatures of 25 °C and above. In the hypothetical MOSFET shown in Figure 16, the rating is 100 V. For the BUK7Y3R5-40H, the voltage is 40 V.

3.1.1 Safe operating area for temperatures above 25 °C

When reading from the SOA curves there are two main considerations:

1. The mounting base temperature is at 25 °C
2. The MOSFET is exposed to a rectangular power pulse

The SOA curves indicate the pulse power required to raise the MOSFET junction temperature, T_j, from 25 °C to its maximum rating of 175 °C, $T_{j(max)}$. The assumption being T_j is at the mounting base temperature $T_{mb} = 25$ °C when power dissipation begins.

Under DC conditions, where a product has been operating for some time (thermally soaked), T_j will be close to the mounting base temperature, T_{mb}.

Under high power short duration pulse conditions T_j, can be much greater than T_{mb}.

A reduction in MOSFET power handling capability results if the initial $T_{mb} > 25$ °C, so it is important to establish an accurate temperature for T_{mb} to determine T_j which is non-trivial activity.

The majority of automotive power applications thermally link the MOSFET mounting base via the PCB footprint and an electrically isolating barrier to a metallic mass (e.g. product housing) to act as a heatsink. Heatsink temperature Ths is in turn thermally linked to the product's ambient temperature, T_{amb}, which may be 85 °C for in-cabin (inside the driver compartment) or 105 °C for under the hood (near and around the engine). In some automotive applications where, for example, the housing is mounted directly to the power train the customer may specify a temperature directly on the heatsink where $T_{hs} \geq 105$ °C.

Unless the offset relationship $T_{mb} > T_{amb}$ is well defined by thermal flow modelling and test verification, the designer can only estimate T_{mb}.

It is important to remember that in a product which has been operating for some time (thermally soaked) MOSFETs which have similar thermal linkages to the same heatsink will have a similar T_{mb}, whether the MOSFET is switched on or switched off.

Calculation to determine the rise in die temperature above mounting base temperature is given below, see Equation (8).

$$T_{j(rise)} = T_{j(max)} - T_{j(mb)} = P_{peak} \cdot Z_{th(t)} \qquad [8]$$

Where:
P_{peak} is the peak power, as this is a rectangular pulsed waveform.

$Z_{th(t)}$ is the thermal impedance value between junction and mounting base for a pulse of t seconds duration.

Note: In DC applications, (where the MOSFET is not pulsed), use $R_{th(j-mb)}$ instead of $Z_{th(j-mb)}$. Generally, for pulses above 100 ms, Z_{th} is indistinguishable from R_{th}. Equation 8 assumes heating is uniformly spread across the whole die. A combination of higher V_{DS} with lower I_{DS} and pulse durations ≥ 100 μs can cause hot spotting (uneven heating) to occur known as the Spirito effect. Refer to TN00008 Section 5 (chapter 13 in this book) - Power and small-signal MOSFET frequently asked questions and answers.

3.1.1.1 Example calculations

Calculate the max DC I_{DS} for BUK7Y3R5-40H, with $V_{DS} = 10$ V at 25 °C

Rewrite Equation (10) to bring out I_{DS} as the main subject (Power is substituted by $I_{DS} \times V_{DS}$). Since Equation (10) is being used for a DC situation, the $Z_{th(t)}$ parameter used in Equation (8) and Equation (9) is replaced by the R_{th} steady state condition.

$$T_{j(rise)} = I_{DS} \times V_{DS} \times Z_{th(t)} \, T_{j(rise)} \qquad [9]$$

$$\frac{T_{j(rise)}}{V_{DS} \times R_{th}} = I_{DS} \qquad [10]$$

$$\frac{175\ °C - 25\ °C}{10\ V \times 1.3\ K/W} = 11.3\ A \qquad [11]$$

When making these calculations always refer to the Safe Operating Area Curve for the device. The SOA curve for the BUK7Y3R5-40H is Figure 4 which can be found in Section 2.4.4. The intersection of I_D = 11.3 A and V_{DS} = 10 V occurs above the DC curve and therefore this condition exceeds device capability. The reason being heat distribution is non-uniform within the die. In other words hot spotting is present, otherwise known as the Spirito effect.

The BUK7Y3R5-40H SOA curve shows for a DC condition the Spirito effect for this device (the point at which a gradient change occurs) is evident at V_{DS} = 0.94 V for I_D= 120 A. As I_D reduces, the allowable V_{DS} increases and by I_D = 11.3 A the maximum permissible V_{DS} = 4.4 V. Thermal consideration are discussed further in Section 3.1.2.

3.1.2 Example using the SOA curve and thermal characteristics

Consider the following application during linear mode operation:
- I_{pulse} = 20 A
- V_{pulse} = 30 V
- f = 2 kHz
- t_{pulse} = 100 µs
- T_{amb} = 25 °C

3.1.2.1 Calculation steps

The SOA curve (Figure 4) is initially checked to see whether any single pulse would cause a problem. Observing the SOA curve, it can be seen that the 20 A, 30 V pulse lies between the 100 µs and 1 ms lines. This indicates that the pulse lies within acceptable limits.

The duty cycle for the pulses is now calculated using a frequency of 2 kHz for 100 µs pulses. These values give a duty cycle of 0.2. The Z_{th} curve (Figure 5) indicates that for 100 µs, the line with the duty cycle (δ) has a transient thermal impedance of 0.35 K/W.

The power dissipation for the square pulse is 20 A × 30 V, which equals 600 W. Using Equation (8), the temperature rise for the 100 µs pulse is calculated as being 600 W × 0.35 K/W, which equals 210 K. With a starting temperature of 25 °C, the temperature rise results in a finishing temperature of 235 °C. As the MOSFET junction temperature must not exceed 175 °C, the MOSFET is not suitable for this application.

If the application requires a single pulse, then the curve shows that the transient thermal impedance for a 100 µs pulse is 0.12 K/W. As a result, the temperature rise is 600 W × 0.12 K/W which equals 72 K. The finishing temperature is then 97 °C for a starting temperature of 25 °C. The device is able to withstand this, thereby confirming what the SOA curve already indicated.

3.1.2.2 Derating for higher starting temperatures

The example Safe Operating Area calculations were performed for a mounting base temperature of 25 °C. At higher mounting base temperatures, the SOA curves must be de-rated, as the allowed temperature rise in the junction is reduced. The allowed power of the pulse is reduced proportionally to the reduced temperature rise. For example, with a mounting base temperature of 25 °C, the allowed temperature rise is 150 °C. At 100 °C, the allowed temperature rise is half of that (75 °C). The allowed power is half of that allowed at 25 °C.

The allowed drain current is de-rated while the allowed drain-source voltage is maintained.

The I_D derating of the SOA curve at 100 °C is shown in Figure 18.

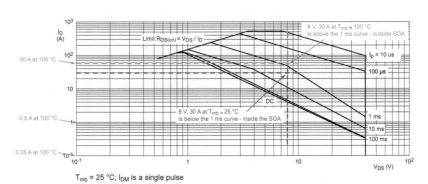

Figure 18 | SOA curve showing derating from T_{mb} = 25 °C to T_{mb} = 100 °C

Example:
Is a 1 ms pulse of 30 A and 8 V allowed at 100 °C?

See Figure 18, the intersection of the blue lines of the rectangular power pulse I_D = 30 A * V_{DS} = 8 V below the 1 ms curve indicates that the device can safely handle this pulse with T_{mb} = 25 °C .

Power handling capability halves with T_{mb} = 100 °C. In Figure 18 the red text shows I_D at 100 °C is half the value at 25 °C.

The intersection of the red lines of the rectangular power pulse I_D = 30 A * V_{DS} = 8 V above the 1 ms curve indicates the device cannot handle this pulse at T_{mb} = 100 °C.

4 References

1. The Impact of Trench Depth on the Reliability of Repetitively Avalanched Low-Voltage Discrete Power Trench nMOSFETs - Alatise et al, IEE Electron Device Letters, Volume 31, No7, July 2010, pages 713-715.

2. Semiconductor Devices - Physics and Technology S.M.Sze, 1985, John Wiley and Sons.

3. Nexperia application note AN10273 - Power MOSFET single-shot and repetitive avalanche ruggedness rating.

4. Nexperia application note AN10874 - LFPAK MOSFET thermal design guide.

5. Nexperia application note AN90001 - Designing in MOSFETs for safe and reliable gate-drive operation.

6. Nexperia technical note TN00008 - Power and small-signal MOSFET frequently asked questions and answerss

Understanding power MOSFET data sheet parameters

5 Tables

1

Understanding power MOSFET data sheet parameters

Nexperia | A Power Design Engineer's Guide

6 Figures

Figure 1. Continuous drain current as a function of mounting base temperature 33
Figure 2. Normalized total power dissipation as a function of mounting base temperature 34
Figure 3. Avalanche current as a function of avalanche period 35
Figure 4. Safe operating area; continuous and peak drain currents as a function of drain-source voltage 36
Figure 5. Transient thermal impedance from junction to mounting base as a function of pulse duration 37
Figure 6. Gate-source threshold voltage as a function of junction temperature 39
Figure 7. Subthreshold drain current as a function of gate-source voltage 39
Figure 8. Drain-source on-state resistance as a function of gate-source voltage at 25 °C and high temperature 41
Figure 9. Normalized drain-source on-state resistance factor as a function of junction temperature 42
Figure 10. Gate charge curve also showing drain-source currents and voltages 44
Figure 11. Features of gate charge curve 46
Figure 12. Capacitances as a function of drain source voltage 47
Figure 13. MOSFET capacitance parameters 47
Figure 14. Reverse recovery waveform definitions 48
Figure 15. Transfer characteristics; drain current as a function of gate-source voltage; typical values 48
Figure 16. Idealized SOA curve at a single time pulse for hypothetical MOSFET 49
Figure 17. Transfer characteristics for a hypothetical MOSFET, showing regions of positive and negative temperature coefficient 51
Figure 18. SOA curve showing derating from T_{mb} = 25 °C to T_{mb} = 100 °C 55

58

Chapter 2

Designing in MOSFETs for safe and reliable gate-drive operation

Application Note: AN90001

The MOSFET gate-source threshold voltage $V_{GS(th)}$ and maximum gate-source voltage (V_{GS-max}) are key parameters that are critical to the reliable operation of MOSFETs. The threshold voltage represents the voltage at which the MOSFET starts to turn on, whilst the maximum gate-source voltage is the maximum gate-source voltage that the MOSFET can withstand safely. V_{GS-max} ratings vary between suppliers and between MOSFETs, which can make it difficult to choose appropriate MOSFETs for the application. This chapter aims to provide the designer with enough knowledge to appreciate these differences and to select an appropriate MOSFET. We also present a new methodology demonstrating where higher V_{GS-max} ratings voltages may be applied for Nexperia's automotive grade MOSFETs.

1 Introduction

The MOSFET can be considered as a voltage-controlled switch. Applying a voltage (V_{GS}) across the gate and source terminals enhances the MOSFET allowing current to flow through the MOSFET-channel between the drain and source terminals. $V_{GS(th)}$ is defined as the V_{GS} for a pre-defined drain current, commonly 1 mA. Increasing the V_{GS} further causes the MOSFET to become fully enhanced. This allows more current to flow for a given drain-source voltage. A fully enhanced MOSFET will also have achieved close to its rated on state resistance $R_{DS(on)}$. Increasing the voltage beyond the full enhancement level will only result in a small reduction in $R_{DS(on)}$. Increasing the V_{GS} further to a level beyond the V_{GS-max} will have direct implications for the MOSFET's reliability. This could lead to destruction of the MOSFET. The design engineer can review the MOSFET data sheet to help ensure that the MOSFET's reliability is not impaired and that it operates as expected. The data sheet gives limits and guidelines, but often the design engineer needs more detail to select a MOSFET.

This chapter aims to bridge this gap. It will provide an overview of what is currently included in the data sheet concerning V_{GS} ratings and it aims to answers questions that may arise when designing in power MOSFETs.

In addition a brief introduction to the physics behind the V_{GS} ratings and the role of the gate-oxide is included. This will provide an appreciation of the reasoning behind the ratings and give confidence in the methodology employed by Nexperia to test, to qualify and to rate the MOSFET's gate-oxide capability.

An analysis of common Power MOSFET applications is also presented. This will highlight the demands imposed on the MOSFET gate-oxide by the application. Different applications have been analysed to develop a mission profile for the V_{GS}. This states what levels of V_{GS} the MOSFET will be exposed to, for how long and at what temperature. This information can then be used to select the correct MOSFET for the application, thus ensuring optimum and reliable operation.

2 Data sheet V_{GS} ratings

In Nexperia data sheets there are typically two main parameters concerning the gate- source voltages. The first being the V_{GS} threshold value or $V_{GS(th)}$. The second is the V_{GS} rating, which in this application note will be called $V_{GS\text{-}max}$.

Some MOSFET data sheets include a value for the plateau (Miller) voltage. This is the V_{GS} voltage during switching events. Its level is poorly defined as it depends on several interdependent electrical and environmental factors. It is not important for MOSFET selection or circuit design and will not be further discussed in this chapter.

2.1 V_{GS} threshold voltage - $V_{GS(th)}$

Figure 1 shows an example of data sheet $V_{GS(th)}$ values; it highlights the voltage required across the gate and source terminals to start to turn the MOSFET on. The conditions for which the $V_{GS(th)}$ is defined are specified here as the V_{GS} necessary for 1 mA of current to flow through the drain terminal. The Nexperia data sheet gives the $V_{GS(th)}$ for a range of temperatures. It also provides minimum and maximum values to account for process variation.

The $V_{GS(th)}$ is the start of MOSFET enhancement, an increase in V_{GS} is required to enhance the MOSFET further. Depending on whether a device is logic-level or standard- level, a MOSFET can be considered fully-enhanced (or fully on) when the V_{GS} is 5 V or 10 V respectively. By this point the MOSFET has achieved its rated $R_{DS(on)}$.

Symbol	Parameter	Conditions	Min	Typ	Max	Unit
$V_{GS(th)}$	gate-sourced threshold voltage	$I_D = 1$ mA; $V_{DS} = V_{GS}$; $T_j = 25$ °C; Figure 9; Figure 10	2.4	3	4	V
		$I_D = 1$ m; $V_{DS} = V_{GS}$; $T_j = -55$ °C; Figure 9	-	-	4.5	V
		$I_D = 1$ mA; $V_{DS} = V_{GS}$; $T_j = 175$ °C; Figure 9	1	-	-	V

Figure 1 | V_{GS} threshold values for a Nexperia automotive grade standard level device

Symbol	Parameter	Conditions	Min	Typ	Max	
$V_{GS(th)}$	gate-sourced threshold voltage	I_D = 1 mA; V_{DS} = V_{GS}; T_j = 25 °C; Figure 9; Figure 10	1.4	1.7	2.1	V
		I_D = 1 m; V_{DS} = V_{GS}; T_j = -55 °C; Figure 9	-	-	2.45	V
		I_D = 1 mA; V_{DS} = V_{GS}; T_j = 175 °C; Figure 9	0.5	-	-	V

Figure 2 | V_{GS} threshold values for a Nexperia automotive grade logic level device

Other differences between standard-level and logic-level devices can be observed in their threshold-voltage values (Figures 1 and 2). It is important to consider these values when selecting a MOSFET for an application. Two questions need to be answered to choose an appropriate MOSFET.

1. Can the gate-driver turn the MOSFET (fully) on?
2. Can the gate-driver turn the MOSFET (fully) off?

To answer these questions, it is necessary to take the worst case conditions in each circumstance. In order to assess question 1 we need to know what is the highest value of $V_{GS(th)}$ that the device may have. From Figures 1 and 2, we can see this occurs at the lower temperature limits. For a standard level device this can be as high as 4.5 V. If the gate-driver output is only 5 V, then a standard level device may not be suitable. This is because the MOSFET is only beginning to turn on and therefore may not operate correctly in the application. A logic level MOSFET with a maximum $V_{GS(th)}$ of ≤ 2.45 V would be more suitable.

It is important to note that $V_{GS(th)}$ has a Negative Temperature Coefficient (NTC): as the junction temperature increases, the V_{GS} for a given I_D decreases. If channel current flows because the V_{GS} is not low enough to drive the MOSFET fully OFF, I_D will increase as die temperature rises. This thermal runaway effect can ultimately cause MOSFET destruction.

Conversely, the designer must consider the upper temperature limit for turning the MOSFET off. At 175 °C a logic level device may conduct channel current at a V_{GS} ≥ 0.5 V. The gate-driver may have a minimum output voltage of 0.6 V. This is not low enough to ensure that a logic level MOSFET is turned fully off. At V_{GS} = 0.6 V channel current could still flow. In this situation it is better to select a standard level device.

2.2 The maximum V_{GS} ratings - V_{GS-max}

V_{GS-max} is the absolute maximum gate-source voltage that can be applied to the device. These values illustrated in Figures 3 and 4 conform to the International Electrotechnical Commission's IEC60134 document -"Rating systems for electronic tubes and valves and analogous semiconductor devices". Referencing paragraph 4 of IEC60134 titled "Absolute maximum rating system" it states [1]:

"Absolute maximum ratings are limiting values of operating and environmental conditions applicable to any electronic device of a specified type as defined by its published data, which should not be exceeded under the worst probable conditions. These values are chosen by the device manufacturer to provide acceptable serviceability of the device, taking no responsibility for equipment variations, environmental variations, and the effects of changes in operating conditions due to variations in the characteristics of the device under consideration and of all other electronic devices in the equipment."

This defines the worst case conditions and highlights the responsibility of the designer to ensure that the absolute maximum value is never exceeded. It does not explicitly place any obligations on the manufacturer in terms of long term reliability.

Symbol	Parameter	Conditions	Min	Max	Unit
V_{GS}	gate-sourced voltage	$T_j \leq 175\ °C$; DC	-20	20	V

Figure 3 | Maximum V_{GS} rating for a Nexperia automotive grade standard level device

Symbol	Parameter	Conditions		Min	Max	Unit
V_{GS}	gate-sourced voltage	$T_j \leq 175\ °C$; DC		-10	10	V
		$T_j \leq 175\ °C$; Pulsed	[1] [2]	-15	15	V

Notice there is an additional pulsed value limited to an accumulated duration of up to 50 hours.

Figure 4 | Maximum V_{GS} rating for a Nexperia automotive grade logic level device

Designing in MOSFETs for safe and reliable gate-drive operation

3 Life Testing

For automotive MOSFETs, AEC-Q101 qualification is required. AEC-Q101 is a list of endurance tests the MOSFET must pass. Each test takes a sample of MOSFETs and places them under various electrical stresses and temperatures. The sample size is a minimum of 77 MOSFETs; each endurance test is repeated 3 times on a different sample of 77 MOSFETs to represent a different process batch. Surviving the endurance tests grants the tested product type Q101 accreditation, allowing the MOSFET to be used in automotive applications [2]. This can be found on all Nexperia automotive qualifed MOSFET data sheets (Figure 5).

BUK9Y3R0-40E
N-channel 40 V 3.0 mΩ logic level MOSFET in LFPAK56

11 November 2014   Product data sheet

1. General description

Logic level N-channel MOSFET in LFPAK56 (Power SO8) package using TrenchMOS technology. This product has been designed and qualified to AEC Q101 standard for use in high performance automotive applications.

2. Features and benefits

- Q101 compliant
- Repetitive avalanche rated
- Suitable for thermally demanding environments due to 175 °C rating
- True logic level gate with $V_{GS(th)}$ rating of greater than 0.5 V at 175 °C

Figure 5 | Front page of a typical Nexperia automotive data sheet, showing the MOSFET is automotive by highlighting that it is Q101 compliant

To qualify the $V_{GS\text{-}max}$ ratings for Q101 the devices undergo a specified life-test procedure. The devices are placed in a chamber at the maximum rated temperature (T_{jmax}) with gate biased at 100% of the data sheet maximum voltage rating for 1000 hours. These tests are performed by Nexperia to ensure that the data sheet ratings of $V_{GS\text{-}max}$ are within specification.

However, life-testing alone is inherently incapable of determining the actual capability of a MOSFET in terms of expected failed parts per million (ppm). In order to satisfy AEC-Q101 criteria no sample devices during the Q101 bias tests should fail. It is possible to extrapolate a failure rate from such data, but the maximum confidence it can provide is in the order of 11000 ppm (based on zero fails in a population of 240 devices under test and using a confidence interval of 95%). With this level of confidence it is not trivial to determine what to specify as the maximum voltage rating. Especially when in addition, Nexeria's own requirements target a sub 1 ppm defectivity level.

To achieve sub-ppm levels Nexperia has developed its own additional testing methodology. Using this, Nexperia can confidently rate the devices to satisfy the AEC-Q101 criteria, while also achieving sub 1 ppm defectivity rates (3). In order to understand this methodology an explanation of the role of a MOSFET's gate-oxide is required and is detailed below.

4 The Gate-oxide

The methodology to determine and qualify the maximum V_{GS} rating of a device is based upon characterisation of the gate-oxide. This is the layer of oxide that insulates the gate polysilicon from the source of the MOSFET and is critical to its operation. Figure 6 shows the location of the gate-oxide in the MOSFET.

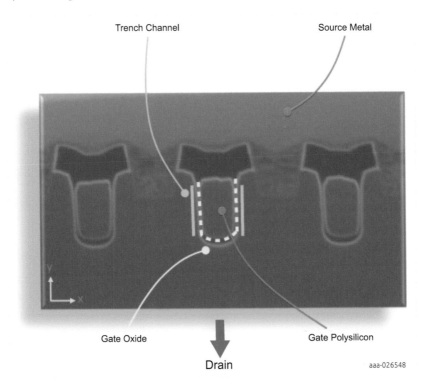

Trench Channel   Source Metal

Gate Oxide   Gate Polysilicon

Drain

aaa-026548

Figure 6 | Cross-section of a power MOSFET at approximately 25,000 magnification showing where the MOSFET channel forms and the location of the gate-oxide. The gate-oxide is present both sides of the trench and a channel forms next to both oxides. Current flows vertically from Drain to Source through the MOSFET channel.

Designing in MOSFETs for safe and reliable gate-drive operation

When designing power MOSFETs, there are two conflicting constraints with respect to the gate-oxide thickness. Achieving a low $R_{DS(on)}$ at a low applied level of V_{GS} requires a thin gate-oxide, conversely withstanding high maximum V_{GS} requires a thick gate-oxide. In most cases, both requirements can be met and gate bias life testing can be performed at 100 % of the absolute maximum rating. However, there are some instances where this is not possible. Logic level devices are designed to provide a guaranteed $R_{DS(on)}$ at V_{GS} = 5 V. This implies a need for a gate-oxide that is thinner than for a standard level device. Consequently a logic-level gate-oxide is not capable of achieving the same maximum $V_{GS\text{-}max}$ rating as a standard-level gate-oxide. For Nexperia's automotive MOSFETs, this is typically 10 V logic-level and 20 V for standard-level devices at the maximum rated temperature, typically 175 °C.

However, caution should be exercised when comparing other manufacturers' data sheets. The $V_{GS\text{-}max}$ rating is not always given at the maximum rated temperature; instead it is often given for 25 °C. The rating given for a temperature of 25 °C may be higher than one given for 175 °C. This will make that MOSFET appear more capable on first review. Because MOSFET gate-oxide reliability decreases with increasing temperature, Nexperia's data sheets show the capability of the MOSFET at maximum rated junction temperature.

Exceeding the $V_{GS\text{-}max}$ rating for the gate-oxide does not mean the device will immediately fail in the application. Applying a V_{GS} to a MOSFET will develop an electric field across the internal gate-oxide (E_{OX}). The oxide electric field strength is a function of oxide thickness (T_{OX}) and V_{GS}.

$$E_{OX} = V_{GS} / T_{OX}$$

If the oxide electric field strength reaches a sufficiently high level, the gate-oxide insulation will break down and will be destroyed. However, for electric field strengths below this critical value the gate-oxide may degrade over time and ultimately fail. The rate at which this occurs depends on both the operating-temperature and the strength of the electric field within the gate-oxide. Expected oxide life-time decreases with increases in either temperature or oxide electric-field stress.

Gate-oxides need to be rated to survive for operating periods of not less than 10 years. Testing for 10 years to assess the reliability of the gate-oxide is not practical. Nexperia performs life tests under accelerated conditions to achieve quicker test results. For assessing the gate-oxide, Nexperia places a group of MOSFETs with known gate-oxide thickness under high temperatures and high oxide field strength. The MOSFETs will therefore degrade much quicker than can be expected in the application. The MOSFETs are monitored until the point of failure, which is observed as a low impedance measurement between the gate and source terminals. This is termed Time Dependant Dielectric Breakdown (TDDB).

Nexperia uses the test data from TDDB to correlate to other operating-temperatures and oxide field-strengths to determine the capability of the oxide in actual application operating conditions. This is applicable to MOSFETs with different gate-oxide thicknesses because the testing characterises oxide field-strength, not V_{GS}.

A gate-oxide production process aims to create a gate-oxide of consistent thickness throughout manufacture. However, in any real fabrication process variation will occur. This means the V_{GS} rating needs to be applicable to the MOSFET with the thinnest gate- oxide that leaves the factory. Production screens are in place that set a lower limit, which corresponds to the MOSFET with the thinnest gate-oxide. Using this value of gate-oxide thickness and the characterisation data from the accelerated TDDB tests, this MOSFET can now have its oxide rated for V_{GS-max} and temperature for a given expected operating life.

For automotive MOSFET the operating requirement is outlined within AEC-Q101; 1000 hours at V_{GS-max} and maximum temperature. Taking this profile into account, and knowing the thinnest oxide that can be supplied, Nexperia can confidently place V_{GS-max} ratings in the data sheet.

Again, for further detail on the mechanics of gate-oxide wear out and Nexperia's methodology towards rating its gate-oxides please refer to [3].

5 Alternative operating profiles

The mission or operating-profile of a MOSFET in an actual application is rarely at the data sheet maximum temperature and at the maximum V_{GS} for 1000 hours as dictated by AEC-Q101. This combination is formulated as a compromise to allow realistic life-testing times that would protect automotive applications. The ultimate rating of a MOSFET V_{GS-max} that meets AEC-Q101 may not meet the application requirements. For example the application may require 12 V V_{GS} but this exceeds the MOSFET of choice's 10 V rating, at first pass this MOSFET cannot be used in the application. However, if the operating profile of the application is outlined with greater detail it may be that the 12 V rating is required for temperatures less than 175 °C and for a cumulative lifetime duration of less than 1000 hours. Here the application criteria can be compared with the true capability of the oxide and therefore be confidently selected for the application.

This chapter assesses several common MOSFET topologies in order to provide an understanding of V_{GS} behaviour. From this it is possible to generate an estimate for what V_{GS} will be applied to the MOSFET and for how long; a V_{GS} profile. Using the V_{GS} profile along with operating-voltage profiles and temperature profiles a full mission profile can be created. An example is shown in Table 1. The mission profile can be used to assess the MOSFET's suitability for the application against the TDDB data.

The first set of analyses presented considers steady state stress on the gate-oxide due to a constant gate-source bias from either an external gate-driver or as a result of the steady state voltages that appear on the gate and source terminals of a MOSFET. Further analysis attempts to estimate the contribution to gate stress from transient gate- source voltages. This could result from capacitive coupling through the Miller capacitance or conduction through the MOSFET body diode. Both require detailed analysis of the application to verify compatibility with the MOSFET features.

Table 1. Example MOSFET mission profile, showing the time spent in hours at a particular V_{GS} and MOSFET junction temperature

V_{GS} =	Time (hours)				
	$T_j = -40\ °C$	$T_j = 25\ °C$	$T_j = 80\ °C$	$T_j = 105\ °C$	$T_j = 125\ °C$
-5 V	1	5	10	1	0
2 V	10	50	100	10	2
5 V	1000	2500	5000	50	10
10 V	100	200	300	100	5
20 V	2	10	5	2	1

5.1 Application assessments

This section assesses several common topologies featuring MOSFETs and focuses on the V_{GS} behaviour. This information will help to produce the mission profile as shown in Table 1.

5.1.1 Single MOSFETs

Starting with the three application topologies shown in Figure 7. Figure 7a and 7b can be considered similar in behaviour as they are both driven gate to source. However, Figure 7c shows the MOSFET being driven gate to ground. It is possible to drive the MOSFET in this manner by ensuring the gate voltage is higher than whatever voltage is currently at the source terminal. However, it is highly recommended not to do so as will become apparent throughout the discussion.

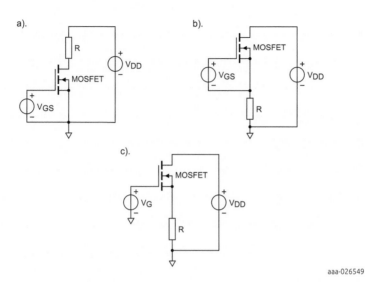

aaa-026549

Figure 7 | a) Low side MOSFET b) High side MOSFET driven Gate to Source c) High side MOSFET driven gate to ground

In Figure 7c, when a V_G is applied, first assumptions may be that the voltage across the load resistor will be close to V_{DD} due to the low on-state resistance of a MOSFET compared to the load. However, the V_{GS} of the MOSFET is $V_{GS} = V_G - V_S$, where V_S is the voltage developed across the load in this example. This means that as V_G rises so, will V_S thus reducing the overall V_{GS} across the MOSFET. The result is a MOSFET that is not fully enhanced and therefore taking a significant portion of the V_{DD} across its drain and source terminals. The MOSFET is now dissipating a considerable amount of power and operating in linear mode, which may have thermal runaway implications. In addition, the load may not behave as expected due to it no longer having the full V_{DD} across it.

In Figure 7a the MOSFET source and gate-driver supply are both grounded and therefore provides a true V_{GS} supply. Likewise in Figure 7b, now the gate-drive is able to float above the source voltage and apply the full drive to the gate-source terminals of the MOSFET. Both the circuits in Figure 7a and 7b the MOSFETs are easily turned fully on and can achieve the low $R_{DS(on)}$. This allows the full V_{DD} to be applied across the load and ensures correct operation of the application.

5.1.2 Half, Full and Three-Phase Bridges

Other application examples include half bridges and by extension full bridges and three phase bridges which can be found in DC-to-DC convertors and motor drives. Here, in any individual leg two MOSFETs are placed in series. When the MOSFETs are off the resistance across the drain-source terminals is not infinite and leakage paths exist. For simplification, these can be treated as resistances across the drain-source terminals. Referencing Figure 8 it can be seen that the V_{GS} on the high side (HS) MOSFET can be -V_{DD}/2. The time the MOSFET V_{GS} is at V_{DD}/2 V may be significant due to this occurring whenever the application is off and connected to the supply voltage. This will need considering in the mission profile and the MOSFET will need to be specified to meet this requirement.

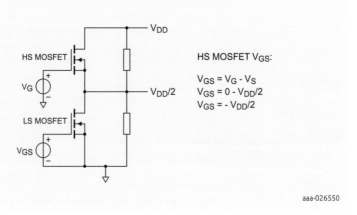

aaa-026550

Figure 8 | Half bridge MOSFET configuration showing leakage paths and potential issues if driving High Side MOSFET with respect to ground

When the MOSFETs are driven with respect to ground the required gate-drive needs to be at least the required V_{GS} for the MOSFET summed with the maximum voltage at the MOSFET's source terminal. For example, an automotive application typically uses a lead acid battery. Potentially the application could see 18 V from the battery and therefore the same voltage may appear on the source terminal of the high side MOSFET. This means to drive a typical SL MOSFET a gate voltage of 28 V (18 V + 10 V) with respect to ground is required to ensure the MOSFET is fully enhanced. Now the gate-drive is fixed at 28 V. However, the battery voltage may be as low as 6 V. This means the V_{GS} will be 22 V (28 V - 6 V). For a SL MOSFET this is outside its safe operating limits and has the potential to reduce its reliability in the application.

Within half bridges the extremes of the V_{GS} have been considered but the source voltage of the high side MOSFET does not depend solely upon the battery-voltage:

load conditions which are variable with temperature and supply-voltage result in not knowing accurately what the source-voltage will be during considerable periods of operation of the application. This makes it very difficult to assess the V_{GS} requirement of the MOSFET when driving them with respect to ground. It is preferred and advisable to have the gate- driver referenced to the source of the MOSFET and not ground. Now, when the source voltage changes the gate-drive will be referencing this and the V_{GS} will be controlled. However, even when driving the MOSFET with respect to source there are still times when the V_{GS} is not fully dictated by the gate-driver. An assessment of transient analysis is required next.

All the applications discussed and their V_{GS} behaviour have been assessed under steady-state conditions, the next few paragraphs take into consideration the dynamic behaviour whilst the MOSFET is switching or commutating currents. In the example figures already shown the gate-drivers have been idealised as perfect voltage sources. However, all gate-drivers will have output impedances and drive current limitations adding to the complexity of transient behaviour for the application. In addition to this the PCB layout will be a factor, with track impedances contributing to the application behaviour. It is beyond the scope of this application note to discuss best layout practices beyond noting that gate-drivers should be placed as close as possible to the MOSFET it is driving. Some of these issues have been addressed in application note AN11599 (chapter 3 of this book) - Using power MOSFETs in parallel.

The transient operation of the half bridge is now reviewed, here solely the case where the MOSFET is driven gate to source is considered. The load is inductive, representing half bridges (DC to DC convertors for example) and three-phase bridges (Brushless DC motors for example). The full operation of these applications is not considered but in each, during the switching of the MOSFETs, the considerations to the gate-drive are similar.

Before describing the application behaviour, it is important to note that all MOSFETs have parasitic capacitances that couple each of the terminals, gate, drain and source (Figure 9). They are C_{GS}, C_{GD} and C_{DS} and exist as part of the MOSFET structure, playing a critical role in the transient behaviour of MOSFETs and therefore the application.

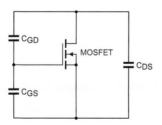

aaa-026551

Figure 9 | Internal parasitic MOSFET capacitances

In half-bridges during an example transient event, one MOSFET is turned off and the second is turned on, this causes the switch node voltage to rise and fall. The switch node is where the source of the high side and the drain of the low side MOSFETs are connected. The dV/dt on the switch node can couple through the C_{GD} of a MOSFET and charge or discharge that MOSFET's C_{GS}, appearing as V_{GS}. Whether the V_{GS} is positive or negative depends on the sign of the dV/dt. It is the function of the driver to compensate for this change in V_{GS} by charging/discharging the V_{GS} to the set level. How effective the gate-driver is at this depends on a couple of factors, the rate of the dV/dt and how well the driver is coupled to the gate and source (how much impedance is between them). Again, being aware that the total impedance is a sum combination of package, resistance and inductances, trace parasitics and intentionally placed components (which have even more parasitics). This behaviour is shown in Figure 9. The consequences of this gate-bounce are biasing of the gate for a cumulative time which needs to be considered in any mission profile and worse, potentially causing cross conduction where both MOSFETs are on simultaneously.

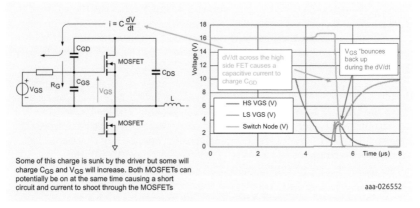

Figure 10 | Dynamic behaviour of a MOSFET half bridge

5.1.3 High side MOSFETs with Inductive loads

Other applications where V_{GS} behaviour may not be as first expected, are when driving inductive-loads. Take again the examples in Figure 7 but now replace the restive-load with an inductive one. The difference in driving methodology, that is with respect to ground or to the source, could result in either the MOSFET operating in linear mode or entering avalanche respectively. Consider now the situation where the gate-drive is referenced to ground. Also assume there is sufficient drive on the gate to compensate for an increase in source voltage, thus allowing the MOSFET to be fully enhanced.

When the MOSFET is turned on current will increase through the inductor, and energy will be stored in its magnetic field. Then the gate-driver is turned off, the inductor starts to demagnetise and produces a back-EMF in order to maintain current flow. As one end of the inductor is grounded this back-EMF appears as a negative voltage on the source. The voltage will continue to decrease until the V_{GS} is great enough such that the MOSFET is partially turned on, maintaining the inductive current flow. Here the MOSFET is in linear mode, the V_{GS} is somewhere between off and fully on and the V_{DS} is significant; remembering that the source is now negative. See Figure 11 for an illustration.

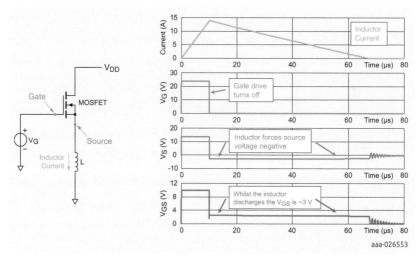

Figure 11 | Circuit and waveforms showing the V_{GS} behaviour whilst driving an inductive load and the gate of the MOSFET is driven gate to ground

Taking the previous example of driving an inductive load but with the gate being driven with respect to the source, the behaviour is similar until the MOSFET is turned off. Again the V_s will go negative until current flow is maintained, however the source is tied firmly to the gate by the driver which is operating at 0 V. No matter how negative the source goes (within operational limits) the MOSFET will stay off. Instead, the V_s will continue to decrease and therefore the V_{DS} will continue to rise. Ultimately the V_{DS} will reach the breakdown voltage of the MOSFET's internal body diode and avalanche (Figure 12). As with linear mode the power dissipation is considerable due to there being voltage and current present in the MOSFET, but avalanche is a preferable method of absorbing the inductive energy. Compared to linear mode, avalanche operation is better at sharing this power dissipation across the silicon die. Further information avalanche can be found in a MOSFET's data sheet and in more detail in application note AN10273 (chapter 4 of this book) - Power MOSFET single-shot and repetitive avalanche ruggedness rating.

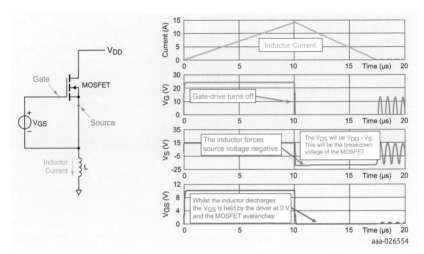

Figure 12 | Circuit and waveforms showing the V_{GS} behaviour whilst driving an inductive load and the gate of the MOSFET is driven Gate to Source

5.1.4 Motor Loads

One final application to be considered is driving motors with a single high side FET. Again the designer is recommended to drive the MOSFET with respect to ground to ensure full control of the MOSFET and application behaviour. Driving with respect to ground and the source voltage will be near V_{DD} due to motor back EMF; all the previous considerations to driving respect to ground apply.

6 Application assessment summary

This chapter has summarised some common application behaviours and their impact on the MOSFET's V_{GS}. The application note has shown that driving a MOSFET with respect to ground causes numerous issues and difficulties. These include operating in linear mode and not knowing what the V_{GS} may be at any point in time. This makes it difficult to formulate a mission profile to select the correct MOSFET. However, driving the gate with respect to source does not remove all of the issues; there are transient events that can induce positive or negative voltages on the V_{GS} that are not fully controlled by the gate-driver. We are still short, however, from producing the mission profile to ensure the correct selection of a MOSFET. The correct MOSFET should not be over-specified and should still operate reliably in the application for its intended life. We now need to create a mission profile.

7 Creating a mission profile

An example mission profile is shown in Table 1, it is a distribution of V_{GS} voltages at a range of temperatures and for how long. However, before generating a profile, several pieces of information need to be gathered. These include but are not limited to:

- How long the application is in operation
  - On and Off times
  - Possible fault conditions
- The distribution of operating temperatures
- The distribution of supply voltages

Along with an understanding of the application as outlined is the previous sections, this information can be used to create a mission profile. The mission profile can be assed against the TDDB data for a given MOSFET, thus determining the MOSFET's suitability for the application.

7.1 Example – Full H-bridge motor drive

An example automotive application is brushed Direct Current (DC) motors such as windscreen wiper motors or seat control motors. For this worked example the MOSFETs are driven with respect to their source terminals and not to ground.

The first part of the exercise is to gather information on how long the application will be operating for. This information can then be translated into how long the MOSFETs are on for and therefore how long they will have a V_{GS} applied. In this instance it is common for the Original Equipment Manufacturer (OEM) to stipulate the usage profile of the system and it may look like (Table 2).

Table 2: Number of motor operations and the total time spent in operation

Operations	Total operation time at 0.5 s per actuation (hours)
180,000	5

Other times when there may be a voltage present at the gate of the MOSFET is when the engine is off but the electronics are on. In the case of the motor, the two high side MOSFETs may be switched on to brake the motor. This time will add cumulatively to the mission profile (Table 3).

Designing in MOSFETs for safe and reliable gate-drive operation

Table 3: Battery voltage whilst the engine is off and the time spent at this voltage whilst the electronic systems are connected to the battery

V_{GS} (V)	Time (hours)
12.5	6,000

Table 3 provides the first piece of information required to build our V_{GS} profile. We need to convert the information in Table 2 into the same. To do so, we need to know the V_{GS} the MOSFET will be driven at. The V_{GS} may be set at 10 V by a power supply or alternatively the MOSFET may be driven directly by the battery voltage. The battery voltage will have its own distribution (Table 4). Using Table 2 and Table 4 we get Table 5.

Table 4: Battery voltage distribution of the life time of the application

Battery voltage	Distribution
14.5	77%
16	15%
17	5%
18	3%

Table 5: V_{GS} profile based on battery voltage distribution and application operation time, including the V_{GS} applied to the MOSFET whilst the engine is off

V_{GS} (V)	Time (hours)
12.5	6000
14.5	19.25
16.0	3.75
17.0	1.25
18.0	0.75
20.0	0.00825

Table 5 is now a V_{GS} profile, it shows the time spent at each V_{GS} value. However, it is missing the temperature profile to make it into a full mission profile to be assessed against the TDDB data. To generate a temperature profile the OEM and the application designer need to work together. Remember that the MOSFET may be operating a little hotter than its ambient (due to self-heating) so engineering margin may need to be added. An example is shown in Table 6.

Table 6: Ambient and junction temperature distribution of the expected life time of the application
The junction temperature is arbitrarily increased by 50 °C, this can be changed based on engineering judgment or calculation when better informed of the systems operational parameters.

T_{amb} (°C)	T_j (°C)	Distribution
-40	10	6%
23	73	20%
40	90	65%
75	125	8%
80	130	1%

Table 5 contains the V_{GS} values, and Table 6 has the temperature distribution. These two together contain the information to make Table 7, the full V_{GS} profile. For example, for 6% of the time the MOSFET junction temperature is at 10 °C. By multiplying the hours at each V_{GS} (from Table 5) by 6% the $T_j = 10$ °C column in Table 7 is populated. It may be the case that the higher V_{GS} voltages only occur at the lower temperatures. The profile in Table 7 will need to be updated to reflect this but can only be done so by the application designer working with the OEM.

Table 7. Full mission profile showing the time in hours for a given V_{GS} voltage and MOSFET junction temperature

V_{GS} (V)	Time at V_{GS} and Temperature (hours)				
	$T_j = 10\,°C$	$T_j = °C$	$T_j = 90\,°C$	$T_j = 125\,°C$	$T_j = 130\,°C$
12.5	360	1200	3900	480	60
14.5	1.155	3.85	12.5125	1.54	0.1925
16	0.225	0.75	2.4375	0.3	0.0375
17	0.075	0.25	0.8125	0.1	0.0125
18	0.045	0.15	0.4875	0.06	0.0075

The profile in Table 7 shows that for a time the MOSFET will see a V_{GS} of 18 V at elevated temperatures. Using solely the datasheet ratings a logic-level MOSFET's $V_{GS\text{-}max}$ rating of 15 V would seem to exclude it from use in this application. However, working with Nexperia to compare the profile to the logic level MOSFETs TDDB data it can be shown that the MOSFET is more than capable of operating reliably in the application. This is because the time spent at these conditions is short.

Once the design engineer has generated a V_{GS} mission profile they are encourage to contact their local Nexperia representative to receive support. Working with Nexperia, the profile can be assessed against the TDDB data and a suitable MOSFET can then be suggested.

8 Summary

The gate-source lifetime and the gate-source turn-on voltage are highly dependent on temperature so one needs to be careful in comparing datasheets from different suppliers where the stated temperature conditions for the gate-source voltages are different.

For devices that do not see the maximum gate-voltage at maximum temperature throughout their intended life, Nexperia has a methodology to provide a better assessment of the required gate-oxide rating for such an application. This would often allow better performance in other parameters without compromising reliability in the application.

This does require the so-called mission profile of the MOSFET in the application, as described in this chapter.

Benefits of low Q_{rr} MOSFETs in motor control applications

Benefits of low Q_{rr} MOSFETs in switching applications

Q_{rr} overlooked and underappreciated in efficiency battle

Automotive Trench 9 Power MOSFETs designed for performance and endurance

The right package for 12 48 V DC-to-DC conversion

9 References

1. Rating systems for electronic tubes and valves and analogous semiconductor devices. IEC. IEC 60134:1961.

2. Failure Mechanism Based Stress Test Qualification For Discrete Semiconductors. AEC. Vol. Rev D. AEC-Q101.

3. A methodology for projecting SiO2 thick gate oxide reliability on trench power MOSFETs and its application on MOSFETs V_{GS} rating. Efthymiou, E, Rutter, P and Whiteley, P. 2015, Microelectronics Reliability.

10 Tables

11 Figures

Chapter 3

Using power MOSFETs in parallel

Application Note: AN11599

Increasing the capability of a MOSFET switch element by using several individual MOSFETs connected in parallel can be useful. However, when designing switch elements careful consideration of the circuit requirements and the MOSFET characteristics and behavior must be applied. This chapter explores some of the problems that can be experienced when several MOSFETs are operated in a paralleled group. It also suggests ways to avoid the problems and minimize their effects.

1 Introduction

One much publicized benefit of power MOSFETs (compared to other semiconductor devices) is that it is easy to parallel them to create a group with increased capability. Although this feature is superficially true, there are several potential problems that can catch out the unwary circuit designer.

A MOSFET consists of a group of paralleled 'cells' fabricated on the surface of a silicon die. All the cells are created at the same time under the same conditions. When the MOSFET is fully enhanced and conducts channel current, the temperatures of all the cells are very similar. As the cells are structurally and thermally closely matched, they share current and power well and the parameters of the MOSFET can be well-defined.

There is a range of values for the parameters of the MOSFET dies on a wafer. There is a wider range for MOSFET dies on different wafers in the same production batch. The range is even wider for all batches even though the MOSFETs are the same type. MOSFETs with parameter values outside the data sheet limits are rejected.

The MOSFETs in a paralleled group should all be the same type, but their parameters could be anywhere within the data sheet range. Their die temperatures are unlikely to be the same. Consequently their power sharing is not perfect.

This chapter contains guidelines on how to design a group of MOSFETs to get the best performance from them. The design must accommodate MOSFET variations within the data sheet limits. It must also allow for MOSFET parameter variations over the range of electrical and environmental conditions. If all the MOSFETs in the group work within their safe maximum limits, the paralleled group of MOSFETs operates reliably.

It is technically and commercially undesirable to have to select MOSFETs and it should be unnecessary. The circuit should be designed to accommodate any MOSFET within the worst case $R_{DS(on)}$ range.

The key data sheet limit which must not be exceeded is the maximum junction temperature $T_{j(max)}$ of 175 °C.

2 Static (DC) operation

This situation is the simplest condition where current flows through a group of paralleled MOSFETs that are fully enhanced (switched ON). A proportion of the total current flows through each MOSFET in the group. At the initial point of turn on, the die temperatures of all the MOSFETs in the group are the same. The drain current I_D flowing in each MOSFET is inversely proportional to its $R_{DS(on)}$ (the drain-source voltage V_{DS} across all the MOSFETs is the same).

The MOSFET with the lowest $R_{DS(on)}$ takes the highest proportion of the current and dissipates the most power (power dissipation $P = V_{DS} \times I_D$).

All the MOSFETs heat up, but the MOSFET with the lowest $R_{DS(on)}$ heats up most (assuming the $R_{th(j-a)}$ of all the MOSFETs is the same).

MOSFET $R_{DS(on)}$ has a positive temperature coefficient. $R_{DS(on)}$ increases as T_j increases. The die temperatures and $R_{DS(on)}$ values of all MOSFETs in the group rise, but the die temperature of the lowest $R_{DS(on)}$ MOSFET increases disproportionately. The effect of this behavior is to redistribute the current towards the other higher $R_{DS(on)}$ MOSFETs in the group.

Stable thermal equilibrium is reached after a period of operation. The lowest $R_{DS(on)}$ MOSFET is the hottest, but carries a lower proportion of the current than it did initially.

The Positive Temperature Coefficient (PTC) of $R_{DS(on)}$ is a stabilizing influence that promotes power sharing between the MOSFETs in the group. However, as stated earlier the most important criterion is that the maximum junction temperature of any MOSFET in the group must not exceed 175 °C.

The cooling of each MOSFET in the group depends on its thermal resistance from junction to ambient. Die temperature influences the heat flow from adjacent MOSFETs. Rather than considering the thermal resistance paths between the MOSFET dies, the main influence is the temperature of the common heatsink. All the MOSFET mounting bases are bonded electrically and thermally to this heatsink.

The lowest $R_{DS(on)}$ MOSFET could be located anywhere in the group. The thermal resistance from mounting base to ambient of all the MOSFETs in the group should be as similar as possible and as low as possible. Cooling is optimised and independent of location.

This thermal resistance solely depends on the thermal characteristics and design of the assembly [Printed-Circuit Board (PCB) or heatsink] to which the MOSFET is thermally bonded.

Sometimes a value for $R_{th(j-a)}$ is given in data sheets but this parameter is of very limited value. It cannot be treated as a well-defined parameter because it also depends on other external factors such as PCB construction, PCB orientation and air flow. The only guaranteed thermal parameter is the thermal resistance from the MOSFET junction to mounting base $R_{th(j-mb)}$.

2.1 Worked examples for static operation

The worked examples that follow are based on the BUK764R0-40E.

Table 1: Thermal characteristics

Symbol	Parameter	Conditions	Min	Max	Unit
$R_{th(j-mb)}$	thermal resistance from junction to mounting base	-	-	0.82	K/W
$R_{th(j-a)}$	thermal resistance from junction to ambient	minimum footprint; mounted on a PCB	-	50	-	K/W

A typical group of MOSFETs has a range of $R_{DS(on)}$ values. The distribution has a peak at around the typical data sheet $R_{DS(on)}$ value; none should have an $R_{DS(on)}$ higher than the data sheet maximum. The $R_{DS(on)}$ of about half of the samples is less than the typical value.

Minimum $R_{DS(on)}$ is not given in the data sheet, but a good estimate is

$$R_{DS(on)(min)} \approx R_{DS(on)(max)} - 2(R_{DS(on)(max)} - R_{DS(on)(typ)}) \qquad [1]$$

The $R_{DS(on)}$ value range means that a group of typical MOSFETs is very unlikely to share power equally when they are operated in parallel.

The worst case would be when one of the MOSFETs has the minimum $R_{DS(on)}$ and all the others have the maximum $R_{DS(on)}$.

Modeling of the electro-thermal system is complex because its electrical and thermal characteristics are mutually dependent. However, an electro-thermally convergent Excel model can be used to estimate the performance characteristics of a paralleled group. As an example, in a worst case situation three BUK764R0-40E MOSFETs are connected in parallel; two have maximum $R_{DS(on)}$ of 4 mΩ. The other has a lower than typical $R_{DS(on)}$ of 2.6 mΩ.

The MOSFET with the lowest $R_{DS(on)}$ value takes the highest proportion of the current. It therefore has the highest power dissipation.

The target is to keep the junction temperature of the hottest MOSFET below 175 °C under worst case operating conditions.

These estimations are simplified illustrations. The thermal representation of the MOSFET group is less complex than a real application. In a real application, there are other factors such as neighboring components and orientation that would influence cooling. However, they show the approximate behavior of the group with two different $R_{th(j-a)}$ values.

The first scenario shows the system with the thermal resistance from junction to ambient for each MOSFET ($R_{th(j-a)}$ = 20 K/W; T_{amb} = 125 °C).

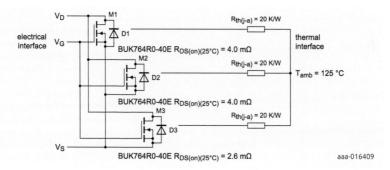

Figure 1 | Electrical and thermal schematic diagram of the three paralleled BUK764R0-40E MOSFETs

Table 2 shows the maximum safe limits of V_{DS}, I_D, P and T_j for all the MOSFETs at thermal equilibrium. At this point, the junction temperature of the hottest MOSFET is almost 175 °C.

MOSFET	V_{DS} [V]	$R_{th(j-a)}$ [K/W]	$R_{DS(on)}$ (25 °C) [mΩ]	Initial $R_{DS(on)}$ (125 °C) [mΩ]	Initial current I_D [A]
M1	0.11	20	2.6	4.16	42.31
M2	0.11	20	4	6.4	27.50
M3	0.11	20	4	6.4	27.50

Initial power P [W]	Initial power share [%]	Final $R_{DS(on)}$ [mΩ]	Final current I_D [A]	Final power P [W]	Final T_j [°C]	Final power share [%]
4.65	43.5	4.92	22.36	2.46	174	42.3
3.03	28.3	7.21	15.26	1.68	159	28.9
3.03	28.3	7.21	15.26	1.68	159	28.9

Total initial power P(M1 + M2 + M3) = 10.70 W

Total final power P(M1 + M2 + M3) = 5.82 W

The second scenario relates to the same electrical system, but with ideal thermal characteristics. The thermal resistance $R_{th(j-a)}$ of each MOSFET is 0.82 K/W. This situation corresponds to the ideal but unrealistic situation where each MOSFET is perfectly thermally bonded to an infinite heatsink (a heatsink with zero thermal resistance).

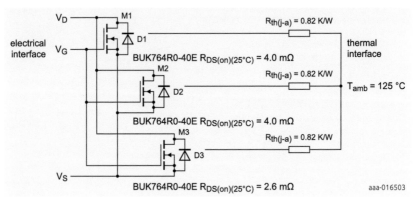

Figure 2 | Electrical and thermal schematic diagram of the three paralleled BUK764R0-40E MOSFETs with ideal thermal conditions

Table 3 shows the values of V_{DS}, I_D, P and T_j for all the MOSFETs at thermal equilibrium. At this point, the junction temperature of the hottest MOSFET is almost 175 °C.

Table 3: MOSFET maximum conditions for $R_{th(j-a)}$ = 0.82 K/W and T_{amb} = 125 °C

MOSFET	V_{DS} [V]	$R_{th(j-a)}$ [K/W]	$R_{DS(on)}$ (25 °C) [mΩ]	Initial $R_{DS(on)}$ (25 °C) [mΩ]	Initial current I_D [A]
M1	0.55	0.82	2.6	4.16	211.54
M2	0.55	0.82	4	6.4	137.50
M3	0.55	0.82	4	6.4	137.50

Using power MOSFETs in parallel

3

Table 3: continued...

Initial power P [W]	Initial power share [%]	Final $R_{DS(on)}$ [mΩ]	Final current I_D [A]	Final power P [W]	Final T_j [°C]	Final power share [%]
116.35	43.5	4.92	111.79	61.48	174	42.3
75.63	28.3	7.21	76.28	41.96	159	28.9
75.63	28.3	7.21	76.28	41.96	159	28.9

Total initial power P(M1 + M2 + M3) = 267.60 W

Total final power P(M1 + M2 + M3) = 145.39 W

Note: This scenario is ideal and unrealistic. It is included to illustrate the benefit of reducing $R_{th(j-a)}$ to maximize the usage of the MOSFET capabilities.

In practice, $R_{th(j-a)}$ is always greater than $R_{th(j-mb)}$. The thermal bonding between the MOSFET mounting base and the heatsink is never perfect and an infinite heatsink does not exist in the real world.

In this case, the drain current (I_D) of the MOSFETs becomes the limiting factor (the data sheet maximum I_D is 75 A).

To optimize MOSFET utilization, the MOSFETs must be able to dissipate as much power as possible. At the same time, the junction temperature of the hottest MOSFET must remain below the maximum safe temperature of 175 °C.

The following conclusions can be drawn from Table 2 and Table 3:

1. It is beneficial to reduce $R_{th(j-a)}$ as much as possible to optimize the MOSFET die cooling.

2. It is beneficial to reduce the maximum ambient temperature to increase the available thermal 'headroom'.

3. As a result of Table 2 and Table 3, it is clear that junction temperature difference between the MOSFETs depends only on their $R_{DS(on)}$ values (assuming the $R_{th(j-a)}$ for each MOSFET is the same).

4. When the paralleled (fully enhanced) MOSFETs heat up during use, their power distribution changes such that the cooler MOSFETs take a greater proportion of the power. This effect is due to the PTC of $R_{DS(on)}$ and it acts to promote thermal stability.

3 MOSFET mounting for good thermal performance and power sharing

To get the most from the MOSFET group, the individual MOSFET should be mounted in a way that causes their mounting base temperatures to be as similar as possible and also as low as possible.

To realize this goal, the thermal resistance between each MOSFET (mounting base) and the mounting bases of all the other MOSFETs in the group should be matched and minimized. They should be mounted symmetrically and as close together as possible on a thermally conductive surface.

Heat flow can be considered to be analogous to electric current flow; so the thermal bonding points of the MOSFETs (usually the drain tabs) should be on a thermal 'ring main'. The low thermal resistance path allows heat to flow easily between the MOSFETs. When heat flows easily between all the MOSFETs in the group, their mounting base temperatures track together closely.

Note: This arrangement does not promote equal current sharing, but promotes better die temperature matching. The temperatures of all the MOSFETs in the group can rise more before the temperature of the hottest MOSFET reaches 175 °C. Hence the power dissipation capability of the group is maximized.

There are practical limits to the physical extent of the thermal ring main; ideally each MOSFET should be next to all its neighbors. This condition limits the group to two or three MOSFETs.

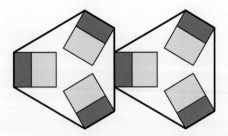

This layout suits standard packaged MOSFETs (e.g. D²PAK, LFPAK and TO-220). The dark shaded area corresponds to the drain tab of the device.

aaa-016511

Figure 3 | A layout for six paralleled MOSFETs to promote good power sharing

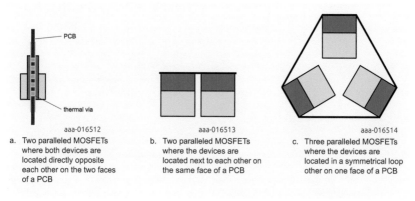

a. Two paralleled MOSFETs where both devices are located directly opposite each other on the two faces of a PCB

b. Two paralleled MOSFETs where the devices are located next to each other on the same face of a PCB

c. Three paralleled MOSFETs where the devices are located in a symmetrical loop other on one face of a PCB

Figure 4 | Good layout arrangements for two paralleled MOSFETs and three paralleled MOSFETs

A good way to parallel a pair of MOSFETs is to locate them on opposite faces of a PCB forming a PCB 'sandwich' as in Figure 4a. Thermal vias between the copper 'land' areas on the PCB reduce the electrical and thermal resistances between their mounting bases.

To parallel a pair of MOSFETs on the same face of a PCB, they can be mounted next to each other as in Figure 4b.

A good way to parallel three MOSFETs is in a ring as in Figure 4c. This arrangement allows all the MOSFET sources in the group to be connected to a 'star' point. The electrical and thermal paths between the MOSFET drains match due to their symmetrical connections to the drain loop.

Minimizing and matching the electrical impedances in the source paths is more important than matching the electrical impedance in the drain paths. This difference is because their gate drives are related to the sources. Good impedance matching in both drain and source is more important in high frequency switching circuits.

If similar electrical and thermal matching can be achieved, larger paralleled groups could be considered. Groups of more than four or five become unwieldy so grouped sub groups should be used.

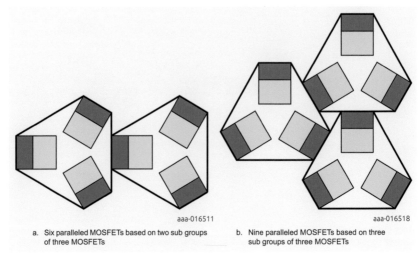

aaa-016511

aaa-016518

a. Six paralleled MOSFETs based on two sub groups
   of three MOSFETs

b. Nine paralleled MOSFETs based on three
   sub groups of three MOSFETs

Figure 5 | Layouts using sub groups of three MOSFETs

In this group of 9 (3 groups of 3), there is a natural drain star point at the center of the group. There are separate source star points at the centers of each sub group. The source star points can be connected on a layer of a multi-layer PCB.

There is a compromise between optimizing layout for power sharing and maximizing PCB usage.

Electrically and thermally optimised layouts always use more PCB area than the minimum possible, but utilization of MOSFET capability should be better. Areas of PCB that are unoccupied by MOSFETs or gate drive components are useful for thermal interfaces with heat sink or cooling air.

4 Power sharing in dynamic operation [pulse and Pulse Width Modulation (PWM) circuits]

Many MOSFET circuits are designed to operate in systems where they are switched repetitively (such as DC-to-DC converters). Paralleled MOSFETs can be used as the switching elements in the system, but in addition to the guidelines set out for optimal steady state power sharing. Some additional points must be considered so that the MOSFETs share current during the switching transitions.

Good circuit and layout design is important. It influences the proportion of current carried by each MOSFET in the group during and after the switching event.

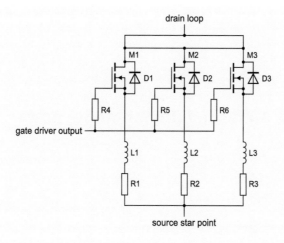

aaa-016505

Figure 6 | Schematic diagram showing the stray source inductances and source resistances

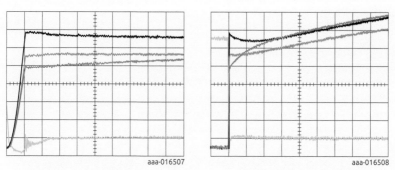

aaa-016507

aaa-016508

a. MOSFET drain current distribution immediately after turn on. The time base scale is 100 ns/division.

b. The same MOSFET drain current distribution as in Figure 7a showing the changes as time progress. The time base scale is 100 μs/division.

Figure 7 | Oscilloscope plots showing the MOSFET drain currents (black, red and blue) and drain source voltage (yellow) after turn on

Figure 7a and Figure 7b show how the current distribution in three paralleled MOSFETs initially depends on the source inductances in the MOSFET current paths, namely L1, L2 and L3. As time progresses the resistances in the MOSFET current paths, namely $R_{DS(on)}$+ R1, $R_{DS(on)}$ + R2 and $R_{DS(on)}$+ R3 determine the current distribution.

The same principles hold about impedance matching of the current paths to the MOSFETs in the group. In this case, it is more important for the rates of change of current in the MOSFETs to match. The source inductances are the key impedance as they affect the gate-source voltages (gate drives) of the MOSFETs in the group.

This effect dominates more in high frequency and short duty cycle applications (e.g. switched-mode power supplies). It may be insignificant in lower frequency applications such as motor drives.

5 Partially enhanced (linear mode) power sharing

If a group of MOSFETs must operate in linear (partially enhanced) mode, great caution is needed. MOSFETs simply paralleled together as they are for fully enhanced conduction are very unlikely to share power or current well.

This behavior is due to the Negative Temperature Coefficient (NTC) of gate threshold voltage $V_{GS(th)}$. As the group of MOSFETs starts to enhance, the MOSFET with the lowest $V_{GS(th)}$ starts to conduct channel current first. It dissipates more power than the others and heat up more. Its $V_{GS(th)}$ decreases even further which causes it to enhance further.

This unbalanced heating causes the hottest MOSFETs to take a greater proportion of the power (and get even hotter). This process is unsustainable and can result in MOSFET failure if the power is not limited. Great care is needed when designing paralleled power MOSFET circuits that operate in the partially enhanced (linear mode) condition.

If all the MOSFETs in the group operate within their Safe Operating Area (SOA), they work reliably. The SOA must be adjusted for the worst case mounting base temperature that occurs in the application. Remember that the data sheet SOA graph applies only if the MOSFET mounting base temperature is 25 °C or less.

Adding external source resistors (R1 to R4 in the schematic; see Figure 8) provides the negative feedback needed for stable operation. The gate-source voltage applied to V_{GS} (M1) = $V_G - I_D$ (M1) × R1.

If the MOSFETs must also operate in fully enhanced mode (e.g. in 'Hot Swap' or 'Soft Start' applications), the inclusion of these resistors is an efficiency disadvantage.

As the MOSFET channel current increases, its gate drive voltage reduces.

As the MOSFETs are operating in partial enhancement (where MOSFET $R_{DS(on)}$ is not important), there is no adverse effect caused by including these resistors. If the MOSFETs must operate in both modes (as with active clamping after fully enhanced conduction), the inclusion of source resistors does have a negative impact.

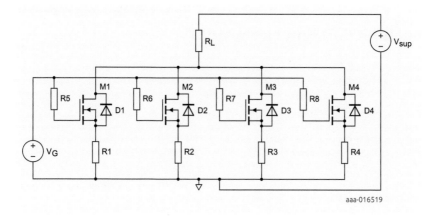

Figure 8 | Schematic diagram of a group of four paralleled MOSFETs intended to operate in linear mode

MOSFETs developed specifically for linear mode operation are available from Nexperia. They can simplify the design of paralleled groups of MOSFETs intended for linear mode operation.

6 Gate drive considerations

It is preferable to fit low value gate resistors between the gate driver and the gate of each MOSFET in the group.

Their main function is to decouple the MOSFET gates from each other so they all receive similar gate drive signals. Without these resistors, at turn on the Miller plateau of the MOSFET with the lowest threshold voltage would act to clamp the gate-source voltages of the other MOSFETs in the group. This clamping effect tends to inhibit and delay the turning on of the other MOSFETs in the group. At turn off a similar process occurs.

Without these resistors, the MOSFET with the lowest threshold voltage would switch on first and switch off last. The consequences of this effect may be insignificant in low frequency high duty cycle applications. In higher frequency PWM applications, it could cause a significant power imbalance between the MOSFETs. Positive feedback also occurs in this case which increases the imbalance and could ultimately cause MOSFET failure.

Gate resistors also help to damp out oscillatory transients on V_{GS}. They also swamp any effects caused by variations in the internal gate resistance $R_{G(int)}$ of the MOSFETs.

6.1 Should individual gate drivers be used for each MOSFET in the group?

Using individual gate drivers for each MOSFET in the group is usually unnecessary. They may be necessary in applications where fast switching of a large group of large die MOSFETs is needed. Here the MOSFETs should be arranged in smaller sub groups, each sub group driven by an individual gate driver. Care should be taken to balance the circuit so the propagation delays of all the gate drivers are similar. This matching ensures that the switching of all the MOSFETs in the group is synchronized. Usually it is sufficient to drive the gate of each MOSFET in the group from the same gate driver. However, it is important to have a gate resistor between the gate driver output and the gate of each MOSFET as mentioned earlier.

7 MOSFET packaging considerations for paralleled groups

Conventionally packaged surface-mounted MOSFETs (DPAK and D^{2}PAK) are the most widely available types so they are considered first for paralleled groups. However, KGD and LFPAK (power SO8) MOSFETs could offer better solutions.

7.1 Bare die (KGD) MOSFETs

These MOSFETs offer the densest and most flexible options for paralleled groups; they are designed to suit a specific application. The die aspect ratio and gate pad location can be designed specifically to suit the application. More source wire bonds can be fitted to the die than can be fitted in a conventionally packaged MOSFET, so overall $R_{DS(on)}$ can be reduced. Maximum drain current can be increased to achieve better performance from a paralleled group of MOSFETs. Special manufacturing facilities are required for KGD assembly.

7.2 LFPAK MOSFETs

The power SO8 (LFPAK) MOSFETs offer the opportunity to manufacture the paralleled MOSFET circuit conventionally. Higher component density and power capability are possible (approaching that of KGDs). The connections to the source and gate are made using copper clips which give better electrical and thermal performance than aluminum wire bonds in conventional packages.

8 Inductive energy dissipation in paralleled MOSFETs

8.1 Avalanching - low side MOSFET group driving a high side inductive load

If the group of paralleled MOSFETs is driving an inductive load, energy stored in this load must be safely dissipated when the current is switched off. A good way to manage this energy is to connect a 'freewheel diode' across the load; see Figure 9. Current flowing in the MOSFET channel diverts into the diode when the MOSFETs switch off and the energy is dissipated in the circuit resistances. However, it is not always possible and energy must then be dissipated safely in the MOSFETs.

If the battery polarity (V_{sup}) is reversed, the low impedance path through the freewheel diode and the body diode can carry large damaging currents. Freewheel diodes are often not used for this reason.

When the group of MOSFETs is switched off, the back e.m.f. from the inductive load may be high enough to cause the drain-source voltage across the group of MOSFETs to exceed the drain-source breakdown voltage $V_{(BR)DSS}$ of one of the MOSFETs. It likely that MOSFETs in the group have a range of $V_{(BR)DSS}$ values (even though they are the same type). The current then flows through the body diode of the MOSFET with the lowest $V_{(BR)DSS}$ in reverse (avalanche) conduction. This condition causes high-power dissipation and temperature rise in the MOSFET die ($P = I_D \times V_{(BR)DSS}$). If the maximum 175 °C junction temperature is exceeded, the thermal stress on the die could degrade or destroy the MOSFET.

In the worst case, all the current which was flowing through the group of MOSFETs could be diverted into the body diode of one MOSFET in the group. If this scenario is possible, it is vital that a single MOSFET in the group can safely handle the total avalanche current under worst case thermal conditions. $V_{(BR)DSS}$ has a positive temperature coefficient which tends to redistribute the current towards other MOSFETs with higher $V_{(BR)DSS}$ values.

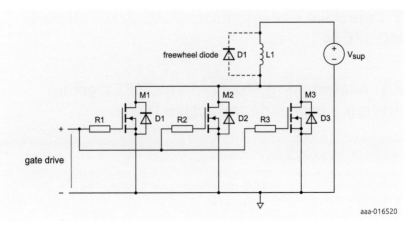

Figure 9 | Low side MOSFET group driving a high side inductive load

8.2 Active clamping - high side MOSFET group driving a low side inductive load

This configuration (see Figure 10) is often used in automotive applications. This topology is useful because the vehicle chassis can be used as the negative supply return path to the battery.

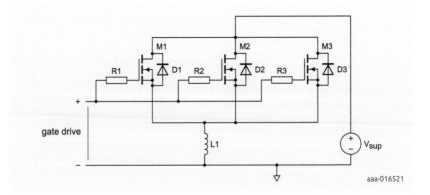

Figure 10 | High side MOSFET group driving a low side inductive load

In this circuit, the difference between the threshold voltages rather than $V_{(BR)DSS}$ spread determines where the load current flows. The MOSFET with the lowest threshold voltage conducts the greatest proportion of the current. The drain-source voltage across the MOSFET group is $V_{sup} + V_{GS}$ and the power dissipation of the group is $(V_{sup} + V_{GS}) \times I_D$. As with the avalanche case, all the current (and hence all the power dissipation) could be diverted into a single MOSFET in the group.

This situation is worse than the avalanche case because MOSFET threshold voltage has a negative temperature coefficient. This characteristic tends to direct the current flow initially to the hottest MOSFET. This MOSFET then gets even hotter so that it retains the current.

9 Summary

1. It is better to use a single large MOSFET rather than a group of smaller MOSFETs.

2. The power capability of a group of n MOSFETs never achieves n times the power capability of a single MOSFET.

3. If it is necessary to use paralleled MOSFETs, use the lowest number possible as the basic group size (3 maximum).

4. If a larger number is needed, use a group of basic groups i.e. 4 = 2 groups of 2; 6 = 2 groups of 3.

5. The circuit layout is a very important factor determining how well a group of paralleled MOSFETs share power dissipation, particularly in higher frequency repetitive switching circuits.

6. Consider LFPAKs (for repetitive switching applications) because of their small size, good thermal performance and low package impedances.

7. Special care is needed when designing groups of MOSFETs that could operate in avalanche or active clamping mode.

10 Tables

11 Figures

Chapter 4

Power MOSFET single-shot and repetitive avalance ruggedness rating

Application Note: AN10273

Power MOSFET single-shot and repetitive avalanche ruggedness rating

1 Introduction

Power MOSFETs are normally measured based on single-shot Unclamped Inductive Switching (UIS) avalanche energy. This chapter describes in detail, the avalanche ruggedness performance, fundamentals of UIS operation and appropriate quantification method for the safe operating condition.

Electronic applications have progressed significantly in recent years and have inevitably increased the demand for an intrinsically rugged power MOSFET. Device ruggedness defines the capacity of a device to sustain an avalanche current during an unclamped inductive load switching event. The avalanche ruggedness performance of a power MOSFET is normally measured as a single- shot Unclamped Inductive Switching (UIS) avalanche energy or $E_{DS(AL)S}$. It provides an easy and quick method of quantifying the robustness of a MOSFET in avalanche mode. However, it does not necessarily reflect the true device avalanche capability (see Ref. 1, Ref. 2 and Ref. 3) in an application.

This chapter explains the fundamentals of UIS operation. It reviews the appropriate method of quantifying the safe operating condition for a power MOSFET, subjected to UIS operating condition. The chapter also covers the discussions on repetitive avalanche ruggedness capability and how this operation can be quantified to operate safely.

2 Single-shot and repetitive avalanche definitions

Single-shot avalanche events are avalanche events that occur due to a fault condition in the application such as electrical overstress. The application does not have an avalanche designed into its operation.

However, repetitive avalanche refers to the applications where avalanche is an intended operation mode of the MOSFET. Here, avalanche is a designed function and has a limited number of operations to ensure reliability of the MOSFET over its life. The number of allowed events is a function of the avalanche energy and can be determined from the data sheet charts found on repetitive avalanche specific parts – ending in suffix R e.g. BUK9K51-60R.

Any customer wishing to operate outside the current avalanche ratings may be considered on an application basis. Contact your local sales team for more information.

3 Understanding power MOSFET single-shot avalanche events

The researchers and the industry have established single-shot avalanche capability of a device (see Ref. 1, Ref. 2 and Ref. 3). The test is carried out on a simple unclamped inductive load switching circuit, as shown in Figure 1.

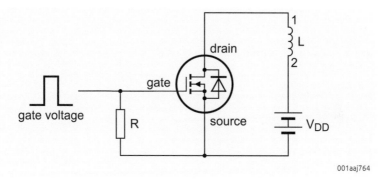

001aaj764

Figure 1 | Unclamped inductive load test circuit for MOSFET ruggedness evaluation

3.1 Single-shot UIS operation

A voltage pulse is applied to the gate to turn on the MOSFET, as shown in Figure 2. It allows the load current to ramp up according to the inductor value (L) and the drain supply voltage (V_{DD}). The phenomenon is shown in Figure 3 and Figure 4. At the end of the gate pulse, the MOSFET is turned off. The current in the inductor continues to flow, causing the voltage across the MOSFET to rise sharply. This overvoltage is clamped at breakdown voltage (V_{BR}) until the load current reaches zero, as illustrated in Figure 3. Typically, V_{BR} is:

$$V_{BR} \approx 1.3 \times V_{(BR)DSS} \qquad [1]$$

The peak load current passing through the MOSFET before turn off is the non-repetitive drain- source avalanche current ($I_{DS(AL)S}$) of the UIS event. $I_{DS(AL)S}$ is illustrated in Figure 4. The following expression is used to determine the rate at which the avalanche current decays, which is dependent on the inductor value:

$$\frac{dI_{DS(AL)S}}{dt_{AL}} = -\frac{V_{BR} - V_{DD}}{L} \qquad [2]$$

The peak drain-source avalanche power ($P_{DS(AL)M}$) dissipated in the MOSFET is shown in Figure 5. It is a product of the breakdown voltage (V_{BR}) and the non-repetitive drain-source avalanche current ($I_{DS(AL)S}$); see Figure 3 and Figure 4. The avalanche energy dissipated is the area under the P_{AV} waveform and is estimated from the following expression:

$$E_{DS(AL)S} = \frac{P_{DS(AL)M} \times t_{AL}}{2} \qquad [3]$$

or

$$E_{DS(AL)S} = \frac{1}{2} \cdot \frac{V_{BR}}{V_{BR} - V_{DD}} \cdot LI^2_{DS(AL)S} \qquad [4]$$

Another crucial parameter involved in a MOSFET avalanche event is the junction temperature. After the avalanche event (τ) has begun, the following expression is used to determine the transient junction temperature variation during device avalanche at a given time:

$$\Delta T_j(\tau) = \int_0^\tau P_{AV}(t) \frac{dZ_{th(\tau-t)}}{d_t} d_t \qquad [5]$$

where Z_{th} is the power MOSFET transient thermal impedance. Alternatively, the following expression approximates the maximum ΔT_j:

$$\Delta T_{j(max)} \approx \frac{2}{3} P_{DS(AL)M} \; Z_{th(t_{AL})}/2 \qquad [6]$$

Assuming that $T_{j(max)}$ occurs at $t_{AL}/2$, $Z_{th(t_{AL})/2}$ is the transient thermal impedance measured at half the avalanche period t_{AL}. Note, the Z_{th} value used for the avalanche calculation is more conservative than the one published in data sheets due to the nature of avalanche.

Therefore, the maximum junction temperature resulting from the avalanche event is:

$$T_{j(max)} \approx \Delta T_{j(max)} + T_j \qquad [7]$$

where T_j refers to the junction temperature prior to turn off.

3.1.1 Single-shot UIS waveforms

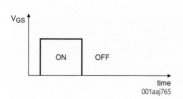

Figure 2 | Gate-source voltage, V_{GS}

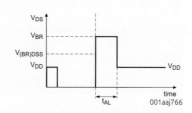

Figure 3 | Drain-source voltage, V_{DS}

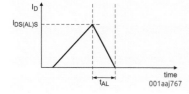

Figure 4 | Drain current, I_D

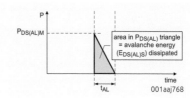

Figure 5 | Peak drain-source avalanche power, $P_{DS(AL)M}$

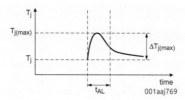

Figure 6 | Transient junction temperature profile of MOSFET during an avalanche event

3.2 Single-shot avalanche ruggedness rating

The failure mechanism for a single-shot avalanche event in a power MOSFET is due to the junction temperature exceeding the maximum temperature rating. In such a case, catastrophic damage occurs to the MOSFET. If the transient temperature resulting from an avalanche event, as shown in Figure 6, rises beyond a recommended rated value, the device risks being degraded. The recommended rated value is de-rated from the maximum temperature for optimum reliability.

Blackburn (see Ref. 2) has discussed a general guideline in detail, on the appropriate method of quantifying the single-shot avalanche capability of a device. It takes the avalanche current and initial junction temperature into consideration. The maximum allowed avalanche current as a function of avalanche time defines the safe operation for a device single-shot UIS event. The maximum allowed avalanche current is set so that a safe maximum junction temperature, $T_{j(max)}$ of 175 °C, is never exceeded. Using Equation 7, Figure 7 is plotted.

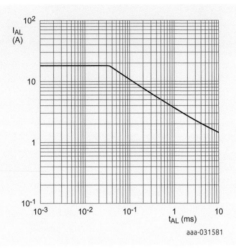

aaa-031581

Figure 7 | BUK9K51-60R avalanche rating; avalanche current as a function of avalanche time

Figure 7 shows the SOA curve of a device single-shot avalanche capability. The 25 °C junction temperature curve shows the maximum allowable IAL for a given t_{AL} at an initial T_j of 25 °C. This maximum I_{AL} results to a maximum allowable junction temperature $T_{j(max)}$ of 175 °C, which means a $\Delta T_{j(max)}$ of 150 °C. The area under the SOA curve is the Safe Operating Area (SOA).

The maximum junction temperature resulting in catastrophic device avalanche failure is approximately 380 °C, which is in excess of the rated $T_{j(max)}$ of 175 °C. However, operating beyond the rated $T_{j(max)}$ may induce long-term detrimental effects to the power MOSFET and is not recommended.

4 Understanding power MOSFET repetitive avalanche events

Repetitive avalanche refers to an operation involving repeated single-shot avalanche events, as discussed earlier. Until recently, most manufacturers have avoided the issues pertaining to the power MOSFET repetitive avalanche capability.

It is primarily due to the complexity in such operations and the difficulties in identifying the underlying physical degradation process in the device.

Due to the traumatic nature of the avalanche event, a repetitive avalanche operation can be hazardous for a MOSFET. It is hazardous even when the individual avalanche events are below the single-shot UIS rating. This type of operation involves additional parameters such as frequency, duty cycle, and thermal resistances $R_{th(j-a)}$ and $R_{th(j-mb)}$ of the system during the avalanche event. However, it is possible to de-rate the single-shot rating to define a repetitive avalanche SOA.

4.1 Repetitive UIS operation

The repetitive UIS test circuit is shown in Figure 1. The gate is fed with a train of voltage pulses at a frequency (f) and for a duty cycle as shown in Figure 8. The resulting breakdown voltage (V_{BR}) and drain current (I_D) passing through the load are the same as for a single-shot UIS. However, the peak I_D is now denoted as repetitive drain-source avalanche current ($I_{DS(AL)R}$), as shown in Figure 9.

The repetitive drain-source avalanche power ($P_{DS(AL)R}$) resulting from the repetitive UIS operation is shown in Figure 10. For finding the value of $P_{DS(AL)R}$, it is necessary to first calculate $E_{DS(AL)S}$ for a single avalanche event using Equation 3. This resultant value of $E_{DS(AL)S}$ is substituted in the following expression, to calculate the value of $P_{DS(AL)R}$:

$$P_{DS(AL)R} = E_{DS(AL)S} \times f \qquad\qquad [8]$$

4.1.1 Repetitive UIS waveforms

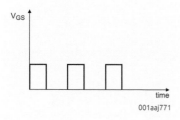

001aaj771

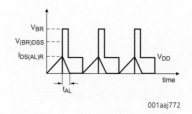

001aaj772

Figure 8 | Gate pulse, V_{GS}

Figure 9 | Drain-source voltage, V_{DS} and repetitive drain-source avalanche current, $I_{DS(AL)R}$

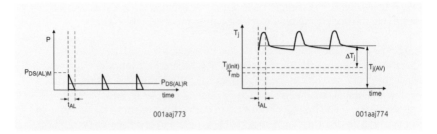

Figure 10 | Repetitive drain-source avalanche power, $P_{DS(AL)R}$

Figure 11 | Transient junction temperature components of MOSFET during repetitive avalanche

4.2 Temperature components

The temperature rise from the repetitive avalanche mode in the power MOSFET is shown in Figure 11.

The temperature ($T_{j(init)}$) comprises the mounting base temperature (T_{mb}) and the temperature rise resulting from any on-state temperature difference (ΔT_{on}).

$$T_{j(init)} = T_{mb} + \Delta T_{on} \qquad [9]$$

In addition, there is a steady-state average junction temperature variation (ΔT_j) resulting from the average repetitive avalanche power loss.

$$\Delta T_j = P_{DS(AL)R} \times R_{th(j-a)} \qquad [10]$$

where $R_{th(j-a)}$ is the thermal resistance from junction to ambient of the device in the application. The summation of Equation 9 and Equation 10 gives the average junction temperature, $T_{j(AV)}$ of a power MOSFET in repetitive UIS operation.

$$T_{j(AV)} = T_{j(init)} + \Delta T_j \qquad [11]$$

5 Repetitive avalanche ruggedness rating

Our investigations show that there is more than one failure or wear-out mechanism involved in repetitive avalanche. Temperature is not the only limiting factor to a repetitive avalanche operation. However, by limiting temperature and the repetitive drain-source avalanche current ($I_{DS(AL)R}$), an operating environment is defined such that the avalanche conditions do not activate device degradation. It allows the power MOSFET to operate under repetitive UIS conditions safely.

Figure 12 shows the repetitive avalanche SOA curve of BUK9K51-60R, where for each avalanche event the T_j rise is limited to 30 K.

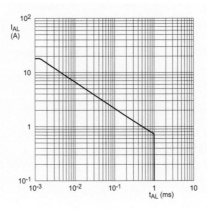

aaa-031582

Figure 12 | Repetitive avalanche rating; avalanche current

The three conditions which must be satisfied for safe operation of a power MOSFET under repetitive avalanche mode are:

1. $I_{(AL)}$ should not exceed the repetitive avalanche SOA curve
2. T_j should not exceed 175 °C
3. The number of cycles should not exceed the avalanche cycle limit chart

The number of allowable cycles can be determined through a second chart in the avalanche MOSFET's data sheet, (see Figure 13).

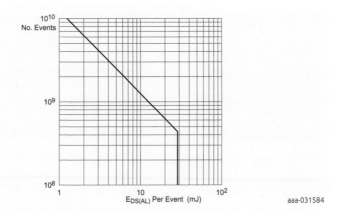

aaa-031584

Figure 13 | Repetitive avalanche rating; maximum number of avalanche events as a function of avalanche energy

Power MOSFET single-shot and repetitive avalanche ruggedness rating

6 Conclusion

Power MOSFETs can sustain single-shot and repetitive avalanche events. Simple design rules and SOA regions are provided.

7 Examples

The following examples examine cases of avalanche operation acceptance:

7.1 Single-shot avalanche case

- Device: BUK9K51-60R; see Figure 7
- $L = 30\ \mu H$
- $I_{AL} = 18\ A$
- $R_{th(j-a)} = 5\ K/W$
- $V_{(BR)DSS} = 60\ V$
- $V_{DD} = 0\ V$

7.1.1 Calculation steps

1. Using the above information, t_{AL} can be determined using Equation 2, which in this case is 7 μs. Transferring the I_{AL} and t_{AL} conditions onto Figure 12, the operating point is under the SOA curve. It suggests that the operating condition may be feasible.

7.2 Repetitive avalanche case

- Device: BUK9K51-60R; see Figure 12 and Figure 13
- $L = 30\ \mu H$
- $I_{(AL)} = 10\ A$
- $f = 3\ kHz$
- $R_{th(j-a)} = 5\ K/W$
- $To = 100\ °C$
- $V_{(BR)DSS} = 60\ V$
- $V_{DD} = 0\ V$

7.2.1. Calculation steps

1. From the above information, t_{AL} can be determined using Equation 2, which in this case is approximately 4 μs. Transferring the I_{AL} and t_{AL} conditions onto

Figure 12, the operating point is under the boundary of the 'Rep. Ava' SOA curve. It suggests that the operating condition is acceptable. Therefore, condition 1 is satisfied.

2. Calculate the non-repetitive drain-source avalanche energy ($E_{DS(AL)S}$) using Equation 3 $E_{DS(AL)S} = 1.56$ mJ).
3. Calculate the repetitive drain-source avalanche power ($P_{DS(AL)R}$) using Equation 8 ($P_{DS(AL)R} = 4.68$ W).
4. Calculate the average ΔTj rise from repetitive avalanche (ΔT_j) using Equation 10 ($\Delta T_j = 123.4$ °C).
5. Determine the average junction maximum temperature in repetitive avalanche operation ($T_{j(AV)}$) using Equation 11 ($T_{j(AV)} = 153$ °C). Therefore, condition 2 is satisfied.
6. Finally based on the energy we can determine the limit number of operations at these conditions from Figure 13, (No. events = $8e^9$)

Based on the above calculations, the operating conditions meet the repetitive avalanche requirements with a limited number of repetitive events of $8e^9$.

▶ Watch video

LFPAK33 Automotive MOSFETs in powertrain applications

▶ Watch video

Single shot avalanche ruggedness of MOSFET

📄 Visit blog

Electrification of the powertrain introduction

📄 Visit blog

LFPAK56D taking the heat out of engine management systems

📄 Visit blog

Talking 48 volts and robust MOSFETs at EEHE Conference

📄 Visit blog

Trench 9 LFPAK33 MOSFETs drive powertrain systems up to 300 W

8 References

1. Turn-Off Failure of Power MOSFETs — D.L. Blackburn, Proc. 1985 IEEE Power Electronics Specialists Conference, pages 429 to 435, June 1985.

2. Power MOSFET failure revisited — D.L. Blackburn, Proc. 1988 IEEE Power Electronics Specialists Conference, pages 681 to 688, April 1988.

3. Boundary of power-MOSFET, unclamped inductive-switching (UIS), avalanche-current capability — Rodney R. Stoltenburg, Proc. 1989 Applied Power Electronics Conference, pages 359 to 364, March 1989.

9 Figures

Chapter 5

Using RC Thermal Models

Application Note: AN11261

1 Introduction

Analysis of the thermal performance of power semiconductors is necessary to efficiently and safely design any system utilizing such devices. This chapter presents a quick and inexpensive way to infer the thermal performance of power MOSFETs using a thermal electrical analogy.

The thermal behaviour of power semiconductor devices can be predicted using RC thermal models. The model types presented in this chapter are known as Foster and Cauer models, consisting in networks of resistors and capacitors. Foster and Cauer models are equivalent representations of the thermal performance of a MOSFET and they can be used within a SPICE environment. This chapter provides some basic theory behind the principle, and how to implement Foster and Cauer RC thermal models. For convenience, Foster and Cauer RC thermal models are referred to as RC models in the rest of this application note. Several methods of using RC thermal models, including worked examples, will be described.

2 Thermal impedance

RC models are derived from the thermal impedance (Z_{th}) of a device (see Figure 1). This figure represents the thermal behavior of a device under transient power pulses. The Z_{th} can be generated by measuring the power losses as a result of applying a step function of varying time periods.

A device subjected to a power pulse of duration > ~1 second, i.e. steady-state, has reached thermal equilibrium and the Z_{th} plateaus becomes the R_{th}. The Z_{th} illustrates the fact that materials have thermal inertia. Thermal inertia means that temperature does not change instantaneously. As a result, the device can handle greater power for shorter duration pulses.

The Z_{th} curves for repetitive pulses with different duty cycles, are also shown in Figure 1. These curves represent the additional RMS temperature rise due to the dissipation of RMS power.

To assist this discussion, the thermal resistance junction to mounting base $R_{th(j-mb)}$ from the BUK7S1R0-40H data sheet, has been included in Table 1. The Z_{th} in Figure 1 also belongs to the BUK7S1R0-40H data sheet.

Table 1: Steady state thermal impedance of BUK7S1R0-40H

Symbol	Parameter	Conditions	Min	Typ	Max	Unit
$R_{th(j-mb)}$	thermal resistance from junction to mounting base	-		0.35	0.4	K/W

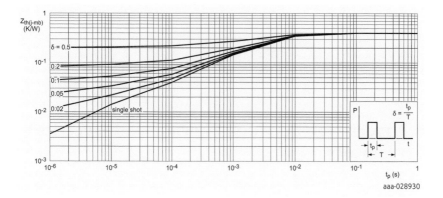

aaa-028930

Figure 1 | Transient thermal impedance from junction to mounting base as a function of pulse duration for the BUK7S1R0-40H

3 Calculating junction temperature rise

To calculate the temperature rise within the junction of a power MOSFET, the power and duration of the pulse delivered to the device must be known. If the power pulse is a square, then the thermal impedance can be read from the Z_{th} chart. The product of this value with the power gives the temperature rise within the junction.

If constant power is applied to the device, the steady state thermal impedance can be used i.e. R_{th}. Again the temperature rise is the product of the power and the R_{th}.

For a transient pulse e.g. sinusoidal or pulsed, the temperature rise within the MOSFET junction becomes more difficult to calculate.

The mathematically correct way to calculate T_j is to apply the convolution integral. The calculation expresses both the power pulse and the Z_{th} curve as functions of time, and use the convolution integral to produce a temperature profile (see Ref. 2).

$$T_{j(rise)} \int_0^\tau P_{(t)} \bullet = \frac{d}{dt} Z_{th} (\tau - t) \, dt \qquad [1]$$

However, this is difficult as the $Z_{th(\tau-t)}$ is not defined mathematically.
An alternative way is to approximate the waveforms into a series of rectangular pulse and apply superposition (see Ref. 1).

While relatively simple, applying superposition has its disadvantages. The more complex the waveform, the more superpositions that must be imposed to model the waveform accurately.

To represent Z_{th} as a function of time, we can draw upon the thermal electrical analogy and represent it as a series of RC charging equations or as an RC ladder. Z_{th} can then be represented in a SPICE environment for ease of calculation of the junction temperature.

4 Association between Thermal and Electrical parameters

The thermal electrical analogy is summarized in Table 2. If the thermal resistance and capacitance of a semiconductor device is known, electrical resistances and capacitances can represent them respectively. Using current as power, and voltage as the temperature difference, any thermal network can be handled as an electrical network.

Table 2: Fundamental parameters

Type	Resistance	Potential	Energy	Capacitance
Electrical $(R = V/I)$	R = resistance (Ohms)	V = PD (Volts)	I = current (Amps)	C = capacitance (Farads)
Thermal $(R_{th} = K/W)$	R_{th} = thermal resistance (K/W)	K = temperature difference (Kelvin)	W = dissipated power (Watts)	C_{th} = thermal capacitance (thermal mass)

5 Foster and Cauer RC thermal models

Foster models are derived by semi-empirically fitting a curve to the Z_{th}, the result of which is a one-dimensional RC network Figure 2. The R and C values in a Foster model do not correspond to geometrical locations on the physical device. Therefore, these values cannot be calculated from device material constants as can be in other modeling techniques. Finally, a Foster RC model cannot be divided or interconnected through, i.e. have the RC network of a heat sink connected.

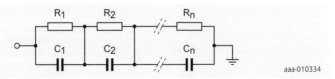

aaa-010334

Figure 2 | Foster RC thermal models

Foster RC models have the benefit of ease of expression of the thermal impedance Z_{th} as described at the end of Section 2. For example, by measuring the heating or cooling curve and generating a Z_{th} curve, Equation 2 can be applied to generate a fitted curve Figure 3:

$$Z_{th(t)} = \sum_{i=1}^{n} R_i \cdot \left[1 - exp\left(-\tfrac{t}{\tau_i} \right) \right] \qquad [2]$$

Where: $\tau i = R i \cdot C i$ $\qquad$ [3]

The model parameters R_i and C_i are the thermal resistances and capacitances that build up the thermal model depicted in Figure 2. The parameters in the analytical expression can be optimised until the time response matches the transient system response by applying a least square fit algorithm.

The individual expression, "i", also draws parallels with the electrical capacitor charging equation. Figure 3 shows how the individual R_i and C_i combinations, sum to make the Z_{th} curve.

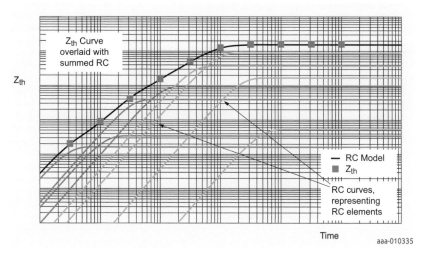

aaa-010335

Figure 3 | Foster RC thermal models

Foster models have no physical meaning since the node-to-node heat capacitances have no physical reality. However, a Foster model can be converted into its Cauer counter-part by means of a mathematical transformation (see Ref. 4).

An n-stage Cauer model can be derived from an n-stage Foster model and they will be equivalent representations of the device thermal performance.

As seen for the Foster model, the Cauer Model also consists of an RC network but the thermal capacitances are all connected to the thermal ground, i.e. ambient temperature as represented in Figure 4. The nodes in the Cauer Model can have physical meaning and allow access to the temperature of the internal layers of the semiconductor structure.

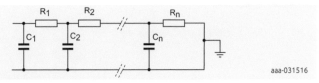

Figure 4 | Cauer RC thermal models

Nexperia provides Foster and Cauer RC models for most of their Automotive Power MOSFET products on the Product Information Pages. The models can be found under the Support tab, demonstrated below with BUK7S1R0-40H, see Figure 5.

Figure 5 | Nexperia RC thermal model documentation

Foster and Cauer RC thermal models allow application engineers to perform fast calculations of the transient response of a package to complex power profiles. In the following sections several examples of using RC thermal models will be presented. Foster models and Cauer models are equivalent representations of the device thermal behaviour but in the described examples Cauer models will be used as more representative of the physical structure of the device.

As shown in Figure 8, a schematic file is available on Nexperia website for BUK7S1R0-40H Cauer model. Other products may not have this schematic file available and may be provided with a netlist file for the Cauer network as shown in Figure 6:

*Part: BUK7S1R0-40H

```
.subckt cauer 1 6 7
R1      1       2       0.00272144
R2      2       3       0.0220255
R3      3       4       0.00713124
R4      4       5       0.185679
R5      5       6       0.182443
C1      1       7       9.29451e-05
C2      2       7       0.000514739
C3      3       7       0.00195047
C4      4       7       0.00305028
C5      5       7       0.0279554
.end cauer
```

Figure 6 | BUK7S1R0-40H Cauer model netlist

The netlist describes the same Cauer network as in Figure 8, and can be used to build the same schematic. Pin 1 in the netlist can be identified as the junction temperature pin T_j in the schematic. Similarly pins 6, 7 as the T_{amb} pins in the schematic.

In order to simulate only the MOSFET pins 6 and 7 will both be tied to the ambient voltage source, as shown in Figure. 8.

However, one of the advantages of using Cauer models is to allow to add external networks to the MOSFET model, for example to model PCBs, heatsinks etc. In order to do so pin 7 will be tied to ambient and pin 6 to the first pin of the external Cauer network. For correct results, it is fundamental to make sure that the end pin of the external Cauer network is tied to the ambient source.

6 Thermal simulation examples

6.1 Example 1

RC thermal models are generated from the Z_{th} curve. This example shows how to work back from an RC model and plot a Z_{th} curve within a SPICE simulator. It allows for greater ease when trying to read values of the Z_{th} curve from the data sheet. This and subsequent examples use the RC thermal model of BUK7S1R0-40H. T_{mb} represents the mounting base temperature. It is treated as an isothermal and for

5

Using RC Thermal Models

this example it is set as 0 °C.

A single shot pulse of 1 W power is dissipated in the MOSFET. Referring to Figure 7; for a single shot pulse, the time period between pulses is infinite and therefore the duty cycle δ = 0. Then the junction temperature T_j represents the transient thermal impedance Z_{th}.

aaa-010337

Figure 7 | Single-shot pulse

$$T_j = T_{mb} + \Delta T = 0 \ ^oC + \Delta T = \Delta T \qquad\qquad [4]$$

$$\Delta T = P \bullet Z_{th} = 1 \ W \bullet Z_{th} \qquad\qquad [5]$$

Equation 5 demonstrates that with P = 1 W, the magnitude of Z_{th} equates to ΔT. The following steps are used to set up and run simulations:

1. set up the RC thermal model of BUK7S1R0-40H in SPICE as shown in Figure 8
2. set the value of voltage source V_{mb} to 0, which is the value of T_{mb}
3. set the value of the current source I1 to 1
4. create a simulation profile and set the run time to 1 s
5. run the simulation
6. Plot the voltage at nod

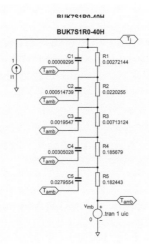

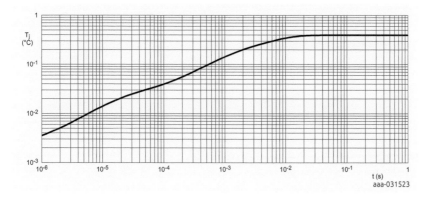

aaa-031522

Figure 8 | BUK7S1R0-40H thermal model setup in SPICE

The simulation result in Figure 9 shows the junction temperature (voltage at T_j) which is also the thermal impedance of BUK7S1R0-40H. The values of Z_{th} at different times can be read using the cursors on this plot within SPICE.

Figure 9 | A plot of T_j from simulation

The value of the current source in this example is set to 1 A to represent 1 W dissipating through the device. It can be easily changed to represent any value of power. The simulation command can be changed for any duration to represent a range of square power pulses.

6.2 Example 2

Another method of generating the power profile, is to use measurements from the actual circuit. This information is presented to the SPICE simulation in the form of a comma-separated value (CSV) file giving pairs of time/power values. It can be generated either as a summary of observations showing the points of change or from an oscilloscope waveform capture.

Two further methods of generating a power profile are discussed. One method is using a PWL file. The other is to generate the power from an MOSFET electrical circuit modeled in SPICE. The former is outlined first.

A source within a SPICE simulator can use a PWL file as an input. The contents of a typical PWL file is shown in Table 3. It can list the current, voltage or in this example, power over time. These files can be generated by typing values into a spreadsheet editor and saving as a .csv file, or alternatively exporting waveforms from an oscilloscope. The actual file itself should not contain any column headings. To implement this procedure within a SPICE environment, follow the same steps as described in Section 6.1 "Example 1", but with the exceptions:

1. Set the property value of the current source to read from a PWL FILE and point it to a .csv file for example: C:\Pulse file\filepulse.csv, which contains the power profile listed in Table 3
2. Set the mounting base T_{mb} (V_{mb}) to 125 °C
3. Set the simulation run time to 0.6 s

Table 3: Data example for use in a PWL file

Time (seconds)	Power (Watts)
0.000000	0
0.000001	120
0.004000	120
0.004001	24
0.004002	24
0.100000	24
0.100001	24
0.100002	80
0.200000	80
0.200002	80
0.200003	0
0.300000	0
0.300001	80
0.315000	80
0.315001	24
0.400000	24
0.400001	0
0.500000	0
0.500001	120
0.515000	120

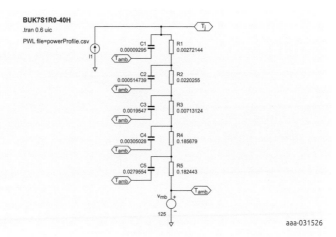

aaa-031526

Figure 10 | SPICE circuit implementing a PWL file with the thermal model of the BUK7S1R0-40H

The simulation result is shown in Figure 11. The junction temperature and thermal impedance values labeled in Figure. 11 demonstrate that the Z_{th} value at 4 ms, and R_{th} value, are in line with Figure 12. It represents the thermal impedance waveform shown in the BUK7S1R0-40H data sheet.

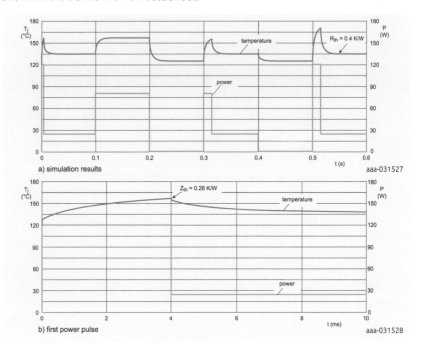

Figure 11 | Simulation results and first power pulse

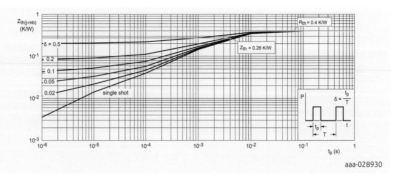

Figure 12 | Transient thermal impedance for BUK7S1R0-40H

The red lines highlight the thermal resistance and impedance for the example shown in Figure 11

6.3 Example 3

The aim of this example is to show how to perform thermal simulation using the power profile generated from a MOSFET circuit.

Following the steps in Section 6.1, set up the thermal model of BUK7S1R0-40H, and set the mounting base temperature to 85 °C.

To set the power value in the current source, construct a MOSFET electrical circuit as provided in Figure 13. The power supply is 12 V. The gate drive supply is assigned a value of 10 V. It is set to run for 50 cycles with a 1 ms period and a 50 % duty cycle.

The power dissipated in the MOSFET can be calculated from Equation 6 or for greater accuracy; the gate current can be included into the calculation to give Equation 7:

$$P = V_{DS} \bullet I_D \tag{6}$$

To improve accuracy:

$$P = V_{DS} \bullet I_D + V_{GS} \bullet I_G \tag{7}$$

The current source into the thermal model can now be defined as:

$$I = V_{(D)} \bullet I\,(V_D) + V_{(G)} \bullet I\,(V_G) \tag{8}$$

Figure 13 demonstrates the link between the electrical circuit and the thermal model circuit.

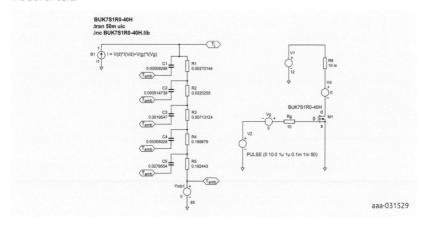

aaa-031529

Figure 13 | SPICE circuit illustrating how to integrate an electrical circuit with a thermal model

The resultant plot of T_j is shown in Figure 14. The maximum temperature of the junction can once again be calculated from data sheet values by following the steps outlined in Ref. 1.

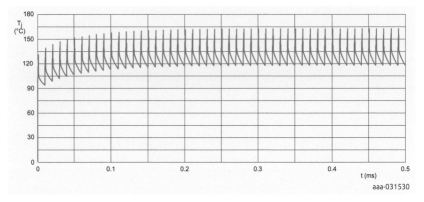

aaa-031530

Figure 14 | Inferred junction temperature (T_j) rise provided by Figure 12

7 Discussions

RC thermal models are not perfect. The physical materials used to build Semiconductors have temperature-dependent characteristics. These characteristics mean that thermal resistance is also a temperature-dependent parameter. Whereas in Ohm's law, the Ohmic resistance is usually considered to be constant and independent of the voltage. So the correspondence between electrical and thermal parameters is not perfectly symmetrical but gives a good basis for fundamental thermal simulations.

In power electronic systems, the thermal resistance of silicon amounts to 2 % to 5 % of the total resistance. The error resulting from the temperature dependence is relatively small and can be ignored for most cases. To obtain a more accurate analysis, replace the passive resistors in the RC model with voltage-dependent resistors. In these resistors, the change in temperature can correspond to change in voltage.

A further limitation of the models presented is that the mounting base temperature of the MOSFET T_{mb}, is set as an isothermal. This is rarely the case in real applications where a rise in the mounting base temperature must be considered. This rise is determined by calculating the temperature rise due to the average power dissipation (i.e. the heat flow) from the mounting base through to ambient. It means that the models are of limited use for pulses greater than 1 s, where heat begins to flow into the environment of the MOSFET. In this situation, the thermal model for the MOSFETs, PCB, heat sink and other materials in proximity must be included.

8 Summary

RC thermal models are available for Nexperia power MOSFETs on the Nexperia website. The models can be used in SPICE or other simulation tools to simulate the junction temperature rise in transient conditions. They provide a quick, simple and accurate method for application engineers to perform the thermal design.

RC thermal simulation of
power MOSFETs

9 References

1. Application note AN11156 - "Using Power MOSFET Z_{th} Curves". Nexperia

2. Application note AN10273 - "Power MOSFET single-shot and repetitive avalanche ruggedness rating". Nexperia

3. Combination of Thermal Subsystems Modeled by Rapid Circuit Transformation. Y.C. Gerstenmaier, W. Kiffe, and G. Wachutka

4. JEDEC Standard JESD51-14 Transient Dual Interface Test Method for the Measurement of the Thermal Resistance Junction-to-Case of Semiconductor Devices with Heat Flow Through a Single Path

10 Tables

11 Figures

Chapter 6

Designing RC snubbers

Application Note: AN11160

1 Introduction

This chapter describes the design of a simple "RC snubber circuit". The snubber is used to suppress high-frequency oscillations associated with reverse recovery effects in power semiconductor applications.

2 Test circuit

The basic circuit is a half-bridge and shown in Figure 1.

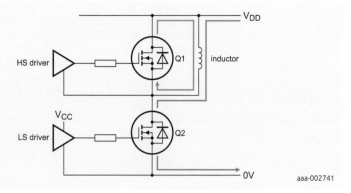

Figure 1 | The half-bridge circuit

Q1 and Q2 are BUK761R6-40E devices. The inductor could also be connected to 0 V rather than V_{DD}.

Inductor current is established in the red loop; Q2 is off and current is flowing through Q1 body diode. When Q2 is turned on, current "commutates" to the blue loop and the reverse recovery effect occurs in Q1. We observe the effect of Q1 reverse recovery on the V_{DS} waveform of Q2; see Figure 2.

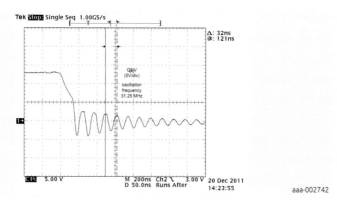

Figure 2 | Reverse recovery-induced oscillation in Q2 V_{DS}

The equivalent circuit is shown in Figure 3.

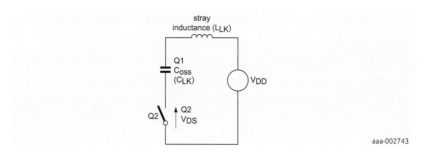

Figure 3 | Equivalent circuit

We are primarily interested in the parasitic elements in the circuit:

- L_{LK} is the total stray or "leakage" inductance comprised of PCB trace inductance, device package inductance, etc.

- The parasitic capacitance C_{LK} is mainly due to C_{oss} of the upper (Q1) device.

Q2 is treated as a simple switch. The oscillation can be eliminated (snubbed) by placing an RC circuit across Q1 drain-source; see Figure 4

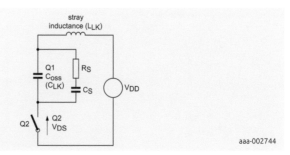

Figure 4 | Equivalent circuit with snubber components R_S and C_S

3 Determining C_{LK} and L_{LK}

Before we can design the snubber, we must first determine C_{LK} and L_{LK}. We could attempt to measure C_{LK} and L_{LK} directly, but a more elegant method can be used. For this LC circuit, we know that:

$$f_{RING0} = \frac{1}{2\pi\sqrt{L_{LK}C_{LK}}}$$ [1]

where f_{RING0} is the frequency of oscillation without a snubber in place; see Figure 2. If we add an extra additional capacitor across Q1 (C_{add}), the initial oscillation frequency from f_{RING0} to f_{RING1} ($f_{RING1} < f_{RING0}$) will change. It can be shown that (see Section 7 "Appendix A; determining C_{LK} from C_{add}, f_{RING0} and f_{RING1}"):

$$C_{LK} = \frac{C_{add}}{x^2 - 1}$$ [2]

where:

$$x = \frac{f_{RING0}}{f_{RING1}}$$ [3]

So if we measure f_{RING0} (without C_{add}), then add a known C_{add} and measure f_{RING1}, we can determine C_{LK} and L_{LK} (two equations, two unknowns).

C_{add} = 3200 pF was added in circuit, and f_{RING1} found to be 22.2 MHz (f_{RING0} previously found to be 31.25 MHz; see Figure 2).

from Equation 3:

$$x = \frac{31.25}{22.2} = 1.41$$ [4]

and from Equation 2:

$$C_{LK} = \frac{3200\,pF}{1.41^2 - 1} = 3239\,pF$$ [5]

Rearranging Equation 1:

$$L_{LK} = \frac{1}{(2\pi f_{RING0})^2 C_{LK}} \qquad [6]$$

So with f_{RING0} = 31.25 MHz and C_{LK} = 3239 pF:

$$L_{LK} = \frac{1}{(2 \times \pi \times 3.125 \times 10^7)^2 \times 3.239 \times 10^{-9}} = 8.01 \times 10^{-9}\,H = 8.0\,nH \qquad [7]$$

and with f_{RING1} = 22.2 MHz and $(C_{LK} + C_{add})$ = 3239 pF + 3200 pF = 6439 pF:

$$L_{LK} = \frac{1}{(2 \times \pi \times 2.22 \times 10^7)^2 \times 6.439 \times 10^{-9}} \quad 7.98 \times 10^{-9}\,H = 8.0\,nH \qquad [8]$$

In other words, the calculated value of L_{LK} remains almost unchanged when we add the additional 3200 pF capacitance. This is a good sanity check of the method for determining C_{LK} and L_{LK}.

4 Designing the snubber - theory

If we replace C_S in Figure 4 with a short-circuit, then we simply have the classic RLC circuit found in text books. The response of this circuit to a step change in voltage (that is Q2 turning on) depends on the degree of damping (ζ or zeta) in the circuit; see Figure 5.

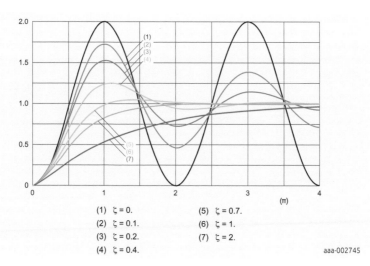

(1) ζ = 0.	(5) ζ = 0.7.
(2) ζ = 0.1.	(6) ζ = 1.
(3) ζ = 0.2.	(7) ζ = 2.
(4) ζ = 0.4.	

aaa-002745

Figure 5 | Step response of an RLC circuit for various values of zeta (ζ)

In theory the circuit oscillates indefinitely if ζ = zero, although this is a practical impossibility as there is always some resistance in a real circuit. As ζ increases towards one, the oscillation becomes more damped that is, tends to decrease over time with an exponential decay envelope. This is an "underdamped" response. The case ζ = one is known as "critically damped" and is the point at which oscillation just ceases. For values of greater than one (overdamped), the response of the circuit becomes more sluggish with the waveform taking longer to reach its final value. There is therefore more than one possible degree of damping which we could build into a snubber, and choice of damping is therefore part of the snubber design process.

For this configuration of RLC circuit, the relationship between ζ, R_S, L_{LK} and C_{LK} is:

$$\varsigma = \left(\frac{1}{2R_S} \right)\sqrt{\frac{L_{LK}}{C_{LK}}} \qquad\qquad [9]$$

The snubber capacitor C_S does not appear in Equation 9.

In some circuits, it is possible to damp the oscillations with R_S alone. However, in typical half-bridge circuits we cannot have a resistor mounted directly across Q1 drain source. If we did, then Q1 is permanently shorted by the resistor and the circuit as a whole would not function as required. The solution is therefore to put C_S in series with R_S, with the value of C_S chosen so as not to interfere with normal operation.

The snubber is a straightforward RC circuit whose cut-off frequency f_C is:

$$F_C = \frac{1}{2\pi R_C C_S} \qquad\qquad [10]$$

Again, we must choose which value of f_C to be used, and there is no single correct answer to this question. The cut-off frequency of the snubber must be low enough to effectively short-circuit the undamped oscillation frequency f_{RINGO}, but not so low as to present a significant conduction path at the operating frequency of the circuit (for example 100 kHz or whatever). A good starting point has been found to be $f_C = f_{RINGO}$.

5 Designing the snubber - in practice

We now have sufficient information to design a snubber for the waveform shown in Figure 2. To recap:

C_{LK} = 3239 pF

L_{LK} = 8.0 nH

f_{RING0} = 31.25 MHz

$$\varsigma = \left(\frac{1}{2R_S}\right)\sqrt{\frac{L_{LK}}{C_{LK}}}$$ [11]

$$F_C = \frac{1}{2\pi R_C C_S} = f_{RING0}$$ [12]

The first task is to choose a value of damping (Figure 5). We have chosen $\zeta = 1$, that is, critical damping. Rearranging Equation 11 we have:

$$R_S = \left(\frac{1}{2\zeta}\right)\sqrt{\frac{L_{LK}}{C_{LK}}} = \left(\frac{1}{2}\right)\sqrt{\frac{8.0 \times 10^{-9}}{3.239 \times 10^{-9}}} = 0.78\ \Omega$$ [13]

use 2 × 1.5 Ω in parallel to give 0.75 Ω.

Rearranging Equation 12 we have:

$$C_S = \frac{1}{2\pi R_S f_{RING0}} = \frac{1}{2 \times \pi \times 0.75 \times 3.125 \times 10^7} = 6.79\ nF$$ [14]

use 4.7 nF + 2.2 nF to give 6.9 nF.

The snubber was fitted across Q1 drain source. The resulting waveform is shown in Figure 6 together with the original (non-snubbed) waveform from Figure 2

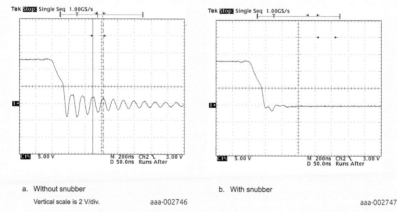

a. Without snubber

Vertical scale is 2 V/div.   aaa-002746

b. With snubber

aaa-002747

Figure 6 | Q2 V_{DS} waveform with and without snubber

As seen in Figure 6, the snubber has almost eliminated the ringing in the V_{DS} waveform. This technique could also be applied to the MOSFET in the Q2 position.

6 Summary

- Reverse recovery effects in power devices can induce high frequency oscillations in devices connected to them.
- A common technique for suppressing the oscillations is the use of an RC snubber.
- Design of an effective snubber requires the extraction of the circuit parasitic capacitance and inductance. A method has been demonstrated for doing this.
- The snubbed circuit has been shown to be a variation on the classic RLC circuit.
- A method of determining values of snubber components has been demonstrated. The method has been shown to work well, using the example of BUK761R6-40E MOSFETs

7 Appendix A; determining C_{LK} from C_{add}, f_{RING0} and f_{RING1}

We know that:

$$f_{RING0} = \frac{1}{2\pi\sqrt{L_{LK}C_{LK}}} \tag{15}$$

where f_{RING0} is the frequency of oscillation without a snubber in place and L_{LK} and C_{LK} are the parasitic inductances and capacitances respectively.

If we add capacitor C_{add} across Q1 drain-source, f_{RING0} is reduced by an amount "x" where:

$$\frac{f_{RING0}}{x} = \frac{1}{2\pi\sqrt{L_{LK}(C_{LK} + C_{add})}} \tag{16}$$

therefore

$$\frac{1}{2\pi\sqrt{L_{LK}C_{LK}}} = \frac{x}{2\pi\sqrt{L_{LK}(C_{LK} + C_{add})}} \tag{17}$$

$$\frac{1}{\sqrt{L_{LK}C_{LK}}} = \frac{x}{\sqrt{L_{LK}(C_{LK} + C_{add})}} \tag{18}$$

$$\sqrt{L_{LK}C_{LK}} = \frac{\sqrt{L_{LK}(C_{LK} + C_{add})}}{x} \tag{19}$$

$$C_{LK} = \frac{C_{LK} + C_{add}}{x^2} \tag{20}$$

$$C_{LK}x^2 - C_{LK} = C_{add} \qquad [21]$$

$$C_{LK}(x^2 - 1) = C_{add} \qquad [22]$$

$$C_{LK} = \frac{C_{add}}{x^2 - 1} \qquad [23]$$

where:

$$x = \frac{f_{RING0}}{f_{RING1}} \qquad [24]$$

8 Figures

Chapter 7

Half-bridge MOSFET switching and its impact on EMC

Application Note: AN90011

1 Introduction

Measuring and improving MOSFET switching behaviour to meet EMC requirements and optimize reliability and efficency in half-bridge switching circuits.

Modern switching converters for low voltages (< 100 V) predominantly use power MOSFETs as the switching devices.

Switching converter applications includes inverters to synthesise AC waveforms, or for use in DC-to-DC converters. The switching devices are often arranged in a simple half-bridge configuration. At some point in time one of the MOSFETs will be actively switching (sometimes called the control FET in DC-to-DC applications) and the other one will be switched off and acting as a diode during the commutation event – this will be switched on once the switching event has finished and acts as a synchronous rectifier, (in DC-to-DC converters this MOSFET is referred to as a syncFET).

The behaviour of the MOSFETs during the switching event strongly influences efficiency and electromagnetic interference (emissions) goals.

In switch mode (PWM) designs, the switching behaviour of the MOSFET (or more generally the switching power devices) can influence the efficiency and the emissions from the system. This will apply to MOSFETs from any vendor, not just those from Nexperia.

This application note describes a technique to measure the switching efficacy and various measures that can be taken to improve the switching behaviour, thus meeting efficiency, EMC requirements and reliability goals.

2 Double pulse testing

This is a relatively simple method of determining the switching behaviour of a pair of MOSFETs in a half-bridge switching circuit. MOSFET Q1 is switched off and acts only as a diode, MOSFET Q2 is actively switched on and off twice: hence "double pulse testing". The behaviour at a particular current level and DC voltage level can be analysed. This testing is useful for comparing MOSFETs from different suppliers, since the detailed design – the technology - of the devices is unlikely to be exactly the same. Figure 1 shows the simplified schematic diagram of the double pulse test circuit.

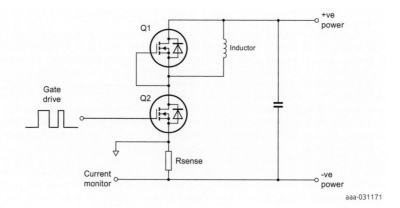

Figure 1 | Simplified schematic diagram of the double pulse test circuit

Simplified switching behaviour is shown in Figure 2

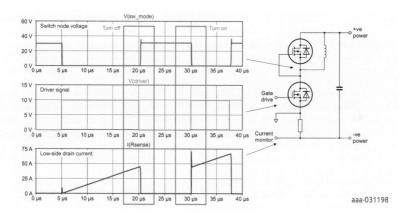

Figure 2 | Simplified switching behaviour

Three waveforms are shown in Figure 2: the top one shows the switch node voltage, the middle one shows the gate driver waveform to the low-side MOSFET and the lower waveform shows the current in the low-side device. The regions of interest are at turn-off of the low-side switch and then at turn-on for the second pulse. Assuming the gap between the first pulse and second pulse is relatively short (but long enough to ensure proper switch off of the switched device before it is switched on again) then the current will be maintained at the target level since the diode will present a voltage of around 1 V to the inductor, so di/dt will be low.

The MOSFET gate driver can be to the user's choice however Nexperia uses a high current driver so that the external gate drive resistor strongly determines the switching speed, rather than this being influenced by the gate driver IC itself.

2.1 Measurement system

Current sensing is a critical consideration. A high bandwidth sensor is required. A coaxial shunt is used in Nexperia's test circuit since the bandwidth can be more than 1 GHz however the additional circuit inductance is in the region of 5 nH. Other methods of measuring current are possible such as Rogowski coils, Hall Effect probes or current transformers but these also suffer from various compromises either in bandwidth or significant additional circuit inductance. Some specialist Rogowski based probes can reach ~80 MHz bandwidth. The goal is to have sufficient bandwidth in the current sensor whilst minimising the additional circuit inductance. It may also be a requirement to have isolation of the probe signal from the circuit (especially if double pulse testing is performed on high voltage systems).

Here are a few tips regarding the measurement system: the current rise time may be in the area of up to 5 ns, so the current signal bandwidth would be 70 MHz, BW ≈ 0.35/trise, see ref (1). A voltage rise time of 5 ns would also be of 70 MHz. The probe BW should be 3x to 5x signal BW to take into account the 3 dB at the quoted BW. The oscilloscope should therefore have an analogue bandwidth the same or higher than the probes when used with x10 voltage probes (1 MΩ input impedance, note that the nominal oscilloscope bandwidth might quoted for a 50 Ω input impedance). The probes should be correctly compensated before use. The sampling rate needs to be at least 2.5x the analogue bandwidth for reasonable resolution. In this example the probes and oscilloscope would need to be 200 MHz analogue BW minimum and the sampling rate would need to be 500 Msamples/s minimum.

Note also that it can take some time for signals to travel along probe cables so the voltage probes and current probe cables should be the same length or the difference in time delay compensated for: a cable difference of 0.5 m could introduce a time difference of around 4 ns. This could have a significant effect on the measurement of switching energy. It is always worth spending a little time to make sure that the measurement system is correctly set up for accuracy, see ref (1). In double pulse testing, the waveforms of interest are low-side V_{DS} (switch node voltage measured as close to the MOSFET terminals as possible), high-side V_{DS} (may be measured using a differential probe method using high-side V_D minus low-side V_{DS}), low-side V_{GS} and low-side I_D. Ideally high-side V_{GS} should also be measured.

2.2 MOSFET switching simulation

SPICE simulation is used to produce some example waveforms. The BUK7S1R0-40H is used for most of this chapter, except where otherwise stated. The simulation circuit is an approximate model of the physical double pulse test circuit with parasitic elements added, see Figure 3. Nexperia has found that there can be a good correlation between SPICE simulation and physical measurements of the real circuit, as long as the device models are accurate (as is the case for Nexperia MOSFET models) and the circuit is realistically modelled, see Appendix A.

Figure 4 shows the MOSFET turn-off event and Figure 5 shows the MOSFET turn-on event.

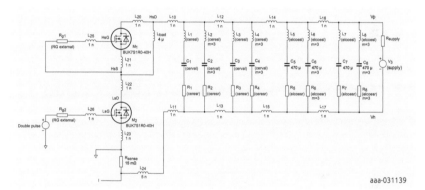

aaa-031139

Figure 3 | SPICE simulation circuit for double pulse test circuit

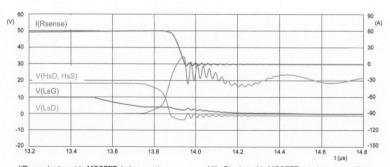

I(Rsense) = low-side MOSFET drain current   V(LsG) = low-side MOSFET gate to source voltage
V(HsD, HsS) = high-side MOSFET drain to source voltage   V(LsD) = low-side MOSFET drain to source voltage

aaa-031185

Figure 4 | Turn-off waveform

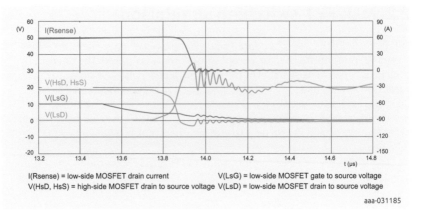

I(Rsense) = low-side MOSFET drain current   V(LsG) = low-side MOSFET gate to source voltage
V(HsD, HsS) = high-side MOSFET drain to source voltage V(LsD) = low-side MOSFET drain to source voltage

aaa-031185

Figure 5 | Turn-on waveform

2.3 MOSFET turn-off waveform description

These waveforms require some explanation as to why they look the way they do. Reference is made to MOSFET capacitances, see Figure 7. Consider first the turn-off waveform in Figure 6. This is divided into 6 time periods t_0 to t_5.

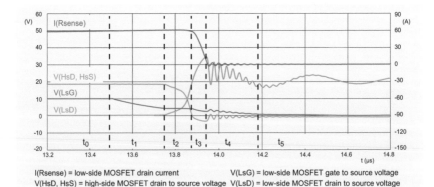

I(Rsense) = low-side MOSFET drain current   V(LsG) = low-side MOSFET gate to source voltage
V(HsD, HsS) = high-side MOSFET drain to source voltage V(LsD) = low-side MOSFET drain to source voltage

aaa-031188

Figure 6 | MOSFET turn-off waveforms, showing reference time periods

During period t0, the low-side device is on and the high-side device is off. This is a steady state condition. During time period t_1, the device turn-off process begins as the gate driver removes charge from the gate capacitance ($C_{ISS} = C_{GS} + C_{GD}$, see Figure 7) of the device and the gate- source voltage starts to fall. V_{DS} rises very slightly as the $R_{DS(on)}$ of the device begins to increase, in accordance with the "drain-source on-state resistance as a function of gate-source voltage" characteristic found in Nexperia MOSFET data sheets.

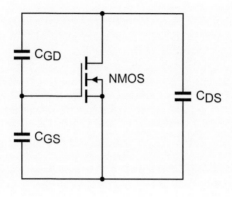

aaa-022333

Figure 7 | MOSFET internal capacitances

During t_2, once V_{GS} falls to the minimum value required to sustain the output inductor current (as determined by the output characteristic, see Figure 8), V_{GS} is approximately constant (this is the "Miller Plateau" and the V_{GS} value = V_p). During this time the gate driver current discharges C_{GD} (causing V_{GS} to fall and V_{DG} to rise), until the switch node voltage has risen to a voltage that allows the diode to conduct current. At this point V_{GS} can fall to its threshold voltage (during t_3) as current is commuted from the low-side MOSFET to the high-side MOSFET body diode.

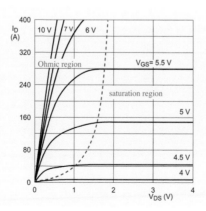

aaa-030487

Figure 8 | Example of MOSFET output characteristics

Towards the end of t_2 and moving into t_3, the low-side MOSFET V_{DS} reaches the level of the DC supply voltage and continues to increase. At this point the body diode of the high-side device can start to turn on and the I_D of the low-side MOSFET can commutate to the high-side device.

The rate at which this happens is now controlled by the gate driver discharging C_{iss} as in period t_1 and the incremental slope of the MOSFET transfer curve (transconductance) of the MOSFET (the transfer curve can be found in Nexperia Power MOSFET data sheets). The resulting rate of change of drain current dI_D/dt causes a voltage to be produced across all circuit inductances affected by the change in I_D. Referring to Figure 3, the inductances affected by dI_D/dt include L10, L11, L20, L21, L22, L23 and L24, as well as any component package inductances (for example L1, L2 and others not shown in Figure 3). This is known as the loop inductance. This results in the large voltage overshoot seen on the low-side MOSFET V_{DS}, the overshoot is 14.5 V. The peak value corresponds to the peak dI_D/dt. The equal change of current in the high-side MOSFET source IS results in a small negative voltage spike across the high-side device due to L20 and L21: note that the measuring point for the voltages includes some circuit impedance contribution in this example and that the MOSFET model includes package parasitics.

This also adds to the voltage spike observed on the low-side MOSFET. The total circuit inductance from the capacitors through both MOSFETs is often referred to as the loop inductance. The sum of the layout (PCB) inductances is 10 nH in Figure 3 however another 1 nH comes from the device internal inductances, then there are additional inductances coming from the DC link capacitors and layout which are not so simple to describe. The peak dI_D/dt is 1.1 A/ns in Figure 4 so 12.1 V is due to the inductances and the voltage overshoot is 13.0 V. Note that the high-side body diode is conducting, so this accounts for about 0.7 V of the difference.

At the end of t_3 and start of t_4, I_D in the low-side MOSFET reaches zero. All the current has transferred to the high-side MOSFET body diode. At this point, the voltage across the low-side MOSFET is still more than 30 V given a supply voltage of 20 V. Oscillation is inevitable and a simple circuit model as shown in Figure 9 illustrates the situation.

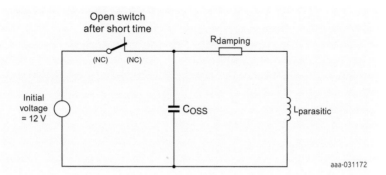

Figure 9 | Oscillation at MOSFET turn-off

C_{OSS} is the low-side MOSFET effective capacitance (C_{DS} in parallel with C_{GD}, C_{GS} is shorted out by the gate driver). This is V_{DS} dependant and the value at 32 V is used in this example). $L_{parasitic}$ is the loop inductance. If C_{OSS} is averaged to 1.6 nF and $L_{parasitic}$ is 11 nH then the oscillation frequency will be 37.9 MHz. This is quite close to the observed oscillation frequency around 35 MHz. The damping resistance which is due to the device construction and resistance due to the layout will reduce the frequency and non-linearity of C_{OSS} results in a slightly bigger effective capacitance being present.

In period t_5, the MOSFET turn-off switching transition is complete. The low frequency oscillation is due to resonance of the ceramic capacitors with the ESL of the electrolytic capacitors and layout inductance. The resonant frequency is approximately 2 MHz in this example. The ceramic capacitors are 100 nH and the ESL of the electrolytic capacitor is 20 nH in the simulated example, on its own the resonant frequency is calculated at of 3.6 MHz. Factoring in the layout inductance would account for the discrepancy. See Section 3.2.1 for more details about low frequency ringing.

The switching loss in the low-side MOSFET at turn-off, (over the t_2 and t_3 time periods), is given by:

$$\int V(LsD) * I(Rsense)dt \qquad [1]$$

Where V(LsD) = low-side MOSFET drain to source voltage. The switching loss in the high-side MOSFET is negligible.

2.4 MOSFET turn-on waveform description

A typical turn-on waveform is shown in Figure 10. In time period t_0 the low-side MOSFET is off. Current is flowing in the body diode of the high-side MOSFET. During t_1 the gate voltage on the low-side MOSFET starts to rise. Nothing happens until the threshold voltage is reached.

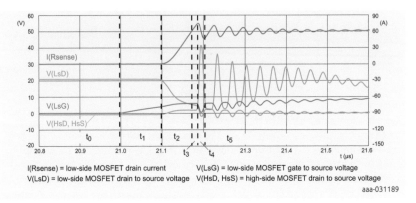

I(Rsense) = low-side MOSFET drain current   V(LsG) = low-side MOSFET gate to source voltage
V(LsD) = low-side MOSFET drain to source voltage   V(HsD, HsS) = high-side MOSFET drain to source voltage

aaa-031189

Figure 10 | MOSFET turn-on waveforms, showing reference time periods

At the start of time period t_2, the gate voltage continues to rise until significant current starts to flow. The rate of change of drain current dI_D/dt increases and then becomes more constant, as defined by the transfer characteristic (see Nexperia MOSFET data sheet) dI_D/dt is also dependant on gate driver current in C_{iss}. The circuit inductances start to interact with the MOSFET. Notice how the MOSFET V_{DS} falls and then plateaus at around 5 V in this example. This corresponds with the highest dI_D/dt observed, interacting with the loop inductance (see Section 2.3). dI_D/dt is therefore limited by the supply voltage and the loop inductance, rather than the MOSFET capability.

Another limitation to dI_D/dt is due to the device source and layout inductance to the connection of the gate drive (represented by L23 in Figure 3). Packages with a source clip such as LFPAK will have a higher dI_D/dt capability compared to wire bonded packages such as DPAK due to the package source inductance. Notice also the high-side V_{DS} shows a "hump" due to dI_D/dt interacting with L20 and L21 (see Figure 3). V_{GS} as observed at the pins of the low-side device is also affected due to inductance of the source leg, the actual V_{GS} applied to the MOSFET die will be fairly constant due to the MOSFET gate capacitance C_{GS}, however the voltage across the package source inductance is added. This can just be observed in Figure 10. At the end of period t_2 the low-side drain current reaches the load inductance current. The low-side V_{DS} doesn't fall at this point. This is because the high-side body diode must be turned off first. Note that the low-side MOSFET is experiencing a relatively high current and also a relatively high V_{DS}, hence there will be some switching loss associated with this condition.

At the start of time period t_3, the current in the low-side MOSFET increases beyond the load current. The high-side MOSFET body diode is being switched off, a negative current is flowing in it and the depletion layer inside the body diode is forming in order to support reverse voltage, charge is being stored in the diode junction. This can be considered as a capacitance (sometimes referred to as the diffusion capacitance C_d, the associated charge may be referred to as Q_s). The low-side drain current approaches its peak value.

Once the depletion layer begins to form, the high-side V_{DS} will begin to increase. This happens at the start of period t_4. The low-side V_{DS} will fall. The low-side drain current will still increase a little further before reaching a peak, partly due to charging the diffusion capacitance C_d but also due to charging the junction capacitance C_j in the high-side body diode. The pn junction can be considered as a parallel plate capacitor, with the distance between the "plates" containing the depletion region as the dielectric material. There comes a point where the current flowing into the depletion region becomes relatively small and the current flowing into the junction capacitance dominates. This is just before the peak current is observed in the low-side MOSFET. The junction capacitance characteristic (especially with respect to V_{DS}) now determines the rate of change of current observed in the body diode and low-side MOSFET. It also determines the rate of rise of the high-side V_{DS}. This is unlike the situation seen during turn-off, where the gate driver and C_{GD} control the dV_{DS}/dt, now this is controlled by the energy stored in the loop inductance and C_{OSS}. The charge stored in C_{OSS} ($C_J = C_{DS}$, $C_{OSS} \approx C_{DS} + C_{GD}$) is referred to as Q_{OSS}. The process of switching off the high-side MOSFET body diode during time periods t_3 and t_4 is known as reverse recovery and is described in ref (5) and other references.

The high-side V_{DS} will usually exceed the nominal DC supply level due to the dI_D/dt and loop inductance. This is referred to as a V_{DS} "spike" and can be problematic. Notice also that the observed low-side V_{GS} waveform shows some oscillations. V_{DS} oscillations are coupled into the MOSFET gate directly as a result of the capacitive divider formed by C_{GD} and C_{GS} (see Figure 7). Secondly, the observed waveform is affected by source lead and layout inductance, represented by L23.

In period t_5, a high-frequency decaying oscillation is observed superimposed on a lower frequency DC link oscillation. The high-frequency oscillation is due to the resonance of the high-side C_{OSS} and the loop inductance $L_{parasitic}$. The low frequency oscillation is due to the resonance of the DC link ceramic capacitors and inductance of the electrolytic capacitors and circuit layout as discussed in the MOSFET turn-off condition, (see Section 3.2.1). The oscillations decay over time.

The switching loss in the low-side MOSFET at turn on, (over the t_2, t_3 and t_4 time periods.), is given by:

$\int V(LsD) * I(Rsense)dt$ [1]

The switching loss in the high-side MOSFET, (over the t4 time period), is given by:

$\int V(HsD, HsS) * (I(Rsense)-I(Lload))dt$ [2]

3 Methods to improve switching performance

In Section 2, the switch on and switch off transients were explored using double pulse testing. In the waveforms presented, some undesirable effects can be seen such as the large voltage spike on the high-side V_{DS} when the low-side MOSFET switches on, also some oscillations at turn-on and turn-off. This is a cause of unwanted noise which may propagate to the outside world and may interfere with the operation of radio systems but may also cause disturbances in other analogue and digital systems (hence the use of the terms such as electromagnetic compatibility or electromagnetic interference: EMC / EMI).

3.1 Voltage spikes

V_{DS} spikes are observed in both the switch off and switch on waveforms. At low-side turn on, it is possible that the high-side V_{DS} might experience a spike which may reach or exceed the rating of the MOSFET. It is good practice to limit this spike to < 80% of the MOSFET rating to achieve good reliability and also to keep the amplitude of the following oscillations quite small.

The following sections consider some methods to minimise these voltage spikes.

3.1.1 Circuit layout

The loop inductance was described in Section 2.3 and Section 2.4. This total inductance should be minimised as far as possible by using compact layout methods, so that the loop area is reduced: if the loop is considered as a turn of a coil then a large coil diameter will result in a larger self inductance. Furthermore, the magnetic field generated by the loop can interfere with nearby wiring according to Faraday's law.

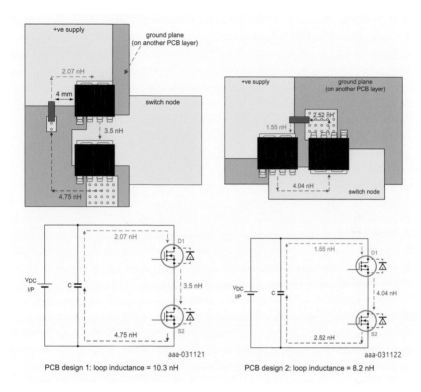

Figure 11 | Half-bridge layout possibilities showing inductances

A layout arrangement as shown in Figure 11 helps to reduce the loop inductance. Design 1 has a loop inductance of 10.3 nH compared to design 2 with a loop inductance of 8.1 nH, according to simulation (ignoring device inductances). Using smaller devices can help to reduce the loop area further.

It was seen in Section 2 that switching behaviour depends on the gate driver voltage and impedance, the package layout source inductance in the gate driver loop and the loop inductance.

3.1.2 Reducing dI/$_D$t

In the case of the low-side MOSFET switch off waveform (Figure 4, Figure 6), the voltage spike depends on the loop inductance and the dI/$_D$t. Since the current is falling, the parasitic inductance will add to the supply voltage as seen at the drain terminal of the MOSFET. The ringing was due to the step voltage change when the drain current (and dI/$_D$t) reaches zero. This can be achieved by slowing the gate drive by some method such as slew rate control at the driver IC, increasing gate resistance or adding capacitance between gate and source. This will increase the switching time and therefore the switch off loss.

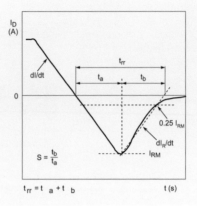

Figure 12 | Reverse recovery waveform definitions

In the case of the low-side MOSFET switch on, it was seen in Figure 10 that there is a significant V_{DS} spike across the high-side MOSFET which is acting as a diode. The spike is due to the loop inductance and dI_R/dt (see Figure 12) which cannot be directly controlled but which is a function of the dI/dt that is controllable. The time t_a is approximately constant and it depends on the time it takes for the depletion region to form in the pn junction of the body diode (i.e. recombination time). A higher dI/dt will therefore result in a higher I_{RM} value and higher energy in the loop inductance.

$dI/_dt$ and dI_R/dt are related by the softness factor of the body diode (t_b/t_a), which is reasonably constant over a range of $dI/_Dt$ values. dI_R/dt multiplied by the loop inductance causes a voltage overshoot. This can be absorbed by the MOSFET output capacitance C_{OSS}. This capacitance is non-linear with respect to V_{DS}, (see Figure 13), which doesn't help with keeping V_{DS} spikes under control. C_{OSS} defines the shape of the tb region (and consequently the dI_R/dt) and is a characteristic of the MOSFET technology.

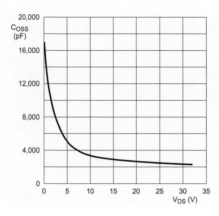

Figure 13 | C_{OSS} as a function of V_{DS}

Adding additional capacitance external to the MOSFET can help to "linearise" the capacitance and reduce the V_{DS} spike. This is the capacitance part of an RC snubber.

3.2 Ringing

This occurs because a stimulus is applied to a resonant circuit. In the half-bridge, inductances are usually attributed to the circuit layout and parasitics within the components, usually the loop inductance. Capacitances are attributed to the MOSFETs (e.g. C_{OSS}) and bypass capacitors

3.2.1 Bypass capacitors

Bypass capacitors should be placed as close to the half-bridge as possible (to minimise the loop area as discussed in 3.2.1), ideally using surface mount devices. The value should be chosen such that resonance will be well damped. A 100 nF 100 V C0G capacitor has an ESL of approximately 1.1 nH and an ESR of 20 mΩ. A 1 µF 100 V X7R capacitor has similar ESL and ESR. This means that the 1 µF capacitor has a better damping capability compared to the 100 nF capacitor, since the characteristic impedance will be closer in value to the capacitor's ESR. The C0G is a more stable dielectric however a higher capacitance is more beneficial. It was shown that the 2 MHz oscillation is due to the capacitance of the ceramic bypass capacitors and the inductance of the layout and electrolytic capacitors. This is also borne out in practice.

In the example simulation circuit, 100 nF capacitors are compared with 1 µF capacitors, see Figure 14.

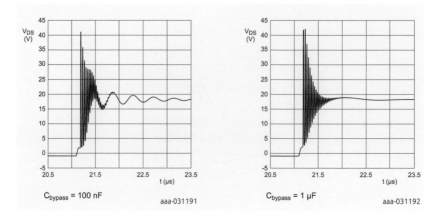

Figure 14 | Effect of bypass capacitor selection: 100 nF vs. 1 µF

The 2 MHz oscillation is shifted to a lower frequency and is a lower amplitude, the ESR and PCB track resistance is providing damping. However the higher frequency oscillation of around 35 MHz remains and is changed only slightly.

3.2.2 Adding a snubber

By adding an RC snubber across the MOSFET drain and source, oscillations can be minimised. AN11160 (chapter 6 in this book) - Designing RC snubbers (ref 3) covers this topic. Another good reference is (ref 4) which proposes a method to optimise the snubber capacitor. The snubber will attenuate the unwanted high frequency oscillations as shown in Figure 15. A 10 nF + 2.2 Ω snubber is applied to the high-side and low-side devices. V_{DS} for the high-side device is shown at low-side turn-on (i.e. high-side body diode turn-off). This also damps the oscillations at low-side turn-off. SPICE programs allow a sweep of parameters to give an indication of the snubber values which are likely to give the desired outcome.

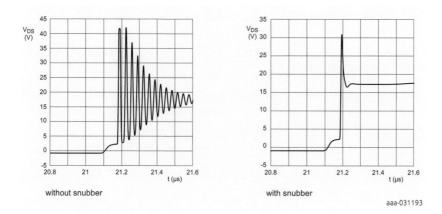

without snubber   with snubber

aaa-031193

Figure 15 | Effect of adding a snubber

3.3 Feedback into the gate signal

There is a risk of feedback into the gate signal due to high dVDS/dt. If this exceeds the gate threshold voltage ($V_{GS(th)}$) then a significant shoot through current can flow in the half-bridge. This is due to the MOSFET capacitances C_{GD}, C_{DS} and the external gate drive resistance forming a potential divider. If a shoot through current occurs, this will significantly increase the switching losses. This is illustrated in Figure 16, see ref (7).

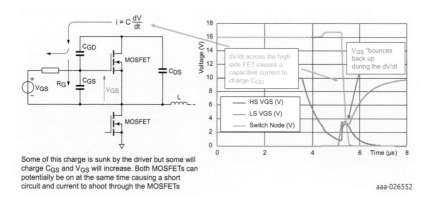

Some of this charge is sunk by the driver but some will charge C_{GS} and V_{GS} will increase. Both MOSFETs can potentially be on at the same time causing a short circuit and current to shoot through the MOSFETs

aaa-026552

Figure 16 | Dynamic behaviour of a MOSFET half-bridge

Additional external capacitance is used to control dV/dt. C_{rss} is relatively small and non-linear giving rise to gate glitches and sudden shoot through current. The external capacitance would be much larger in value and quite linear, producing a controlled dV/dt. See section 3.4.2.

3.4 Switching speed control

3.4.1 Effect of varying R_G

Varying the external gate resistance will affect switching losses in the low-side MOSFET; see Figure 17, Figure 18 and Figure 19. In this case, measurements have been made using the BUK7S1R5-40H.

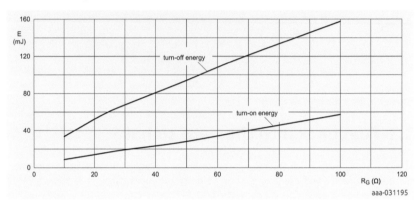

Figure 17 | Effect of varying R_G on switching loss (example values only)

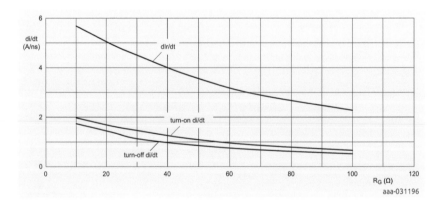

Figure 18 | Effect of varying R_G on di/dt, dIr/dt and turn-off di/dt (example values only)

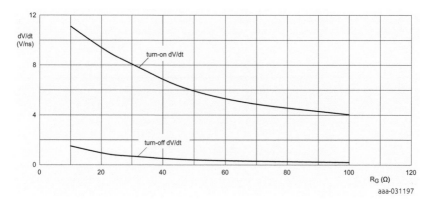

Figure 19 | Effect of varying R_G on turn-on dV/dt and turn-off dV/dt (example values only)

Increasing R_G will increase switching loss but the benefit is better controlled switching and improvements in spiking and ringing. There may also be an increased risk of gate bounce so it may be necessary to add a small capacitor between gate and source.

For best performance, R_G for turn-on should be large than R_G for turn-off. di/dt is controlled by the V_{GS} value around the Miller plateau voltage V_p:

$I_G = (V_{GS} - V_p) / R_G$ for example:

$I_{G(on)} = (10 - 4.3) / 10 = 0.57$ A

$I_{G(off)} = (0 - 4.3) / 10 = -0.43$ A

Hence turn on $dI/_Dt$ may be different to turn off $dI/_Dt$ depending on the value of R_G. $dI/_Dt$ can also be controlled by carefully selecting the location of the gate drive ground connection point, this is equivalent to adjusting L23 in Figure 3.

3.4.2 Effect of adding external gate to source capacitance

In case of gate bounce risk, (see Section 3.3), an external C_{GS} can be added to reduce the high frequency impedance of the gate driver whilst still having relatively high R_G The effect on switching speed ($dI/_Dt$) is relatively modest, as seen below in Figure 20. This is for a BUK7S1R0-40H with an R_G external value of 22 Ω.

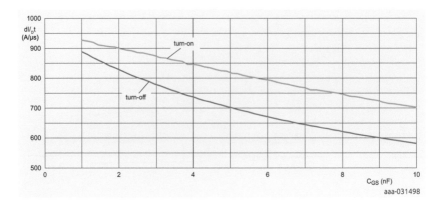

Figure 20 | C$_{GS}$ effect on MOSFET dI/$_D$t

3.4.3 Effect of adding gate to drain capacitance

Adding some drain voltage feedback via a gate – drain capacitor would reduce dV/dt without affecting dI/$_D$t and will reduce the voltage spike at turn-off. Losses are increased. Reducing dV/dt is beneficial because in a motor drive, the switch node voltage is presented directly to the motor windings. The motor windings can act as antennae so that the frequency domain content of the waveform can radiate into the environment. The highest frequency component of the waveform will be approximately 0.35/rise time or 0.35/fall time.

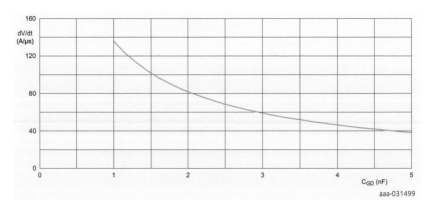

Figure 21 | External C$_{GD}$ effect on controlling MOSFET turn-off

Figure 21 shows the effect of adding a capacitor to a BUK7S1R0-40H with a series resistor of 10 Ω. Usually a series resistor R$_{GD}$ is added to C$_{GD}$ in order to prevent oscillations, see Figure 22. The value of C$_{GD}$ can be in the range of 1 – 5 nF for a device such as BUK7S1R0-40H, much bigger than the value of the MOSFET internal C_{rss}. The value of R_{GD} can be in the range of 10 – 50 Ω for this device, higher values start to diminish the effect of having the external C_{GD}. Note that Figure 22 applies to the low-side controlling switch in the case of the double pulse test circuit.

In the case of the MOSFET acting as a synchronous rectifier then the effect of adding external C_{GD} will reduce dv/dt however the value of dV/dt can be much higher. See Figure 23.

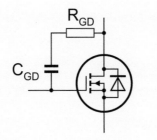

aaa-031501

Figure 22 | Adding C_{GD} and R_{GD}

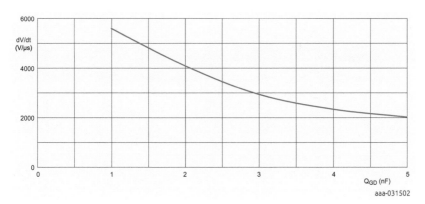

aaa-031502

Figure 23 | External C_{GD} effect on the synchronous rectifier MOSFET

It is recommended that some SPICE simulation is performed first before experimenting to determine the optimum values of external resistors and capacitors.

4 Impact on EMC and efficiency

The significant voltage transients and oscillations which have been described in Section 2 are the source of electromagnetic interference. This must be suppressed in order to meet CISPR25 based requirements for automotive and CISPR 11 and the like for industrial, telecoms and consumer equipment. These kinds of standards consider conducted and radiated emissions. How do these transient voltages and currents cause interference? In the next paragraphs, emissions from digital circuits will be ignored however the same basic principles apply, the difference being that the voltages are much lower than in the power circuit and the frequency rise and fall times are much faster.

In an ideal PWM controlled half-bridge MOSFET circuit, it is still necessary to take care of EMI by using screening and filters. This is because simple analysis of the half-bridge waveforms feature rectangular blocks of current with fast rising and falling edges from the DC link and the output switch node will feature fast rising and falling voltages. See Figure 24.

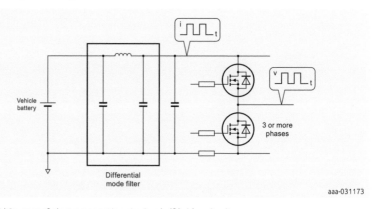

Figure 24 | Sources of electromagnetic noise in a half-bridge circuit

5 Conclusions

This chapter is intended to give the reader a reasonably detailed understanding of how the half-bridge switching circuit is a source of electromagnetic noise and power loss. In particular, the reverse recovery characteristic of the MOSFET body diode can be a key factor to achieving good EMC behaviour and lower losses. Some techniques to reduce switching noise at source have been considered and a brief overview of how the noise propagates to the outside world have been considered.

🔲 Watch video

Benefits of low Q_{rr} MOSFETs in motor control applications

🔲 Watch video

Benefits of low Q_{rr} MOSFETs in switching applications

🔲 Watch video

Developing reliable MOSFETs how difficult can it be

📋 Visit blog

Q_{rr} overlooked and underappreciated in efficiency battle

📋 Visit blog

Automotive Trench 9 Power MOSFETs designed for performance and endurance

6 References

1. High Speed Digital Design – a Handbook of Black Magic, Howard Johnson & Martin Graham

2. Power and small-signal MOSFET frequently asked questions and answers TN00008, section 7.8, Nexperia

3. Designing RC snubbers" AN11160, Nexperia

4. Optimising snubber design through frequency-domain analysis", EDN

5. Semiconductor device modelling with SPICE 2nd Edition, Giuseppe Massobrio & Paulo Antognetti

6. EMC for product designers, Tim Williams

7. Designing in MOSFETs for safe and reliable gate-drive operation AN90001, Nexperia

Half-bridge MOSFET switching and its impact on EMC

7 Appendix A: Comparison between SPICE simulation and practical measurements for the BUK7S1R0-40H in a double pulse test circuit

The SPICE circuit used is as shown in Figure 3. The following values were used in the simulation: ceresr = 20 m, ceresl = 1.13 n, cerval = 100 n, cerval1 = 100 n, elcoesr = 40 m, elcoesl = 20 n.

Both turn-on and turn-off conditions are considered.

SPICE model is modified from standard: TT parameter is approximately half of published value (to give better reverse recovery alignment with double pulse measurements).

The following test conditions were applied: R_G = 30 Ω, I_L = 60 A, V_{DC} = 20 V.

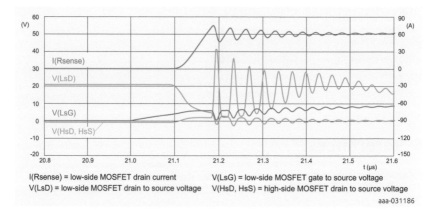

I(Rsense) = low-side MOSFET drain current
V(LsD) = low-side MOSFET drain to source voltage

V(LsG) = low-side MOSFET gate to source voltage
V(HsD, HsS) = high-side MOSFET drain to source voltage

aaa-031186

Figure 25 | SPICE turn-on waveform

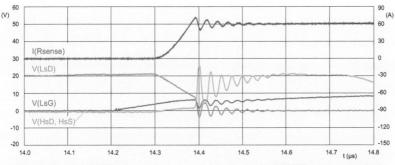

I(Rsense) = low-side MOSFET drain current   V(LsG) = low-side MOSFET gate to source voltage
V(HsD, HsS) = high-side MOSFET drain to source voltage V(LsD) = low-side MOSFET drain to source voltage

aaa-031238

Figure 26 | Measurement turn-on waveform

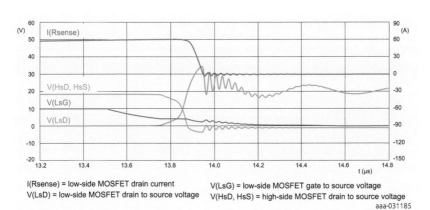

I(Rsense) = low-side MOSFET drain current   V(LsG) = low-side MOSFET gate to source voltage
V(LsD) = low-side MOSFET drain to source voltage   V(HsD, HsS) = high-side MOSFET drain to source voltage

aaa-031185

Figure 27 | SPICE turn-off waveform

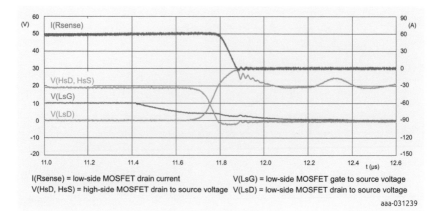

I(Rsense) = low-side MOSFET drain current   V(LsG) = low-side MOSFET gate to source voltage
V(HsD, HsS) = high-side MOSFET drain to source voltage V(LsD) = low-side MOSFET drain to source voltage

aaa-031239

Figure 28 | Measurement turn-off waveform

Table 1: Meausrement and SPICE simluation values

	Turn-on (measured)	Turn-on (SPICE)		Turn-off (measured)	Turn-off (SPICE)
dI/$_D$t	1.12 A/ns	1.12 A/ns	dI/$_D$t	0.82 A/ns	1.05 A/ns
dIr/dt	2.96 A/ns	2.78 A/ns	dV/dt	0.31 V/ns	0.45 V/ns
ΔIRM	10.09 A	12.2 A	V(LsD)	29 V	34.2 V
t$_a$	11.43 ns	12.8 ns	-	-	-
t$_b$	5.17 ns	7.2 ns	-	-	-
dV/dt	4.54 V/ns	5.7 V/ns	-	-	-
V(HsD, HsS)	27 V	41.2 V	-	-	-

8 Tables

Half-bridge MOSFET switching and its impact on EMC

9 Figures

Chapter 8

Failure signature of electrical overstress on power MOSFETs

Application Note: AN11243

1 Introduction

When Power MOSFETs fail, there is often extensive damage. Examination of the size and location of the burn mark, the failure signature, provides information about the type of fault condition which caused the failure. This chapter provides a catalogue of failure signatures from common electrical overstress failure modes. The catalogue can be used in forensic investigation of the underlying root cause of failure to improve module design and reliability.

Power MOSFETs are used to switch high voltages and currents, while minimizing their own internal power dissipation. Under fault conditions however, it is possible to apply voltage, current and power exceeding the MOSFET capability. Fault conditions can be either due to an electrical circuit failure or a mechanical fault with a load such as a seized motor. This leads to Electrical Overstress (EOS). Typically the consequence of EOS is the short circuiting of at least 2 of the 3 MOSFET terminals (gate, drain, source). In addition, high local power dissipation in the MOSFET leads to MOSFET damage which manifests as burn marks, die crack and in extreme cases as plastic encapsulation damage.

Examination of the size and location of the burn mark, the failure signature, provides information about the type of fault condition which caused the failure. Common fault conditions are:

- ElectroStatic Discharge (ESD)
- Unclamped Inductive Switching (UIS) - commonly called Avalanche or Ruggedness
- Linear Mode operation
- Over-current

Packaged MOSFETs have been deliberately destroyed under these conditions. Images recorded of the ensuing burn marks on the silicon surface, provide a 'Rogue's Gallery' to aid the explanation of EOS failures.

Section 1.1 to Section 1.4 gives an overview of the common failure signatures. Appendices in Section 2.1 to Section 2.17 provide further images.

1.1 ESD - Human body model

1.1.1 EOS method

ESD pulses were applied using a standard Human-body Model ESD circuit; for details see *AEC - Q101 - REV - May 15, 1996*. Voltage of the applied pulse was progressively increased until device failure was observed.

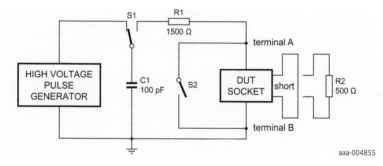

Figure 1 | Typical circuit for Human body Model ESD simulation

1.1.2 Fault condition simulated

Human body model ESD simulates situations when a voltage spike is applied to the MOSFET exceeding the maximum voltage that can be sustained by the gate oxide of either gate-source or gate-drain. The pulse is applied with 1500 Ω series resistance between the voltage origin and the MOSFET, which limits the rate of rise of the MOSFET gate voltage. Either human handling, electrical test equipment or malfunctioning circuits can easily apply such voltage pulses.

1.1.3 Signature

Failure site is found in an edge cell of the MOSFET structure. Outer edge cells and cells near the gate are the first to be subjected to the incoming voltage pulse and are thus the first sites where the voltage exceeds the gate-oxide capability. The signature differs from Machine Model failures in that the fail site does not show such a strong tendency to group near the gate, due to the slower rise in gate voltage.

Table 1: Examples of Human Body Model ESD failure signature

Device name	Cell pitch (μm)	Image	Comments
BUK9508-55A	9 (hexagon)	 aaa-004856	Fail site is gate oxide of edge cell; see Section 2.1 "Human body model EOS of BUK9508-55A" for further images
BUK9Y40-55B	4 (stripe)	 aaa-004857	Fail site is gate oxide of edge cell; see Section 2.2 "Human body model EOS of BUK9Y40-55B" for further images
PSMN011-30YL	2 (stripe)	 aaa-004858	Fail site is gate oxide of edge cell; see Section 2.3 "Human body model EOS of PSMN011-30YL" for further images
PSMN8R5-100PSF	2.5 (stripe)		Fail site is gate oxide of edge cell, see Section 2.4 "Human body model EOS of PSMN8R5-100PSF" for further images.
BUK7Y3R0-40H	1.5 (stripe)		Fail site is gate oxide of edge cell, see Section 2.5 "Human body model EOS of BUK7Y3R0-40H" for further images.

1.2 Unclamped Inductive Switching (UIS) (Avalanche or Ruggedness)

1.2.1 EOS method

Inductive energy pulses were applied using a standard UIS circuit; for details see *AEC - Q101-004 - REV - May 15, 1996*. A fixed inductance value is selected. Current in the inductor prior to switching the MOSFET was progressively increased until device failure was observed.

Table 2. UIS ruggedness test circuit and waveforms

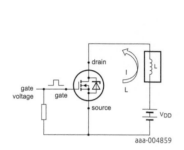

aaa-004859

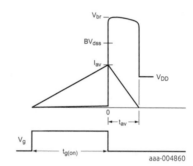

aaa-004860

Figure 2 | Circuit diagram for UIS ruggedness test   Figure 3 | Waveforms obtained from UIS test

1.2.2 Fault condition simulated

UIS simulates situations when a MOSFET is switched off in a circuit in which there is inductance. The inductance can be deliberate (such as an injector coil in a diesel engine system), or parasitic. As the current cannot decay to zero instantaneously through the inductance, the MOSFET source-drain voltage increases to take the device into avalanche breakdown. The energy stored in the inductance is then dissipated in the MOSFET.

1.2.3 Signature

Failure site is found in an active MOSFET cell. The burn-mark is usually round in shape, indicating a central failure site and subsequent thermal damage.

If the avalanche event is long in duration (~ ms), then burn marks locate at central sites on the die, where there is maximum current flow and reduced heat dissipation. The sites are often adjacent to wire bonds/clip bonds where current density is high, but not directly under the wire bond/clip bond as it provides a local heat sink. Failure is at the hottest location of the die.

For short avalanche events (~ μs), the burn marks can take on more random locations over the die surface. The temperature rise in the chip is more uniform with negligible chance for current crowding and local heating on these time scales. For even shorter avalanche events, the burn marks can locate at die corners due to the discontinuity in cell structure at these locations.

Table 3: Examples of Unclamped Inductive Switching failure signature

Device name	Cell pitch (µm)	Image	Comments
BUK7L06-34ARC	9 (hexagon)	 aaa-004861	Round burn in active area; see Section 2.6 "Unclamped inductive switching EOS of BUK7L06-34ARC" for further images
BUK9Y40-55B	4 (stripe)	 aaa-004862	Round burn in active area; see Section 2.7 "Unclamped Inductive Switching EOS of BUK9Y40-55B" for further images
PSMN7R0-30YL	2 (stripe)	 aaa-004863	Round burn in active area; see Section 2.8 "Unclamped inductive switching EOS of PSMN7R0-30YL" for further images

Device name	Cell pitch (µm)	Image	Comments
PSMN8R5-100PSF	2.5 (stripe)	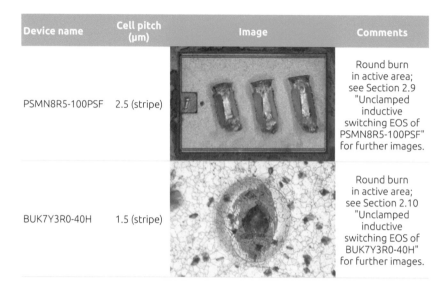	Round burn in active area; see Section 2.9 "Unclamped inductive switching EOS of PSMN8R5-100PSF" for further images.
BUK7Y3R0-40H	1.5 (stripe)	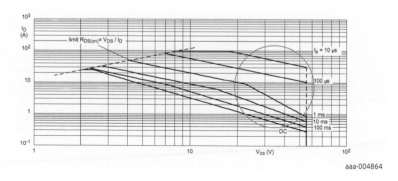	Round burn in active area; see Section 2.10 "Unclamped inductive switching EOS of BUK7Y3R0-40H" for further images.

1.3 Linear mode operation

1.3.1 EOS method

A Safe Operating Area (SOA) graph is included in all power MOSFET data sheets. Outside the defined safe region, the power dissipated in the FET cannot be removed, resulting in heating beyond the device capability and then device failure. MOSFETs were taken and a fixed source-drain voltage applied. Current pulses of defined duration were applied and the current was increased until MOSFET failure was observed.

Figure 4 | Safe operating area; continuous and peak drain currents as a function of drain-source voltage

1.3.2 Fault condition simulated

Linear mode operation is common during device switching or clamped inductive switching and is not a fault condition unless the SOA is exceeded. Linear mode EOS simulates situations when a MOSFET is operated in Linear mode for too long. This situation can also occur if, when intending to turn the FET on, the gate signal voltage to the FET is too low. This condition can also arise when intending to hold the FET in the Off-state with high drain-source voltage. If the gate connection is lost, the gate voltage capacitively rises and the same Linear mode fault condition occurs

1.3.3 Signature

The hottest location of the die is a failure site that is usually at central sites on the die. The center of the die is where there is maximum current flow and reduced heat dissipation. The sites are often adjacent to wire bonds/clip bonds where current density is high, but not directly under the wire bond/clip bond as it provides a local heat sink.

Table 4: Examples of linear mode failure signature

Device name	Cell pitch (µm)	Image	Comments
BUK7L06-34ARC	9 (hexagon)	aaa-004865	Burns located in center of die adjacent to wire-bonds; see Section 2.11 "Linear mode EOS of BUK7L06-34ARC" for further images
BUK9Y40-55B	4 (stripe)	aaa-004866	Burn adjacent to location of clip bond in center of die; see Section 2.12 "Linear mode EOS of BUK9Y40-55B" for further images

Failure signature of electrical overstress on power MOSFETs

8

Device name	Cell pitch (µm)	Image	Comments
PSMN7R0-30YL	2 (stripe)	aaa-004867	Burn adjacent to location of clip bond in center of die; see Section 2.13 "Linear mode EOS of PSMN7R0-30YL" for further images
PSMN8R5-100PSF	2.5 (stripe)		Burn between source bond wires in active area, see Section 2.18 "Linear mode EOS of PSMN8R5-100PSF" for further images
BUK7Y3R0-40H	1.5 (stripe)		Burn close to the source clip location in the active area, see Section 2.19 "Linear mode EOS of BUK7Y3R0-40H" for further images

1.4 Over-current

1.4.1 EOS method

The maximum current-handling capability is specified on the data sheet for Power MOSFETs. This capability is based on the current handling capability of wires or clips, before which fusing will onset, combined with the ability to dissipate heat. Exceeding this rating can result in catastrophic failure.

I_D	drain current	V_{GS} = 10 V; T_{mb} = 100 °C; see Figure 1	-	53	A
		V_{GS} = 10 V; T_{mb} = 25 °C; see Figure 1	-	76	A
I_{DM}	peak drain current	t_p ≤ 10 µs; pulsed; T_{mb} = 25 °C; see Figure 3	-	260	A

aaa-005071

Figure 5 | Example of maximum current rating from the data sheet of PSMN7R0-30YL

1.4.2 Fault condition simulated

Over-current occurs if a FET is turned on with no element in the circuit to limit the current, resulting in a supply voltage being applied fully over the drain-source terminals of the FET. Typically this occurs if a load has been short-circuited. Alternatively if 2 FETs are operating in a half-bridge, over-current can ensue if both are turned on together.

1.4.3 Signature

Failure site is initially where the current handling connections (wires or clips) meet the die. Normally damage is extensive however in over-current conditions, and spreads over the entire die surface with evidence of melted metallization and solder joints.

For wire-bonded packages, there is often evidence of fused wires. For clip-bonded packages, die crack is commonly observed.

Table 5: Examples of over-current failure signature

Device name	Cell pitch (µm)	Image	Comments
BUK7L06-34ARC	9 (hexagon)	aaa-004868	Burns located in center of die adjacent to wire- bonds. Secondary damage of remelted top metal and solder die attach; see Section 2.14 "Over-current EOS of BUK7L06-34ARC" for further images

Device name	Cell pitch (µm)	Image	Comments
PSMN7R0-30YL	2 (stripe)	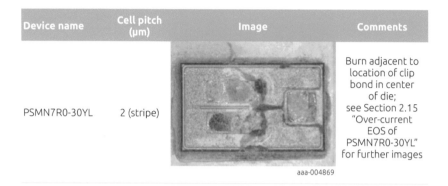 aaa-004869	Burn adjacent to location of clip bond in center of die; see Section 2.15 "Over-current EOS of PSMN7R0-30YL" for further images

2 Appendices

2.1 Human Body Model EOS of BUK9508-55A

Table 6: Human body model EOS

BUK9508-55A

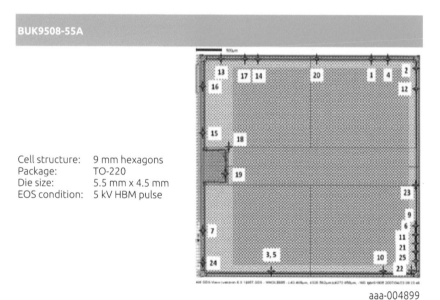

Cell structure: 9 mm hexagons
Package: TO-220
Die size: 5.5 mm x 4.5 mm
EOS condition: 5 kV HBM pulse

aaa-004899

Fails located in edge cells, distributed around edge of device

Failure signature of electrical overstress on power MOSFETs

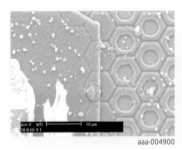

Figure 6 | Sample image 4; after Al removal

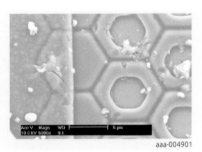

Figure 7 | Sample image 4; after Al removal, close-up

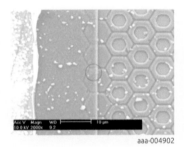

Figure 8 | Sample image 19; after Al removal

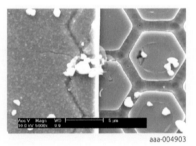

Figure 9 | Sample image 19; after TEOS removal, close-up

2.2 Human Body Model EOS of BUK9Y40-55B

Table 7: Human body model EOS

BUK9Y40-55B

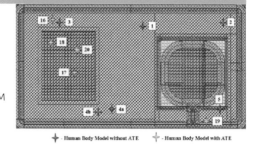

Cell structure: 4 μm stripe
Package: LFPAK (clip bond)
Die size: 2.5 mm x 1.35 mm
EOS Condition: 450 V to 650 V HBM
                  pulse

✛ - Human Body Model without ATE   ✛ - Human Body Model with ATE

aaa-004904

Fails located randomly over die with increased grouping in edge cells. Some fails subjected to ATE testing to create additional damage to highlight fail site

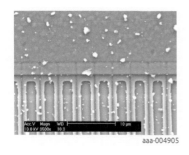

aaa-004905

aaa-004906

Figure 10 | Sample image 5; after Al removals

Figure 11 | Sample image 5; after TEOS removal, close-up

Failure signature of electrical overstress on power MOSFETs

∞

2.3 Human Body Model EOS of PSMN011-30YL

Table 8: Human body model EOS

PSMN011-30YL

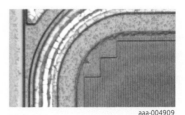

Cell structure: 2 µm stripe
Package: LFPAK (clip bond)
Die size: 1.7 mm x 1.2 mm
EOS Condition: 200 V to 210 V HBM pulse

aaa-004907

Fails located in edge cells

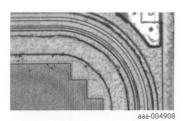

aaa-004908

Figure 12 | Device 4; after Al removals

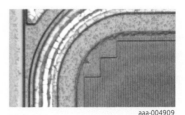

aaa-004909

Figure 13 | Device 7; after Al removal

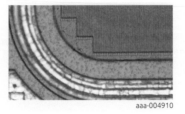

aaa-004910

Figure 14 | Device 5; after Al removals

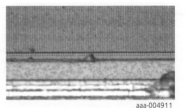

aaa-004911

Figure 15 | Device 10; after Al removal

Failure signature of electrical overstress on power MOSFETs

2.4 Human Body Model EOS of PSMN8R5-100PSF

Table 9: Human body model EOS

PSMN8R5-100PSF

Cell structure:	2.5 µm stripe
Package:	SOT78
Die size:	4 mm x 2.67 mm
EOS Condition:	1.4 kV to 1.8 kV HBM pulse

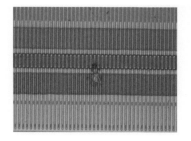

Figure 16 | Device 4 after Al removals

Figure 17 | Device 7 after Al removal

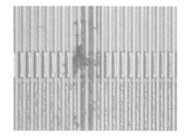

Figure 18 | Device 5 after TEOS removal

Figure 19 | Device 10 following decapsulation

Failure signature of electrical overstress on power MOSFETs

2.5 Human Body Model EOS of BUK7Y3R0-40H

Table 10: Human body model EOS

BUK7Y3R0-40H

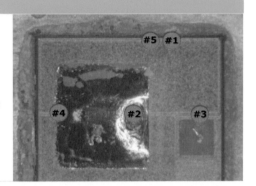

Cell structure: 1.5 µm stripe
Package: SOT669
Die size: 2.65 mm x 2.15 mm
EOS Condition: 2 kV HBM pulse

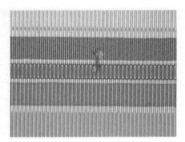

Figure 20 | Device 2 after Al, barrier and TEOS etch   Figure 21 | Device 3 after Al, barrier and TEOS etch

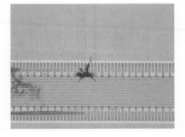

Figure 22 | Device 4 after Al, barrier and TEOS etch

2.6 Unclamped Inductive Switched EOS of BUK7L06-34ARC

Table 11: Unclamped inductive switching EOS

BUK7L06-34ARC

Cell structure:	9 mm hexagons	Small round burn marks, randomly distributed over active area, close to but not directly under wire-bonds
Package:	TO-220 (clip bond)	
Die size:	4.3 mm x 4.3 mm	
EOS Condition:	0.2 mH; 80 A to 110 A	

aaa-004912

Figure 23 | Sample image 1

aaa-004913

Figure 24 | Sample image 2

aaa-004914

Figure 25 | Sample image 3

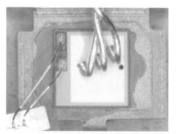

aaa-004915

Figure 26 | Sample image 4

Failure signature of electrical overstress on power MOSFETs

8

2.7 Unclamped Inductive Switched EOS of BUK9Y40-55B

Table 12: Unclamped inductive switching EOS

BUK9Y40-55B

Cell structure: 4 µm stripe
Package: LFPAK (clip bond)
Die size: 2.5 mm x 1.35 mm
EOS Condition: Red dots: 0.1 mH, 76 A to 80 A
Yellow dots: 15 mH, 7 A to 9 A

○ - Burn mark location for 15 mH inductor
● - Burn mark location for 100 µH inductor

aaa-004916

Small round burn marks, randomly distributed over active area, close to but not directly under clip bond

aaa-004917

Figure 27 | Sample image 41; 0.1 mH

aaa-004918

Figure 28 | Sample image 43; 0.1 mH

aaa-004919

Figure 29 | Sample image 51; 15 mH

aaa-004920

Figure 30 | Sample image 55; 15 mH

Failure signature of electrical overstress on power MOSFETs

8

2.8 Unclamped Inductive Switched EOS of PSMN7R0-30YL

Table 13: Unclamped inductive switching EOS

PSMN7R0-30YL

Cell structure: 2 µm stripe
Package: LFPAK (clip bond)
Die size: 2.5 mm x 1.35 mm
EOS Condition: Red dots: 0.1 mH,
48 A to 51 A
Yellow dots: 15 mH,
16 A to 18 A

aaa-004921

Small round burn marks, randomly distributed over active area, close to but not directly under clip bond

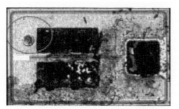

aaa-004922

Figure 31 | Sample image 6; 0.1 mH

aaa-004923

Figure 32 | Sample image 8; 0.1 mH

aaa-004924

Figure 33 | Sample image 18; 3.5 mH

aaa-004925

Figure 34 | Sample image 20; 3.5 mH

2.9 Unclamped Inductive Switched EOS of PSMN8R5-100PSF

Table 14: Unclamped inductive switching EOS

PSMN8R5-100PSF

Cell structure: 2 µm stripe
Package: SOT78
Die size: 4 mm x 2.67 mm
EOS Condition: Teal dot - 25 mH
                  Orange dot - 100 uH

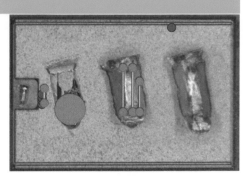

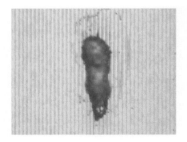

Figure 35 | Device 1 upper (orange) hotspot

Figure 36 | Device 1 lower (orange) hotspot

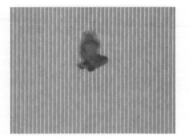

Figure 37 | Device 4 upper (orange) hotspot

Figure 38 | Device 4 lower (orange) hotspot

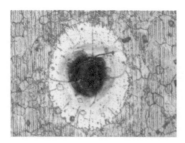

Figure 39 | Device 6 (teal) hotspot

Figure 40 | Device 7 (teal) hotspot

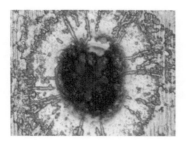

Figure 41 | Device 8 (teal) hotspot

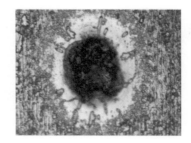

Figure 42 | Device 9 (teal) hotspot

2.10 Unclamped Inductive Switched EOS of BUK7Y3R0-40H

Table 15: Unclamped inductive switching EOS

BUK7Y3R0-40H

Cell structure:	1.5 µm stripe
Package:	SOT699
Die size:	2.65 mm x 2.15 mm

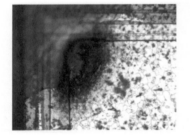

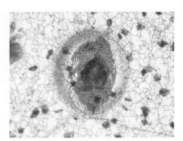

Figure 43 | Device 1

Figure 44 | Device 2

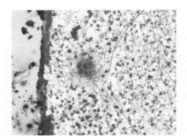

Figure 45 | Device 3

Failure signature of electrical overstress on power MOSFETs

8

2.11 Linear mode EOS of BUK7L06-34ARC

Table 16: Linear mode EOS

BUK7L06-34ARC

Cell structure: 9 mm hexagon
Package: TO-220 (clip bond)
Die size: 4.3 mm x 4.3 mm
EOS condition: 15 V, 3 A Burn marks located in middle of the die adjacent to wire bonds
30 V, 1.5 A Burn mark and location are more discrete at 20 V, 1.5 A

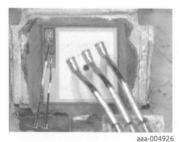

aaa-004926

Figure 46 | Sample image 1: 15 V, 3 A

aaa-004927

Figure 47 | Sample image 2: 15 V, 3 A

aaa-004928

Figure 48 | Sample image 3: 15 V, 3 A

aaa-004929

Figure 49 | Sample image 4: 15 V, 3 A

Failure signature of electrical overstress on power MOSFETs

Failure signature of electrical overstress on power MOSFETs

aaa-004930

Figure 50 | Sample image 1: 30 V, 1.5 A

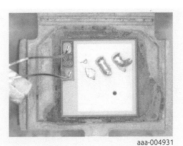

aaa-004931

Figure 51 | Sample image 2: 30 V, 1.5 A

aaa-004932

Figure 52 | Sample image 3: 30 V, 1.5 A

aaa-004933

Figure 53 | Sample image 4: 30 V, 1.5 A

2.12 Linear mode EOS of BUK9Y40-55B

Table 17: Linear mode EOS

BUK9Y40-55B

Cell structure: 4 µm stripe
Package: LFPAK (clip bond)
Die size: 2.5 mm x 1.35 mm
EOS condition: 20 V, 3.5 A, 30 ms
20 V, 3 A, 60 ms
30 V, 1.4 A, 60 ms

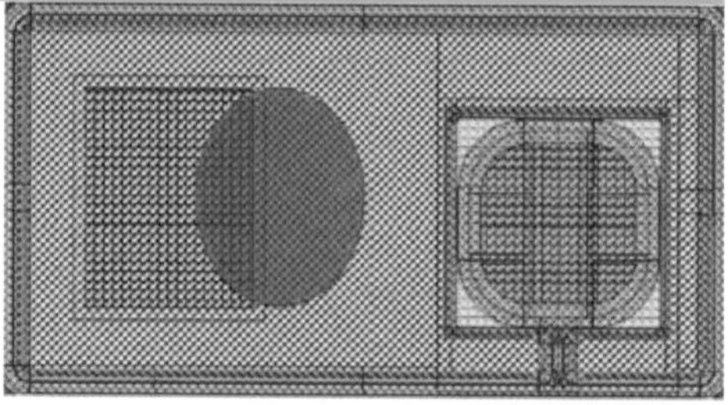

● - Burn mark location   aaa-004916

Burn marks in center of die, adjacent but not directly under clip bond

aaa-004935

Figure 54 | Sample image 61; 20 V, 3.5 A, 30 ms

aaa-004936

Figure 55 | Sample image 62; 20 V, 3.5 A, 30 ms

aaa-004937

Figure 56 | Sample image 63; 20 V, 3.5 A, 30 ms

aaa-004938

Figure 57 | Sample image 64; 20 V, 3.5 A, 30 ms

Failure signature of electrical overstress on power MOSFETs

8

Failure signature of electrical overstress on power MOSFETs

aaa-004937

Figure 58 | Sample image 66; 20 V, 3 A, 60 ms

aaa-004938

Figure 59 | Sample image 67; 20 V, 3 A, 60 ms

aaa-004942

Figure 60 | Sample image 68; 20 V, 3 A, 60 ms

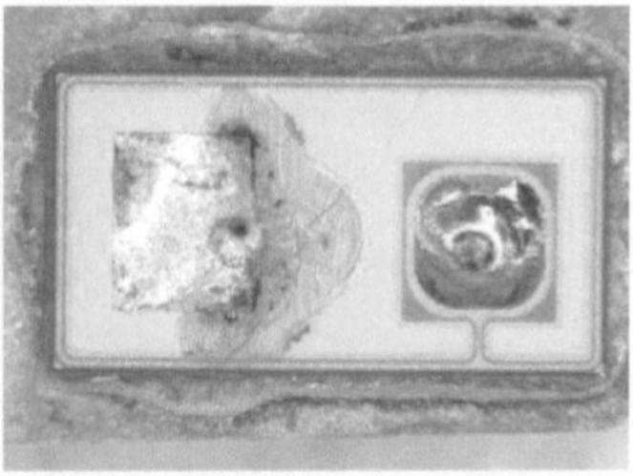

aaa-004943

Figure 61 | Sample image 69; 20 V, 3 A, 60 ms

aaa-004944

Figure 62 | Sample image 71; 30 V, 1.4 A, 60 ms

aaa-004946

Figure 63 | Sample image 72; 30 V, 1.4 A, 60 ms

aaa-004945

aaa-004947

Figure 64 | Sample image 73; 30 V, 1.4 A, 60 ms

Figure 65 | Sample image 74; 30 V, 1.4 A, 60 ms

2.13 Linear mode EOS of PSMN7R0-30YL

Table 18: Linear mode EOS

PSMN7R0-30YL		
Cell structure:	2 µm stripe	
Package:	LFPAK (clip bond)	
Die size:	2.3 mm x 1.35 mm	Burn marks in center of die, adjacent but not directly under clip bond
EOS condition:	0.1 mH, 48 to 51 A	
	3.5 mH, 16 A to 18 A	

aaa-004948

aaa-004951

Figure 66 | Sample image 1; 15 V, 2.5 A, 100 ms

Figure 67 |Sample image 2; 15 V, 2.5 A, 100 ms

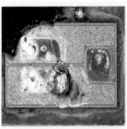

aaa-004953

Figure 68 | Sample image 4; 15 V, 2.5 A, 100 ms

aaa-004954

Figure 69 | Sample image 5; 15 V, 2.5 A, 100 ms

aaa-004955

Figure 70 | Sample image 11; 15 V, 5 A, 1 ms

aaa-004956

Figure 71 | Sample image 12; 15 V, 5 A, 1 ms

aaa-004957

Figure 72 | Sample image 13; 15 V, 5 A, 1 ms

aaa-004958

Figure 73 | Sample image 14; 15 V, 5 A, 1 ms

2.14 Linear mode EOS of PSMN8R5-100PSF

Table 19: Linear mode EOS

PSMN8R5-100PSF

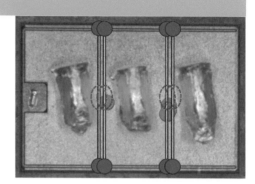

Cell structure: 2.5 µm stripe
Package: SOT78
Die size: 4 mm x 2.67 mm
EOS condition: Teal dot - 50 V
10 ms pulse length
Orange dot - 70 V
1 ms pulse length

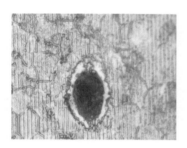

Figure 74 | Device 5 upper (orange) hotspot

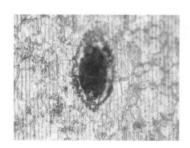

Figure 75 | Device 6 lower (orange) hotspot

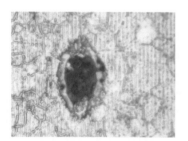

Figure 76 | Device 7 upper (orange) hotspot

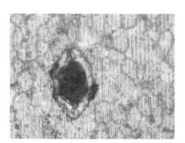

Figure 77 | Device 8 lower (orange) hotspot

Figure 78 | Device 1 (teal) hotspot

Figure 79 | Device 2 (teal) hotspot

Figure 80 | Device 3 (teal) hotspot

Figure 81 | Device 4 (teal) hotspot

2.15 Linear mode EOS of BUK7Y3R0-40H

Table 20: Linear mode EOS

BUK7Y3R0-40H

Cell structure: 1.5 μm stripe
Package: LFPAK (clip bond)
Die size: 2.3 mm x 1.35 mm
EOS condition: 0.1 mH, 48 A to 51 A
                 3.5 mHm 16 A to 18 A

Burn marks in center of die, adjacent but not directly under clip bond

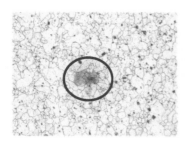

Figure 82 | Sample image 1; 15 V, 2.5 A, 100 ms

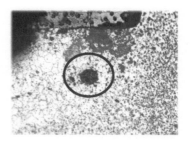

Figure 83 | Sample image 2; 15 V, 2.5 A, 100 ms

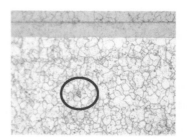

Figure 84 | Sample image 4; 15 V, 2.5 A, 100 ms

2.16 Over-current EOS of BUK7L06-34ARC

Table 21: Over-current EOS

BUK7L06-34ARC

Cell structure:	9 mm hexagon
Package:	TO-220 (clip bond)
Die size:	4.3 mm x 4.3 mm
EOS condition:	120 A

Extensive damage starting from die where wire bonds meet die.
Secondary damage of reflowed solder and even fused wires are visible.

aaa-004959

Figure 85 | Sample image 1

aaa-004960

Figure 86 | Sample image 2

aaa-004961

Figure 87 | Sample image 3

aaa-004962

Figure 88 | Sample image 4

2.17 Over-current EOS of PSMN7R0-30YL

Table 22: Over-current EOS

PSMN7R0-30YL

Cell structure:	2 µm stripe	Burn marks in center of die, adjacent but not directly under clip bond Some evidence of die-cracking.
Package:	LFPAK (clip bond)	
Die size:	2.3 mm x 1.35 mm	
EOS condition:	35 A, 35 ms	

aaa-004963

Figure 89 | Sample image 6

aaa-004964

Figure 90 | Sample image 7

aaa-004965

Figure 91 | Sample image 8

aaa-004966

Figure 92 | Sample image 9

Failure signature of electrical overstress on power MOSFETs

8

Failure signature of electrical overstress on power MOSFETs

3 Tables

4 Figures

Chapter 9

LFPAK MOSFET
thermal design guide

Application Note: AN90003

1 Introduction

This chapter is a guide to assist design engineers in understanding the power dissipation limits of the LFPAK family of packages. The maximum power that a MOSFET can dissipate is considered as a function of the Printed Circuit Board (PCB) design, using some common configurations. The application notes comprises of three main sections. The first section gives some background on MOSFET power loss and the thermal environment. The next two sections address separately the low power LFPAKs (LFPAK56D and LFPAK33) and the high power LFPAKs (LFPAK56 and LFPAK88).

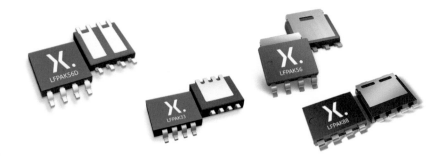

2 MOSFET power dissipation and the design environment

During normal operation, MOSFETs can exhibit three kinds of power losses:

- Switching losses – due to voltage and current being non-zero during the transition between the ON and OFF states.
- Conduction losses – when the device is fully on due to its on-state resistance $R_{DS(on)}$.
- Avalanche losses – if the device breakdown voltage is exceeded and an avalanche event occurs.

The shape of the power can change depending on the nature of the load. A generalized model of the total power dissipated by a MOSFET is the sum of these three losses, see Equation (1).

$$P_{tot} = P_{sw} + P_{cond} + P_{av}$$ [1]

In addition to electrical requirements another challenge is often the harsh environment that a device needs to operate in, particularly in terms of temperature. For instance, in automotive and industrial applications it's not uncommon to encounter high ambient temperature requirements, (from 85 °C up to 125 °C), this limits the amount of power that a MOSFET can safely handle.

Semiconductor devices are not the only parts to consider when dealing with high temperatures. For instance, the PCB material FR4 has a maximum operating temperature of around 130 °C, depending on manufacturer and chemistry, this is much lower than the limit specified for the junction of a silicon die (175 °C).

Modern applications continue to push the limits of power MOSFETs, while searching for better and better performances. As a consequence thermals have become one of the most important aspects of systems design. One way to address thermal issues is to carefully choose a device with the appropriate performances and provide a good enough path through which heat can flow freely, avoiding any impact on the device reliability.

2.1 Heat propagation phenomena

Heat propagates because of a temperature difference between the junction and the outside/ambient. Propagation occurs from junction and the outside/ambient through different material, from solids (silicon, copper, FR4, aluminum) to fluids (surrounding air or even air pockets trapped in the solder joints on the PCB). Heat finds a path whether it's defined by an engineer or not. This means that if the path is not designed correctly then heat might get trapped and raise the temperature of one or multiple mediums.

The physical phenomena by which heat can propagate are: conduction, convection and radiation.

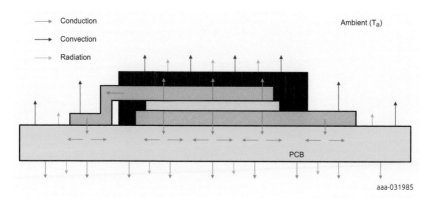

Figure 1 | Thermal propogation phenomena

9

2.1.1 Conduction

Conduction is the propagation of heat in a solid medium due to a temperature difference within it, and it is caused by the random movement of atoms and molecules. The rate of heat flow Q is directly proportional to the cross-section area A, temperature difference and thermal conductivity k. It is inversely proportional to the length x of the heat path, see Equation (2).

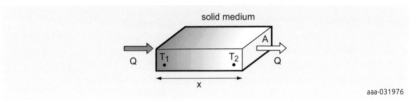

aaa-031976

Figure 2 | Conduction in a solid medium

$$Q = k \cdot A \cdot \frac{T_1 - T_2}{x}$$ [2]

Thermal conductivity, measured as W/(mK), is a physical property of a material and defines its ability to conduct heat. The higher its value the higher the rate of heat transfer, therefore the better thermal conductor. From Equation 2 it can be derived that rate of heat flow is measured in W. Therefore, heat is measured in Joule (Ws).

Table 1 lists some materials with their thermal conductivity values. Air is a very bad conductor of heat, thus a good thermal insulator. It's thermal conductivity is 2,000 times lower than that of steel. Notice how thermal glue has a very low thermal conductivity of less than 2, (generic brand). Thermal glue is not a good thermal conductor, however its main function is to create a good fit between two surfaces that otherwise would form trapped pockets of air, which is 100 times a better insulator than the glue itself.

Table 1: Typical thermal conductivity values

Material	k (W/mK)
Air (not moving)	0.024
Brick	0.6
Glass	0.8
Thermal glue	1.78
Steel	50.2
Brass	109
Silicon	130

Material	k (W/mK)
Aluminium	205
Copper	385
Silver	406
Diamond	1000

2.1.2 Convection

Convection is the transfer of heat from a solid body to a fluid due to its movement with respect to the surface of the body, and it is promoted by a difference in temperature between the two mediums. The fluid may be a gas (air) or a liquid.

Here the rate of heat flow depends only on surface A, temperature difference and convection coefficient h, see Equation (3).

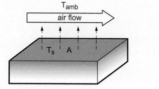

Figure 3 | Convection in free air

aaa-031977

$$Q = h \cdot A \cdot (T_s - T_{amb}) \qquad [3]$$

The convection coefficient is not a physical property of the fluid (like the conduction coefficient) but an abstract quantity verified by experimentation. It depends on fluid density, velocity, viscosity, turbulence and on the solid medium surface geometry.

The convection coefficient is measured in $W/(m^2K)$. Table 2 lists some values measured in different scenarios of free/natural and forced cooling.

Table 2: Thermal convection coefficient values

Flow type	h (W/m²K)	
	Free air	Forced cooling
Gases	2 - 20	25 - 300
Air	10	100
Liquids	50 - 1,000	100 - 40,000
Phase change	2,500 - 100,000	

As can be seen during a phase change the convection coefficient rises dramatically up to 100,000. This is due to the fact that during a phase change all the energy involved, and transferred to the fluid, is used to rearrange molecules structure and does not result in a temperature change.

2.1.3 Radiation

Radiation is the propagation of heat via infrared radiation.

The main benefit of radiation is that as the ambient temperature increases, and the component temperature with it, the heat transfer by radiation increases as well. As you can see in Equation (4), it depends on the fourth power of temperature. The radiation is bigger but not by a lot and the overall effect is that radiation does not help a body get cooler.

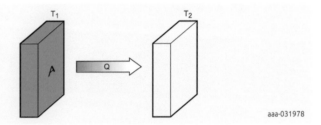

aaa-031978

Figure 4 | Radiation

$$Q = \varepsilon \cdot \sigma \cdot A \cdot (T_1^4 - T_2^4)$$
[4]

The amount of radiation is determined by the surface emissivity. Emissivity of a material is measured between 0 and 1. A perfect emitter is called a black body because it emits 100% of the energy it absorbs, and is assigned an emissivity value of 1. Table 3 below gives emissivity values for different materials.

Table 3. Typical emissivity values

Material	Emissivity coefficient (ε)
Aluminium, polished	0.05
Aluminium, oxidized	0.25
Black electrical tape	0.95
Copper, polished	0.01
Copper, oxidized	0.65
Steel, oxidized	0.88
Water	0.98

A new piece of polished aluminum has emissivity of 0.05, (not good), its emissivity increases as it oxides by 5 times. Every object emits thermal radiation, the amount of radiation that a particular object emits as a function of wavelength looks as a bell shaped curve. Energy is emitted at all frequencies but the major part of the emission occurs at a certain wavelength range which depends on the source temperature. The higher the temperature the higher the frequency (lower the wavelength), that is why we see materials change color as they heat up.

At the receiving side, for most of the surfaces, the same graph looks quite flat but to a very small range of wavelengths at which the object absorbs all the impinging radiation. These surfaces are called selective surfaces, because they absorb only certain wavelengths.

2.2 Thermal – Electrical analogy

When considering thermal propagation, classical methods of analysis may be used. These are based on the thermal equations and thermal networks. These describe the paths through which heat propagates through mediums or from one medium to another.

Any thermal network can be modelled by means of an electrical circuit. An analogy for every thermal parameter can be found in the electrical domain. The respective analogues of electric potential and current are temperature difference and rate of heat flow. Based on these it may be observed that the thermal resistance is the ratio of temperature and rate of heat flow similarly to how the voltage and current ratio defines the electrical resistance using Ohm's law. The main analogies may be seen in Table 4 below. Based on these, thermal networks can be solved using many of the electrical theory laws such as Ohm's and Kirchhoff's laws. Also circuits can be simplified by means of series and parallel resistor equivalences.

Table 4. Thermal and electrical analogous parameters

Thermal	Electrical
Temperature T (°C)	Voltage V (V)
Rate of heat flow Q (W)	Current I (A)
Thermal resistance R_{th} (K/W)	Resistance R (Ω)
Thermal capacitance C_{th} [W·s/K]	Capacitance C (A·s/V = F)

An example of a thermal circuit modelled in the electrical domain using a SPICE software may be seen in Figure 5. Figure 6 shows the response of this example circuit as a temperature plot, where the transient and steady state thermal behaviour may be seen.

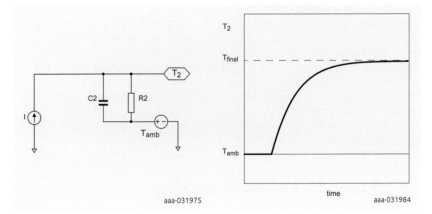

aaa-031975

time
aaa-031984

Figure 5 | SPICE model   **Figure 6** | Response

2.2.1 Thermal resistance

Thermal resistance is a measure of the inertia of a material or medium towards heat flow, just like the electrical resistance is to the movement of electrons. It is therefore a physical property of the specific component. It is calculated as the ratio of the temperature difference between two points and the rate of heat flow, therefore as K/W. The thermal and electrical models may be seen in the pictures below.

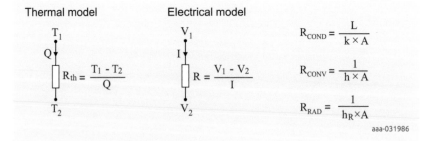

Thermal model   Electrical model

$$R_{th} = \frac{T_1 - T_2}{Q}$$ $$R = \frac{V_1 - V_2}{I}$$

$$R_{COND} = \frac{L}{k \times A}$$

$$R_{CONV} = \frac{1}{h \times A}$$

$$R_{RAD} = \frac{1}{h_R \times A}$$

aaa-031986

Figure 7 | Thermal and electrical resistance models

Every phenomenon governing how heat flows, namely conduction, convection and radiation, has its own thermal resistance. Each one of them depends inversely on a coefficient and surface or cross section area of the material from where heat is generated or simply passing through. In conduction the resistance depends directly to the length of the medium.

LFPAK MOSFET thermal design guide

9

2.2.2 Thermal capacitance

Thermal capacitance, sometimes known also as thermal mass, is a property of a material which represents how much heat (thermal energy) it can store in time, similar to its electrical counterpart with electrical energy. Thermal capacitance provides also a quantity of the inertia against temperature fluctuations, the higher the value the harder it will be to drive the stored energy in or out.

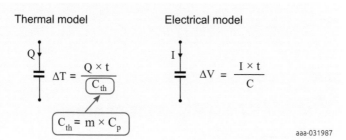

Thermal model   Electrical model

$$\Delta T = \frac{Q \times t}{C_{th}}$$

$$C_{th} = m \times C_p$$

$$\Delta V = \frac{I \times t}{C}$$

aaa-031987

Figure 8 | Thermal and electrical capacitance models

Thermal capacitance is typically referred to using the symbol C_{th}, and it's measured as J/K. For a body of uniform composition, it can be approximated as the product of mass (m) of the body and specific heat capacity (C_p), which is the heat capacity of a sample of the substance divided by the mass of the sample.

2.2.3 Transient and steady state thermal behavior

- Thermal transients describe temperatures which are changing, even at the end of the analysis window. An example may be observed below in the yellow part of the junction temperature plot.
- Steady state thermals describe the stable region where temperatures show minimal to no change at all. These temperature remain unchanged with the passing of time and thus represent the final values a system might show under constant conditions.

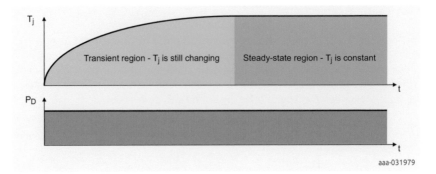

Figure 9 | Transient and steady state thermal behavior

2.3 MOSFET steady state thermal characteristics

This section focuses on two important MOSFET thermal aspects. The junction to mounting base thermal resistance as well as the junction to ambient thermal resistance. The aim in this chapter is to overview the two thermal paths and to show the thermal network which describes these paths.

2.3.1 Thermal resistance junction to mounting base - $R_{th(j-mb)}$

The thermal heat path between the MOSFET junction to its mounting base is one of the most important thermal specifications on a data sheet. It is represented by the overall junction to mounting base thermal resistance which is a value describing the ease with which heat is conducted along this path due to the different materials is going through. In Figure 10, a MOSFET depiction is represented with the thermal resistive network between the junction to mounting base.

As the MOSFET and its parts are 3 dimensional so is the mentioned heat path, thus the 2 dimensional resistor network seen below is actually 3 dimensional in reality. Referring back to the $R_{th(j-mb)}$, it is important to remember that the value encompasses the whole network. Lastly, the parameter describes the steady state thermal characteristics, thus one should use average power dissipation values in order to obtain the temperatures reached by the MOSFET.

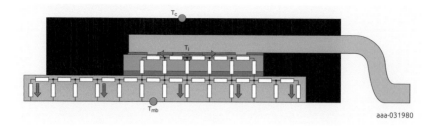

Figure 10 | Thermal path junction to mounting base

2.3.2 Thermal resistance junction to ambient - $R_{th(j-a)}$

The thermal heat path between the MOSFET junction and the ambient encompasses paths within the MOSFET itself as well as additional ones when a MOSFET is mounted onto a PCB. Hence, heat may spread from the junction towards the mounting base and the case. Afterwards, when the extremities of the MOSFET are reached, the heat will flow into the surroundings via the PCB or directly from the case. These heat paths are depicted in Figure 11.

Figure 11 a) shows the heat moving from the junction to the mounting base and to the case top and afterwards to the ambient. Figure 11 b) shows the heat moving from the mounting base to the PCB and through it in order to reach the ambient.

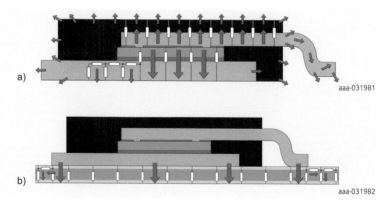

Figure 11 | Thermal path junction to ambient

A simplified thermal circuit may be seen in Fig. 12. It is important to notice that the two thermal paths from the component to the ambient are in parallel, thus improving both may be redundant.

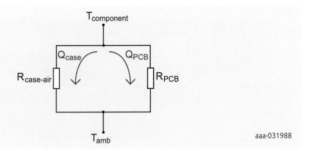

Figure 12 | Simplified $R_{th(j-a)}$ thermal paths

A more cost effective method of reducing the thermal resistance between the MOSFET to the surroundings may be to focus on one of the thermal paths and improve it in the best way possible.

Figure 13 shows a thermal circuit which encompasses the MOSFET the PCB and the environment, it may be observed that the three heat spreading methods are shown by individual thermal resistors. In this particular case, the heat spreads:

- Through conduction from the junction towards the outside of the MOSFET, represented by the mounting base and the case.
- From the case to the ambient the heat propagates through convection and radiation.
- From the mounting base to the PCB and into it, conduction is again the main way of propagation.
- From the PCB into the environment convection and conduction are the main methods through which heat propagates to the ambient, radiation is usually negligible.

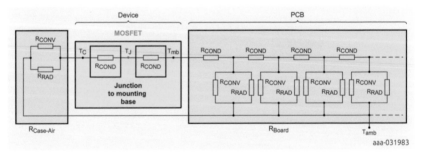

Figure 13 | Thermal circuit, MOSFET, PCB and environment

The thermal circuit seen in Figure 13 is also represented in Figure 1. Finally, the two thermal resistor networks highlighted in green are also represented in Figure 12.

2.3.3 PCB thermal limitation and the 1 Watt rule

As previously described, the junction to ambient thermal path contains the board or PCB. This is often made from FR4 material, which from a thermal and electrical perspective is an insulator. Moreover, planes, pours and traces of copper are also present as these provide the circuit interconnections. Altogether we can consider them as forming the board and giving it a certain thermal characteristic called the board thermal resistance. It was found that this value is approximately **50-60 K/W**, depending on the amount of copper, insulation layer thickness and other factors. Since this is specific to the materials and dimensions of a board, this limit is imposed.

Moreover, the ambient temperature in which a board operates, the thermal limitations of a system, the FR4 temperature limit of 120 °C to 140 °C, as well as the temperature ranges within which a board needs to function in, gives rise to a power limitation. These same dependencies can be noted from the following equations:

$$Thermal\ resistivity\left[\frac{W}{mK}\right] = \frac{1}{Thermal\ conductivity\left[\frac{mK}{W}\right]} \quad [5]$$

$$Thermal\ resistance\left[\frac{K}{W}\right] = Thermal\ resitivity\left[\frac{W}{mK}\right] \times \frac{Thickness\ [m]}{Area\ [m^2]} \quad [6]$$

$$Thermal\ resistance\left[\frac{K}{W}\right] = \frac{Temperature\ difference\ [K]}{Power\ [m]} \quad [7]$$

PCB thickness, area and thermal resistivity determine the PCB thermal resistance, given in K/W. Hence, given a specific ambient temperature and a maximum FR4 temperature, or the system maximum operation temperature, a ΔT is obtained.

Example: calculate the power dissipation of a MOSFET mounted on an FR4 PCB within an automotive environment where the ambient temperature is 80 °C.

- The FR4 PCB material has a thermal resistance $R_{th(FR4\ PCB)}$ = 50 K/W
- The FR4 PCB material maximum temperature ($T_{FR4(max)}$) = 130 °C
- The ambient temperature T_{amb} = 80 °C

$$\Delta T = T_{FR4(max)} - T_{(amb)} = 130\ °C - 80\ °C = 50\ °C \quad [8]$$

$$P = \frac{R_{th(FR4\ PCB)}}{\Delta T} = \frac{50\ K}{50\ K/W} = 1\ W \quad [9]$$

Given the above ambient temperature and FR4 PCB characteristics, approximately 1 watt of power may be dissipated in a MOSFET within this automotive environment.

LFPAK MOSFET thermal design guide

2.3.4 Thermal nomenclature

Terminology surrounding thermal characterization of power MOSFETs has been revised multiple times over the years. Regardless of these efforts, standards organizations and semiconductor manufacturers may still use different names when referring to the same thermal parameter, or to slightly different variations of it. The terms often used to indicate one or the other type of thermal resistance are: R and θ. In the case of junction to ambient, the $R_{th(j-amb)} = R_{\theta(j-amb)} = \theta_{(j-amb)}$.

3 LFPAK56D and LFPAK33

3.1 Simple configuration with a single layer

In this section, we will present the maximum power dissipation results for a simple PCB configuration using a single layer with varying copper area.

Results for the LFPAK56D and LFPAK33 packages are given, for the LFPAK56D with only one or with both MOSFETs conducting.

3.1.1 LFPAK56D

Set-up:
- 1 layer on the top
- MOSFET power dissipation is 0.1 W, 0.5 W and 1 W applied to each MOSFET
- Maximum junction temperature of 175 °C
- PCB material is standard FR4, 1.6 mm thickness, dimension 100 x 100 mm
- Maximum PCB operating temperature of 120 °C
- Copper thickness is 2 oz./ft^2 (70 μm)
- The PCB is suspended in free air at ambient temperature of 20 °C
- The simulation is carried out for conduction, convection and radiation heat transfer
- There is no forced air cooling applied, i.e. only natural convection is modeled

The simplest possible PCB stack-up is that of a single top copper layer, see Figure 14.

In this analysis, we will examine the variation in device junction temperature (T_j) as a function of the top copper area.

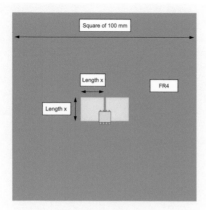

Figure 14 | Copper area configuration: LFPAK56D, single top copper layer

The graph in Figure 15 captures two important factors:

- T_j depends greatly on length "x" and thus copper area, the bigger the area the better the thermal performance
- However, the ability of the top copper to provide heatsinking for the MOSFET shows a "law of diminishing returns". In other words, we cannot keep on adding more copper area in the hope of continuing to reduce T_j. As can be seen from Figure 15 below, T_j will plateau at around 50 °C (for 0.5 W per MOSFET) no matter how much copper area we provide.

Care must be taken for T_j above 120 °C as PCB temperature directly under the transistor would be close to the MOSFET T_j.

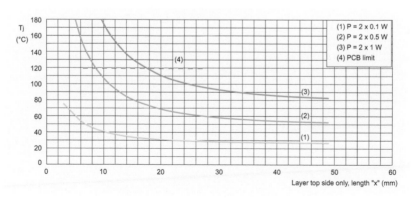

Figure 15 | Junction temperature as a function of copper side length x for LFPAK56D

An alternative to the previous approach is to look at the maximum power allowed before reaching $T_{j(max)}$ = 175 °C (MOSFET absolute max). Maximum power allowed is shown for different ambient temperature and copper length. In this example the PCB temperature was not considered so care must be taken for the resulting heat on the PCB.

In Figure 16 the maximum power for the conditions given is as follows:
T_{amb} = 20 °C: Max power is 2.6 W per MOSFET (2 × 2.6 W permissible in this package)
T_{amb} = 80 °C: Max power is 1.65 W per MOSFET (2 × 1.65 W permissible in this package)

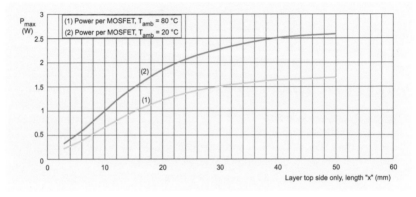

Figure 16 | Maximum permissible power dissipation as a function of copper side length x for LFPAK56D

3.1.2 LFPAK56D only one MOSFET active at a time

In a typical half bridge application only one MOSFET conducts at a time. In the graph below, Figure. 17, 1 W is dissipated in the left MOSFET (blue curve). We can see that 1 W dissipation in one MOSFET is not equivalent to 0.5 W dissipation in each of the two MOSFETs (yellow curve).

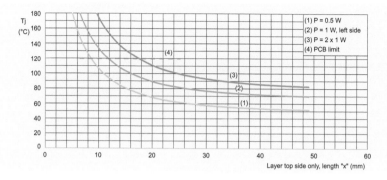

Figure 17 | Junction temperature as a function of copper side length x for LFPAK56D; one MOSFET conducting

As can be seen temperature is higher in the case of one MOSFET dissipating 1 W than it is with two MOSFETs each dissipating 0.5 W. When only one MOSFET is active the second MOSFET does not make a significant contribution to the total dissipation capability - meaning that if one MOSFET is off the heating is not shared equally between the two. This is further explained by the thermal network shown in Figure 19.

An alternative to the previous approach is to look at the maximum power allowed before reaching $T_{j(max)} = 175\ °C$ (MOSFET absolute max). Maximum power allowed is shown for different ambient temperature and copper length. In this example the PCB temperature was not considered so care must be taken for the resulting heat on the PCB. In Figure 18 the maximum power for the conditions given is as follows:
- $T_{amb} = 20\ °C$: Max power is 3.35 W with only left MOSFET
- $T_{amb} = 80\ °C$: Max power is 2.1 W with only left MOSFET

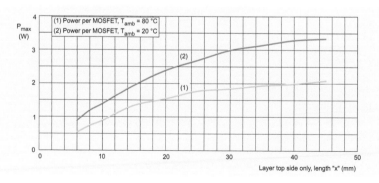

Figure 18 | Maximum power as a function of side length x for LFPAK56D; one MOSFET conducting

The concept of the second MOSFET half-sharing the thermal dissipation when turned off is not true
– see Figure 19

Dual MOSFET thermal resistance configuration:

We can see that the thermal path between both MOSFETs inside the package is highly resistive (100 K/W).

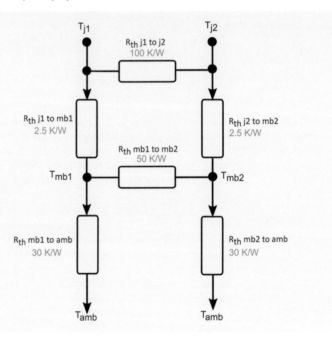

Figure 19 | Thermal resistance configuration

3.1.3 LFPAK33

Set-up:
- 1 layer on the top
- MOSFET power dissipation is 0.1 W, 0.5 W and 1 W applied in the MOSFET
- Maximum junction temperature of 175 °C
- PCB material is standard FR4, 1.6 mm thickness, dimension 100 x 100 mm
- Maximum PCB operating temperature of 120 °C
- Copper thickness is 2 oz./ft^2 (70 µm)
- The PCB is suspended in free air at ambient temperature of 20 °C
- The simulation is carried out for conduction, convection and radiation heat transfer

- There is no forced air cooling applied i.e. only natural convection is modeled

The simplest possible PCB stack-up is that of a single top copper layer. In this analysis, we will examine the variation in device junction temperature (T_j) as a function of top copper area.

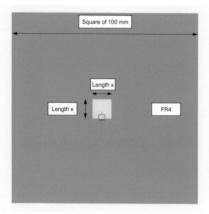

Figure 20 | Copper area configuration: LFPAK33, single top copper layer

The graph in Figure 21 captures two important factors:

- T_j depends greatly on length "x" and thus copper area, the bigger the area the better the thermal performance
- However, the ability of the top copper to provide heatsinking for the MOSFET shows a "law of diminishing returns". In other words, we cannot keep on adding more copper area in the hope of continuing to reduce T_j. As can be seen from Figure 21 below, T_j will plateau at around 40 °C (for 0.5 W per MOSFET) no matter how much copper area we provide.

Care must be taken for T_j above 120 °C as PCB temperature directly under the transistor would be close to the MOSFET T_j.

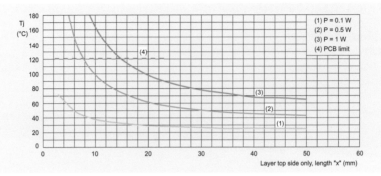

Figure 21 | Junction temperature as a function of copper side length x for LFPAK33

An alternative to the previous approach is to look at the maximum power allowed before reaching $T_{j(max)}$ = 175 °C (MOSFET absolute max). Maximum power allowed is shown for different ambient temperature and copper length. In this example the PCB temperature was not considered so care must be taken for the resulting heat on the PCB.

In the graph below, Figure 22, the maximum power for the conditions given is as follows:

T_{amb} = 20 °C: Max power is 3.7 W in the MOSFET
T_{amb} = 80 °C: Max power is 2.4 W in the MOSFET

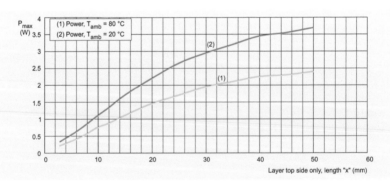

Figure 22 | Maximum permissible power dissipation as a function of copper side length x for LFPAK33

3.2 Usual configuration: 4 layers + vias

In this section, we will present the maximum power dissipation results for a PCB configuration using 4 layers + vias for dissipation on the bottom layer, with varying copper area.

Results for the LFPAK56D and LFPAK33 packages are given, for the LFPAK56D with only one or with both MOSFETs conducting.

3.2.1 LFPAK56D

Set-up:
- 4 layers + vias (vias number increases with the copper area with a maximum of 25 vias for each side)
- MOSFET power dissipation is 0.1 W, 0.5 W and 1 W applied to each MOSFET
- Maximum junction temperature of 175 °C
- PCB material is standard FR4, 1.6 mm thickness, dimension 100 x 100 mm
- Maximum PCB operating temperature of 120 °C
- Copper thickness on all layers (external and internal) is 2 oz./ft^2 (70 μm)
- The PCB is suspended in free air at ambient temperature of 20 °C
- The simulation is carried out for conduction, convection and radiation heat transfer
- There is no forced air cooling applied i.e. only natural convection is modeled

The common PCB stack-up is 4 layers with vias under MOSFETs to create a dissipation path to the heatsink.

In this analysis, we will examine the variation in device junction temperature (T_j) as a function of top copper area. In Figure 23 below, we can see the vias configuration:

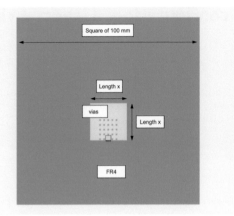

Figure 23 | Copper area configuration: LFPAK56D, 4 layers with vias

Vias configuration: square vias used for ease of simulation.

Figure 24 | Sectional view: LFPAK56D

Table 5: Limitation of number of vias

X (mm)	Vias configuration	Comments	Vias information
minimal footprint	2+2 vias	Maximum number of vias able to be inserted in the copper surface	
6	9+9 vias		
8	12+12 vias		Vias pitch 2.5 mm
10	20+20 vias		Vias side length 0.7 mm
15	25+25 vias		Copper thickness 70 µm
20	25+25 vias		No solder fill
25	25+25 vias	25 vias maximum	
30	25+25 vias		
35	25+25 vias		
40	25+25 vias		
50	25+25 vias		

The graph in Figure 25 captures two important factors:

- T_j depends greatly on length "x" and thus copper area, the bigger the area the better the thermal performance
- However, the ability of the top copper to provide heatsinking for the MOSFET shows a "law of diminishing returns". In other words, we cannot keep on adding more copper area in the hope of continuing to reduce T_j. As can be seen from the graph in Figure 25, T_j will plateau at around 36 °C (for 0.5 W per MOSFET) no matter how much copper area we provide.

Care must be taken for T_j above 120 °C as the PCB temperature directly under the transistor would be close to the MOSFET T_j.

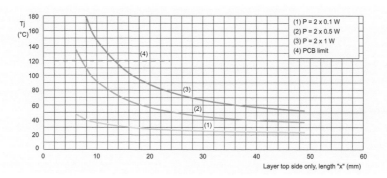

Figure 25 | Junction temperature as a function of copper side length x for LFPAK56D

An alternative to the previous approach is to look at the maximum power allowed before reaching $T_{j(max)}$ = 175 °C (MOSFET absolute max). Maximum power allowed is shown for different ambient temperature and copper length. In this example the PCB temperature was not considered so care must be taken for the resulting heat on the PCB.

In the graph below, Figure 26 the maximum power for the conditions given is as follows:

T_{amb} = 20 °C: Max power is 5.3 W per MOSFET (2 × 5.3 W permissible in this package)
T_{amb} = 80 °C: Max power is 3.55 W per MOSFET (2 × 3.55 W permissible in this package)

9

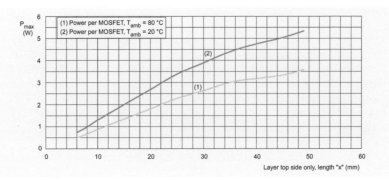

Figure 26 | Maximum permissible power dissipation as a function of copper side length x for LFPAK56D

3.2.2 LFPAK56D only one MOSFET active at a time

In a typical half bridge application only one MOSFET conducts at a time. Figure 27 below shows the results for 1 W applied to the left MOSFET (blue curve). We can see that 1 W dissipated in one MOSFET is not equivalent to 0.5 W dissipation in each of the two MOSFETs (yellow curve).

As can be seen temperature is higher in the case of one MOSFET conducting with 1 W than it is with two MOSFETs each dissipating 0.5 W.

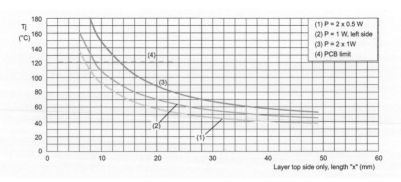

Figure 27 | Junction temperature as a function of copper side length x for LFPAK56D; one MOSFET

An alternative to the previous approach is to look at the maximum power allowed before reaching $T_{j(max)} = 175\,°C$ (MOSFET absolute max). Maximum power allowed is shown for different ambient temperature and copper length. In this example the PCB temperature was not considered so care must be taken for the resulting heat on the PCB.

In Figure 28 the maximum power for the conditions given is as follows:

- T_{amb} = 20 °C: Max power is 6 W with only left MOSFET
- T_{amb} = 80 °C: Max power is 4 W with only left MOSFET

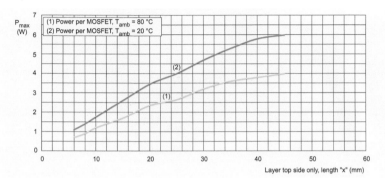

Figure 28 | Power dissipation as a function of copper side length x for LFPAK56D; one MOSFET

As previously mentioned, when only one MOSFET is active the second MOSFET does not make a significant contributution to the total dissipation capabilty – see Figure 19.

3.2.3 LFPAK33

Set-up:
- 4 layers + vias (vias number increases with the copper area with a maximum of 25 vias for each side)
- MOSFET power dissipation is 0.1 W, 0.5 W and 1 W applied in the MOSFET
- Maximum junction temperature of 175 °C
- PCB material is standard FR4, 1.6 mm thickness, dimension 100 x 100 mm
- Maximum PCB operating temperature of 120 °C
- Copper thickness on all layers (external and internal) is 2 oz./ft^2 (70 μm)
- The PCB is suspended in free air at ambient temperature of 20 °C
- The simulation is carried out for conduction, convection and radiation heat transfer
- There is no forced air cooling applied i.e. only natural convection is modeled

The common PCB stack-up is 4 layers with vias under the MOSFETs to create a dissipation path to the heatsink.

In this analysis, we will examine the variation in device junction temperature (T_j) as a function of top copper area.

In Figure 29 below, we can see the vias configuration:

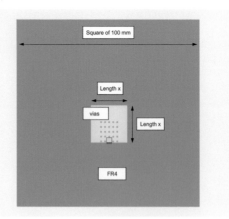

Figure 29 | Copper area configuration: LFPAK33, 4 layers with vias

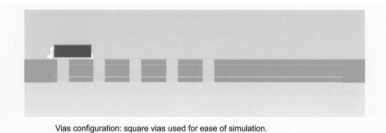

Vias configuration: square vias used for ease of simulation.

Figure 30 | Sectional view: LFPAK33

Table 6: Vias configuration

X (mm)	Vias configuration	Comments	Vias information
minimal footprint	1 via	Maximum number of vias able to be inserted in the copper surface	
6	6 vias		
8	9 vias		
10	20 vias		Vias pitch 2.5 mm
15	25 vias		Vias side length 0.7 mm
20	25 vias		Copper thickness 70 μm
25	25 vias		No solder fill
30	25 vias	25 vias maximum	
35	25 vias		
40	25 vias		
50	25 vias		

The graph Figure 31 captures two important factors:

- T_j depends greatly on length "x" and thus copper area, the bigger the area the better the thermal performance
- However, the ability of the top copper to provide heatsinking for the MOSFET shows a "law of diminishing returns". In other words, we cannot keep on adding more copper area in the hope of continuing to reduce T_j. As can be seen from Figure 31 below T_j will plateau at around 33 °C (for 0.5 W per MOSFET) no matter how much copper area we provide.

Care must be taken for T_j above 120 °C as PCB temperature directly under the transistor would be close to the MOSFET T_j.

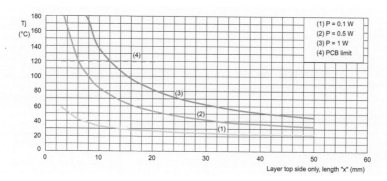

Figure 31 | Junction temperature as a function of copper side length x for LFPAK33

An alternative to the previous approach is to look at the maximum power allowed before reaching $T_{j(max)}$ = 175 °C (MOSFET absolute max). Maximum power allowed is shown for different ambient temperature and copper length. In this example the PCB temperature was not considered so care must be taken for the resulting heat on the PCB.

In the graph below the maximum power for the conditions given is as follows:

T_{amb} = 20 °C: Max power is 6.5 W in the MOSFET
T_{amb} = 80 °C: Max power is 4.3 W in the MOSFET

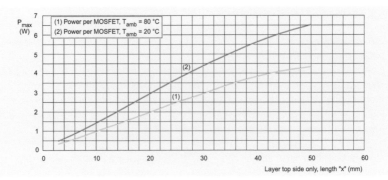

Figure 32 | Maximum permissible power dissipation as a function of copper side length x for LFPAK33

3.3 Placement advice for improved dissipation

In this section, we will present some results for two MOSFETs placed close to each other on a single layer PCB with varying copper area.

3.3.1. LFPAK56D

Simulation of two MOSFETs placed next to each other is carried out and checked against results seen in section 2.1. The aim is to understand the dissipation effect that the two LFPAK56D have on one another.

Set-up
- 1 layer on the top side
- MOSFET power dissipation is 0.5 W applied to each MOSFET
- Maximum junction temperature of 175 °C
- PCB material is standard FR4, 1.6 mm thickness, dimension 200 x 150 mm
- Maximum PCB operating temperature of 120 °C
- Copper thickness on all layers (external and internal) is 2 oz./ft^2 (70 μm)
- The PCB is suspended in free air at ambient temperature of 20 °C
- The simulation is carried out for conduction, convection and radiation heat transfer
- There is no forced air cooling applied i.e. only natural convection is modeled

The simplest possible PCB stack-up is that of a single top copper layer. In this analysis, we will examine the variation in device junction temperature (T_j) as a function of top copper area.

- 2 mm gap between right and left copper layers
- Simulation carried out for different length "x"
- 0.5 W applied on each internal MOSFET

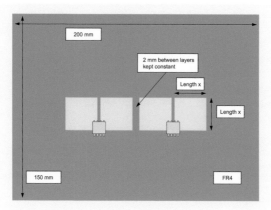

Figure 33 | Copper area configuration: LFPAK56D, single top copper layer

The graph in Figure 34 shows:

- The results (in green) are similar to the ones observed in section 2.1 (slightly higher +3 °C)
- This is due to the low conductivity of FR4, despite only 2 mm gap it showed no heat transfer from one copper area to the other

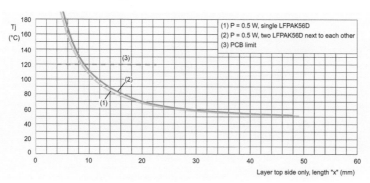

Figure 34 | Junction temperature as a function of copper side length x for 2 LFPAK56D

3.3.2 LFPAK33

Simulation of two MOSFETs placed next to each other is carried out and checked against results seen in section 2.3. The aim is to understand the dissipation effect that the two MOSFETs have on one another.

Set-up:
- 1 layer on the top
- MOSFET power dissipation is 0.5 W applied in the MOSFET
- Maximum junction temperature of 175 °C
- PCB material is standard FR4, 1.6 mm thickness, dimension 200 x 150 mm
- Maximum PCB operating temperature of 120 °C
- Copper thickness is 2 oz./ft^2 (70 μm)
- The PCB is suspended in free air at ambient temperature of 20 °C
- The simulation is carried out for conduction, convection and radiation heat transfer
- There is no forced air cooling applied i.e. only natural convection is modeled

The simplest possible PCB stack-up is that of a single top copper layer. In this analysis, we will examine the variation in device junction temperature (T_j) as a function of top copper area.

- 2 mm gap between right and left copper layers
- Simulation carried out for different length "x"
- 0.5 W applied on each MOSFET

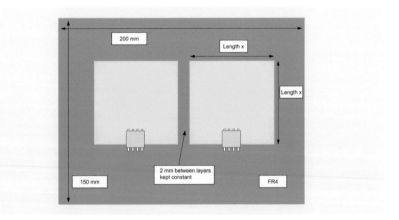

Figure 35 | Copper area configuration: LFPAK33, single top copper layer

The graph in Figure 37 shows:

- The results for x > 20 mm are similar to the ones observed in section 2.3 (slightly higher +3 °C)
- This is due to the low conductivity of FR4, despite only 2 mm gap it showed no

heat transfer from one copper area to the other
- For x < 20 mm results show up to 20 °C higher compared to the results from section 2.3.
- This is due to the MOSFETs being brought closer to each other as a result of reduced copper area – note that in this case the space between MOSFETs is half the space between MOSFETs in the case of LFPAK56D

In Figure 36 you can see that for x = 10 mm, the distance between the LFPAK33 MOSFETs is approximatively 10 mm. Less than 20 mm apart, the MOSFETs are close enough to heat each other, hence we start to see a temperature difference.

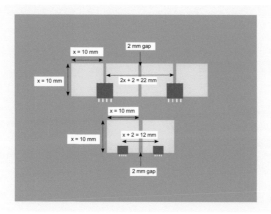

Figure 36 | Copper area configuration: 2 x LFPAK33, 2 x LFPAK56D; separation between MOSFETs

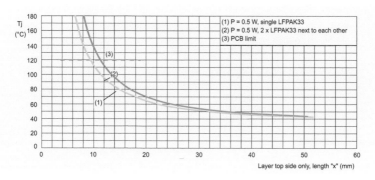

Figure 37 | Junction temperature as a function of copper side length x for 2 LFPAK33

3.4 Comparison between two LFPAK56 and one LFPAK56D, then one LFPAK56D and two LFPAK33

In this section we will present some comparative results for different package devices on a single layer board with varying copper area.

3.4.1 Two LFPAK56 to LFPAK56D

In this section the results of two single LFPAK56 MOSFETs are compared to the results of one dual LFPAK56D MOSFET (see Section 3.1.1)

The aim is to highlight the benefit of using one LFPAK56D dual MOSFET instead of two single LFPAK56 MOSFETs.

Set-up:
- 1 layer on the top
- MOSFET power dissipation is 0.5 W applied to each MOSFET
- Maximum junction temperature of 175 °C
- PCB material is standard FR4, 1.6 mm thickness, dimension 100 x 100 mm
- Maximum PCB operating temperature of 120 °C
- Copper thickness is 2 oz./ft^2 (70 μm)
- The PCB is suspended in free air at ambient temperature of 20 °C
- The simulation is carried out for conduction, convection and radiation heat transfer
- There is no forced air cooling applied, i.e. only natural convection is modeled

The simplest possible PCB stack-up is that of a single top copper layer. In this analysis, we will examine the variation in device junction temperature (T_j) as a function of top copper area.

- Same gap between copper layer was used for both single LFPAK56 and dual LFPAK56D
- Simulation carried out for different length "x".
- 0.5 W applied on each MOSFET

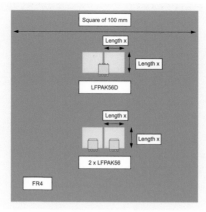

Figure 38 | Copper area configuration: 1 x LFPAK56D, 2 x LFPAK56, single top copper layer

The graph in Figure 39 shows:

- Overall two single LFPAK56 show better heat dissipation than one dual LFPAK56D by up to approximately 10 °C. This is due to the larger surface area of the LFPAK56 drain tab giving improved heat spreading and thermal dissipation.
- Note that the 10 °C is the relative figure between the two packages, the most important factor is the operating junction temperature
- If there is enough margin before reaching 175 °C at the junction, then LFPAK56D offers an attractive option due to its space saving

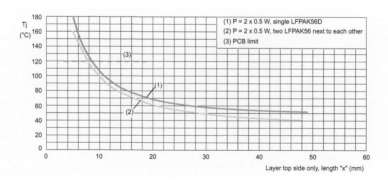

Figure 39 | Junction temperature as a function of copper side length x for 2 LFPAK56 and 1 LFPAK56D

3.4.2 LFPAK56D to two LFPAK33

In this section the results of one dual LFPAK56D MOSFET are compared to the results of two single LFPAK33 MOSFETs (see section 4.2)

Aim is to highlight the benefit of using one LFPAK56D dual instead of two single LFPAK33.

Set-up:
- 1 layer on the top
- MOSFET power dissipation is 0.5 W applied to each MOSFET
- Maximum junction temperature of 175 °C
- PCB material is standard FR4, 1.6 mm thickness, dimension 100 x 100 mm
- Maximum PCB operating temperature of 120 °C
- Copper thickness is 2 oz./ft^2 (70 μm)
- The PCB is suspended in free air at ambient temperature of 20 °C
- The simulation is carried out for conduction, convection and radiation heat transfer
- There is no forced air cooling applied, i.e. only natural convection is modeled

The simplest possible PCB stack-up is that of a single top copper layer. In this analysis, we will examine the variation in device junction temperature (T_j) as a function of top copper area.

- Same gap between copper layer was used for both single LFPAK33 and dual LFPAK56D
- Simulation carried out for different length "x"
- 0.5 W applied on each MOSFET

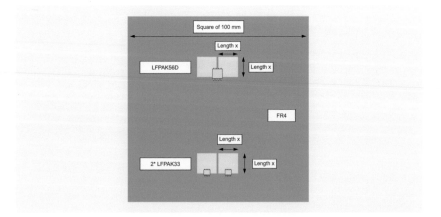

Figure 40 | Copper area configuration: 1 x LFPAK56D, 2 x LFPAK33, single top copper layer

The graph in Figure 41 shows:

- Overall two single LFPAK33 show better heat dissipation than a dual LFPAK56D by up to approximately 5 °C. This is due to the larger drain surface area of the LFPAK33 offering better thermal dissipation, (less improvement than with LFPAK56 as LFPAK33 is a smaller package).
- Note that the 5 °C is the relative figure between the two packages, the most important factor is the operating junction temperature.
- If there is enough margin before reaching 175 °C at the junction, then LFPAK56D offers an attractive option due to all the advantages that one component offers versus two in terms of PCB layout, placement, cost effectiveness, etc.

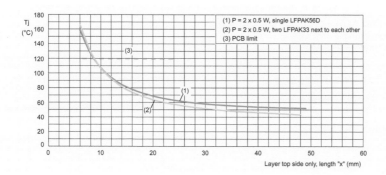

Figure 41 | Junction temperature as a function of copper side length x for 1 LFPAK56D and 2 LFPAK33

3.5 Impact of $R_{th(j-mb)}$ compared to $R_{th(mb-a)}$

Dissipation losses from the MOSFET junction are not mainly limited by the thermal resistance $R_{th(j-mb)}$ as this is very low. The high thermal path for heat dissipation is presented by the thermal resistance $R_{th(mb-amb)}$ (mounting base to PCB to ambient).

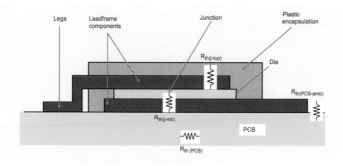

Figure 42 | View of thermal resistances in and outside the MOSFET

Example: for the part number BUK7M15-60E (LFPAK33, 15 mΩ, 60 V) the maximum thermal resistance junction to mounting base is 2.43 K/W:

Table 7: Thermal resistance BUK7M15-60E

Symbol	Parameter	Conditions	Min	Typ	Max	Unit
$R_{th(j\text{-}mb)}$	thermal resistance from junction to mounting base	Fig. 5	-	2.01	2.43	K/W

Using thermal simulation (Flotherm) with the following conditions:

0.5 W of losses in the MOSFET, air ambient is 20 °C, 35 µm copper, we can calculate some thermal resistance.

- $R_{th(j\text{-}mb)}$ is 0.8 K/W
  - This is a lower value than given in the data sheet due to the simulation using ideal conditions
- As can be seen in Table 8 below, thermal resistance for other items have high value compared $R_{th\,j\text{-}mb}$
- The total thermal resistance, junction to ambient, is 59.4 K/W when using 65.4 °C as (ambient) reference point.

Table 8 lists temperatures for different points captured in the simulation and shown in Figure 43.

Table 8: Breakdown of thermal resistance for a simple case

Thermal resistance part	Temperature (°C)	R_{th} (K/W)
Junction	95.1	-
Mounting base	94.7	0.8
PCB under MOSFET	88.6	12.2
PCB to the right of the MOSFET	86.6	4
Ambient air 0.5 mm over the top of the PCB	79.1	15
Ambient air 1 mm over the top of the PCB	65.4	27.4

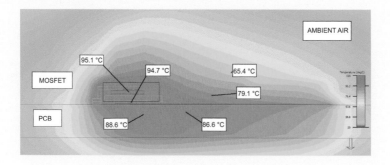

Figure 43 | Thermal result, LFPAK33, 0.5 W, 20 °C ambient

Due to the very low thermal resistance between junction and mounting base it is very important to take care of design surrounding the MOSFET, (i.e. thermal vias, copper area, heat sink, water cooling, air cooling), in order to reduce the total thermal resistance.

4 LFPAK56 and LFPAK88

4.1 Simple configuration with a single layer

In this section, we will present the maximum power dissipation results for a simple PCB configuration using a single layer with varying copper area.

Results are given for the LFPAK56 and LFPAK88 packages. Models used are based on 1 mΩ LFPAK56E and LFPAK88.

4.1.1 Set-up:
- 1 copper layer on the top
- MOSFET power dissipation is 1 W, 1.5 W and 2 W
- Maximum junction temperature of 175 °C
- PCB material is standard FR4, 1.6 mm thickness, dimension 100 x 100 mm
- PCB operating temperature of 120 °C and T_j of 175 °C are highlighted in graphs
- Copper thickness is 2 oz./ft^2 (70 µm)
- The PCB is suspended in free air at ambient temperature of 20 °C
- The simulation is carried out for conduction, convection and radiation heat transfer
- There is no forced air cooling applied, i.e. only natural convection is modeled

The simplest possible PCB stack-up is that of a single top copper layer, see Figure 44.

In this analysis, we will examine the variation in device junction temperature (T_j) as a function of the top copper area and calculate the maximum power that can be safely dissipated in the MOSFET to reach a T_j of 175 °C.

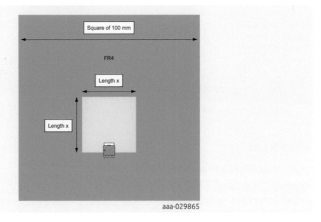

Figure 44 | Copper area configuration: LFPAK56, single top copper layer, the configuration is the same for LFPAK88

4.1.2 Junction temperature as a function of copper area

The graphs in Figure 45 and Figure 46 capture two important factors:

- T_j depends greatly on length "x" and thus copper area, the bigger the area the better the thermal performance
- However, the ability of the top copper to provide heatsinking for the MOSFET shows a "law of diminishing returns". In other words, we cannot keep on adding more copper area in the hope of continuing to reduce T_j. As can be seen from Fig. 45 below, for LFPAK56, 1 W profile, T_j will plateau at around 55 °C.

Note: Standard FR4 PCBs operate at a maximum temperature of 120 °C, care must be taken for $T_j > 120$ °C as the PCB area directly under the transistor will be close to the MOSFET junction temperature, (due to low $R_{th(j\text{-}mb)}$).

The graphs below also shows the absolute minimum copper area needed for $T_j \leq$ 175 °C.

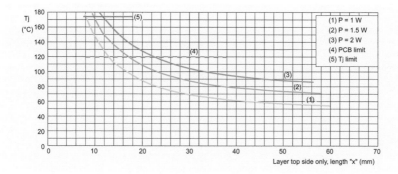

Figure 45 | Junction temperature as a function of copper side length x for LFPAK56

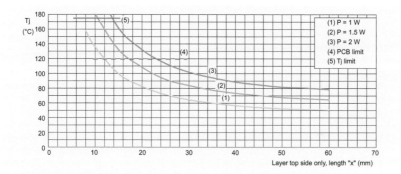

Figure 46 | Junction temperature as a function of copper side length x for LFPAK88

4.1.3 Maximum allowed power dissipation as a function of copper area

The maximum allowed power dissipation is shown in Figure 47 and Figure 48 below, for different ambient temperature and copper side length. In this example the PCB temperature was not considered so care must be taken for the resulting heat on the PCB.

From graphs in Figure 47 and Figure 48 the maximum permissible power, (T_{amb} = 20 °C), is 5.05 W and 5.9 W for the LFPAK56 and LFPAK88 packages respectively:

Table 9: Maximum power dissipation

Device	$T_{amb} = 20\,°C$	$T_{amb} = 80\,°C$
LFPAK56	5.05 W	3.2 W
LFPAK88	5.9 W	3.8 W

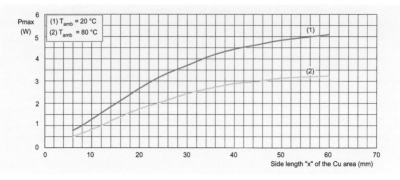

Figure 47 | Maximum permissible power dissipation as a function of copper side length "x" for LFPAK56

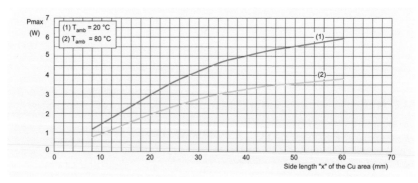

Figure 48 | Maximum permissible power dissipation as a function of copper side length "x" for LFPAK88

9

LFPAK MOSFET thermal design guide

4.2 Usual configuration: 4 layers + vias

In this section, we will present the maximum power dissipation results for a PCB configuration using 4 layers + vias for dissipation on the bottom layer, with varying copper area.

Results are given for the LFPAK56 and LFPAK88 packages.

4.2.1 Set-up:

- Four layers with vias (max number of vias is 25 and for small copper areas this number will decrease accordingly, see Table 10)
- MOSFET power dissipation is 1 W, 1.5 W and 2 W
- Maximum junction temperature of 175 °C
- PCB material is standard FR4, 1.6 mm thickness, dimension 100 x 100 mm
- PCB operating temperature of 120 °C and T_j of 175 °C are highlighted in graphs
- Copper thickness of all layers is 2 oz./ft^2 (70 µm)
- The PCB is suspended in free air at ambient temperature of 20 °C
- The simulation is carried out for conduction, convection and radiation heat transfer
- There is no forced air cooling applied, i.e. only natural convection is modeled

The common PCB stack-up is 4 layers with vias under the MOSFET to create a dissipation path to heatsink (no heat sink was used in simulation).

In this analysis, we will examine the variation in device junction temperature (T_j) as a function of copper area (same area size applied to all layers).

The configuration of the vias is shown below in Figure 49 and Figure 50:

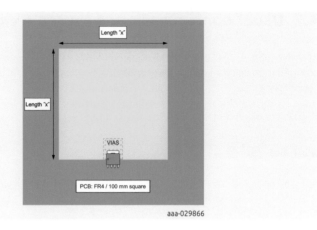

aaa-029866

Figure 49 | Copper area configuration: LFPAK56, 4 layers with vias, the configuration is similar for LFPAK88

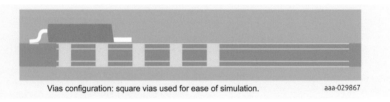

Vias configuration: square vias used for ease of simulation.   aaa-029867

Figure 50 | Sectional view: LFPAK56

Table 10: Limitation of number of vias

X (mm)	Vias configuration	Comments	Vias information
6	9 vias	Maximum number of vias able to be inserted in the copper area	
8	9 vias		
10	20 vias		Square vias length 0.7 mm Vias pitch: 2.5 mm (between vias in columns) 2.0 mm (between vias in rows) Copper thickness: 70 µm No solder fill
15	25 vias		
20	25 vias		
25	25 vias		
30	25 vias		
35	25 vias	25 vias maximum	
40	25 vias		
45	25 vias		
50	25 vias		
60	25 vias		

4.2.2 Junction temperature as a function of copper area (4 layers and vias)

The graphs in Figure 51 and Figure 52 below show the junction temperature as a function of drain copper area following the same trend as the single layer PCB configuration in that:

- T_j depends greatly on copper area
- The ability of the top copper to provide heatsinking for the MOSFET shows a "law of diminishing returns".

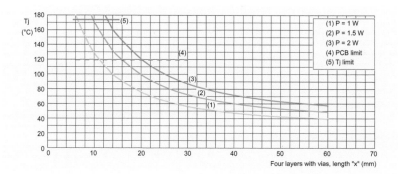

Figure 51 | Junction temperature as a function of copper side length x for LFPAK56

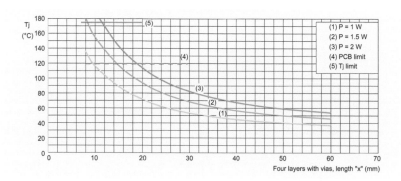

Figure 52 | Junction temperature as a function of copper side length x for LFPAK88

4.2.3 Maximum allowed power dissipation as a function of copper area (4 layers and vias)

From graphs in Figure 53 and Figure 54 the maximum power for a given package and conditions are as follows:

Table 11: Maximum power dissipation

Device	$T_{amb} = 20\ °C$	$T_{amb} = 80\ °C$
LFPAK56	9.6 W	6.3 W
LFPAK88	10.65 W	6.9 W

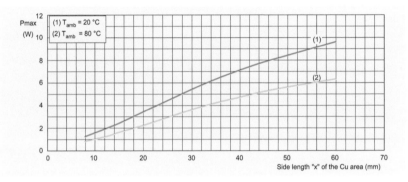

Figure 53 | Maximum permissible power dissipation as a function of copper side length "x" for LFPAK56

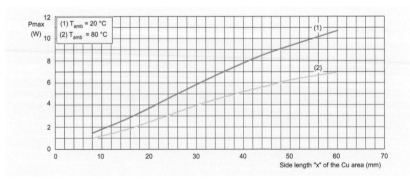

Figure 54 | Maximum permissible power dissipation as a function of copper side length "x" for LFPAK88

4.3 Simple configuration with a single split layer of copper

In this section, we will present the maximum power dissipation results as per the previous section for a simple PCB configuration using a single layer and varying copper area, but with copper layer split in two part (one part placed under the drain tab of the MOSFET and the other under the source pins).

Results are given for the LFPAK88 package only.

4.3.1 Set-up:

- 1 copper layer on the top - split into two areas:
  - 3/5 of area under drain tab
  - 2/5 of area under source pins
- MOSFET power dissipation is 1 W, 1.5 W and 2 W
- Maximum junction temperature of 175 °C
- PCB material is standard FR4, 1.6 mm thickness, dimension 100 x 100 mm
- PCB operating temperature of 120 °C and T_j of 175 °C are highlighted in graphs
- Copper thickness is 2 oz./ft^2 (70 µm)
- The PCB is suspended in free air at ambient temperature of 20 °C
- The simulation is carried out for conduction, convection and radiation heat transfer
- There is no forced air cooling applied, i.e. only natural convection is modeled

The simplest possible PCB stack-up is that of a single top copper layer, see Figure 55.

In this analysis, we will examine the variation in device junction temperature (T_j) as a function of the top copper area.

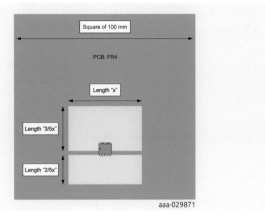

Figure 55 | Split copper area configuration: LFPAK88, single top layer with copper

The graph in Figure 56 captures what has been previously mentioned in terms of copper area and heat dissipation i.e. the bigger the area the better the thermal performance. More importantly in this configuration, it shows the importance in considering the source pins of an LFPAK MOSFET as a thermal path for efficiently dissipating heat.

The graph in Fig. 56 also shows that coper area of length "x" = 40 mm in split copper configuration provides a performance equivalent of that provided in the solid (non-split) copper area of length "x" = 60 mm.

Split copper configuration for length "x" = 40 mm is as follows:

- 24 mm x 40 mm copper area placed under the drain tab of the LFPAK MOSFET
- 16 mm x 40 mm copper area placed under the source pins of the LFPAK MOSFET

   Note: Standard FR4 PCBs operate at maximum temperature of 120 °C, care must be taken for T_j > 120 °C as PCB area directly under the transistor would be close to the MOSFET junction temperature (due to low $R_{th(j\text{-}mb)}$).

Results are for LFPAK88, but the principle applies to all Nexperia clip bond LFPAK devices. T_{amb} = 20 °C: Max power of ~6 W is achieved with an area of 40 mm x 40 mm single copper layer in split configuration, whist previously shown to require an area of 60 mm x 60 mm for single solid copper layer.

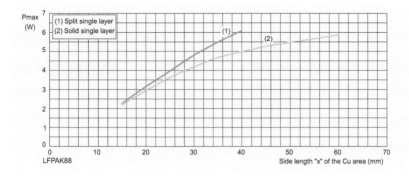

Figure 56 | Maximum permissible power dissipation as a function of copper side length "x" for LFPAK88

4.4. Impact of $R_{th(j\text{-}mb)}$ compared to $R_{th(mb\text{-}amb)}$

The thermal resistance $R_{th(j\text{-}mb)}$ of the MOSFET is very low and therefore dissipation losses are mainly limited by the high thermal resistive path presented by $R_{th(mb\text{-}amb)}$ (mounting base to ambient).

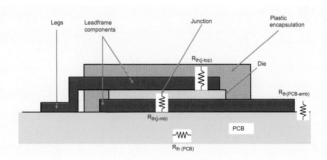

Figure 57 | View of thermal resistances in and outside the MOSFET

Example: for the part number BUK7S1R0-40H (LFPAK88, 1 mΩ, 40 V) the maximum thermal resistance junction to mounting base is 0.4 K/W, see Table 12:

Table 12: Thermal resistance BUK7S1R0-40H

Symbol	Parameter	Conditions	Min	Typ	Max	Unit
$R_{th(j-mb)}$	thermal resistance from junction to mounting base	-		0.35	0.4	K/W

Using thermal simulation (Flotherm) with the following conditions:

- 1 W of losses in the MOSFET
- Ambient air temperature of 20 °C
- 70 μm copper

we can calculate the thermal resistance for different paths, example:

- 1 W of losses in the MOSFET
- Junction temperature = 52.2 °C
- Mounting base temperature = 52.0 °C
- $R_\Theta = \Delta T / P => R_{th(j-mb)} = 0.\,2$ K/W.

This is lower than the measured value given in the data sheet due to simulation using ideal conditions.

As can be seen in Figure 58 below, the thermal resistance between mounting base and ambient is of much higher value (~30 K/W) than $R_{th(j-mb)}$.

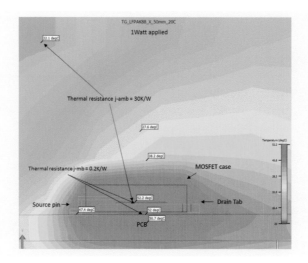

Figure 58 | Thermal resistance LFPAK88: single layer copper profile (50 x 50 mm)

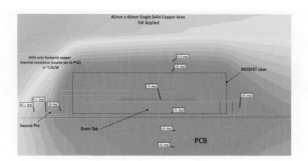

Figure 59 | Thermal resistance LFPAK88: single layer copper profile (40 x 40 mm)

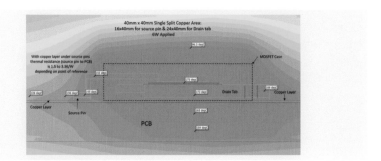

Figure 60 | Thermal resistance LFPAK88: single split layer copper profile (40 x 40 mm: split into 24 x 40 mm and 16 x 40 mm)

5 Conclusion

All the LFPAK packages offer a very good junction to mounting base thermal performance, meaning that the mounting base can be near to the junction temperature, but this is often limited by the PCB high temperature capability.

It is very important for designs to reduce the thermal resistance between mounting base and the ambient environment as this will present the bottleneck in heat dissipation. All of Nexperia LFPAK packages use clip bond technology making their source pins a good thermal path in addition to the thermal path provided by the drain tab. To take full advantage of this feature, it is important for PCB layout designs to consider placing a good amount of copper under the source pins. The drain tab still presents the main thermal path for heat dissipation and should be the focus for any thermal design layout.

In all cases a configuration with 4 layers with vias substantially improves the heat dissipation.

This thermal guide establishes the necessary principles in thermal design approaches, combined with LFPAK packages features (i.e. low $R_{th(j\text{-}mb)}$ and source clip bond) offer the designer good options in optimizing PCB thermal design.

Good thermal design practices should be applied to take advantage of the very good thermal performance LFPAK packages and $T_{j(max)}$ must be kept < 175 °C for safe operation.

LFPAK Vs DPAK thermal performance comparison

Addressing thermal concerns LFPAK88 Vs D²PAK

Increasing thermal capability in small signal MOSFETs

LFPAK56D taking the heat out of engine management systems

Weighing the benefits of LFPAK

LFPAK88 A very cool customer

High current 3 phase BLDC motor drive application using Nexperia LFPAK88 MOSFETs

Using Nexperia Power MOSFETs to handle high currents up to 380 A

6 Tables

7 Figures

Chapter 10

Maximum continuous currents in Nexperia LFPAK power MOSFETs

Application Note: AN90016

1 Introduction

This chapter examines the factors that determine the maximum permissible current ratings for LFPAK (copper-clip package) MOSFETs.

Modern electronics using low-voltage (<100 V) MOSFETs has seen an increase in high-power demand in both automotive and industrial applications. Power output in kilowatt terms for applications such as motor drive is now a very common requirement. Combined with the existing space constraint in modules this means that the need to handle more power is being passed on to the components, particularly MOSFETs.

The current limit given in data sheets for power MOSFETs is one of the most important parameters in such high-power applications where the handling of very high currents is required.

As the MOSFET is a three terminal device – Gate, Source and Drain – current can flow through any of these terminals as I_G, I_S and I_D respectively. Only maximum continuous current I_D (drain- source) and continuous current I_S (source-drain/body diode) will be considered. Leakage currents (I_{GSS}, I_{DSS}) and pulsed currents such as I_{DM} are not in the scope of this document

This chapter gives a comprehensive insight into the methodology in determining the maximum continuous current rating of Nexperia power MOSFETs.

It is critical to fully understand the capabilities, the boundaries and the relevant environmental conditions so that electronics engineers and designers select the right MOSFET for the right application - all of which will be discussed and addressed in this document.

This chapter is specific for LFPAK and its copper clip bond technology – Nexperia's flagship package.

2 LFPAK, superior performance

LFPAK packages are compact in size, they offer much higher power density and reduced parasitic inductances compared with wire bond devices. Combined with their copper clip bond technology, they have played an important role in MOSFETs achieving a very high current capability.

As illustrated in Figure 1 below, LFPAK copper clip bond packages have the following benefits:
- Prevents localised current crowding shown in Fig 1 b) D²PAK wire bond package

- Allows for a more uniform current spread
- Acts as a heat sink to the die

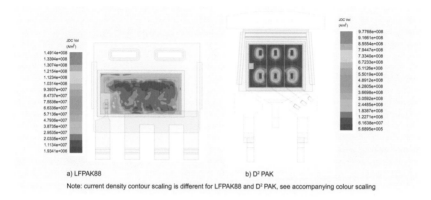

a) LFPAK88   b) D² PAK

Note: current density contour scaling is different for LFPAK88 and D² PAK, see accompanying colour scaling

Figure 1 | Current crowding contours for a) LFPAK88 and b) D²PAK packages

3 Key parameters that set out the boundaries

Before discussing what maximum current a MOSFET can achieve, it is important to highlight the parameters governing the boundaries of the environment within which the MOSFET must operate. These boundaries are mainly set by the thermal environment, but also by the conditions that impact the MOSFET data sheet parameters; both have a direct effect on the performance and the capabilities of the MOSFET.

Thermal environment and thermal parameters

This section discusses the thermal parameters and explains their direct impact on the maximum current in a MOSFET.

Temperature range and the 175 °C limit

-55 °C is the lowest temperature given in the data sheet. Although normally this is associated with storage temperature, MOSFETs' characteristics in Nexperia data sheet are given against this value. Note - the lowest temperature associated with real life application is usually **-40 °C**

25 °C (unless otherwise stated) is the reference temperature that all maximum capabilities of MOSFETs are based upon. In Nexperia MOSFET data sheets, this is given as a mounting base temperature parameter – T_{mb} – referring to the central point of the MOSFET drain tab. Note - other MOSFET venders commonly use T_c

(case temperature), which refers to the same point, i.e. drain tab and not to the plastic part of the MOSFET.

175 °C refers to the junction, i.e. the silicon die, temperature of the MOSFET and the parameter for this is given as **T_j**. All MOSFETs must operate below this temperature – more details are given later.

The 175 °C limit explained

With high temperatures, it is understandable to think that the plastic mould should be the first cause of concern.

Historically plastic moulds have caused issues and although improvements have been made in this industry, if the right compound is not properly selected it can still cause issues and leads to device failures. However, plastic mould compound alone does not give the full story nor is it the source of setting the 175 °C limit, as will be discussed in the next section.

4 MOSFET structure

This section briefly discusses the main components in the internal structure of LFPAK MOSFETs and their temperature properties:

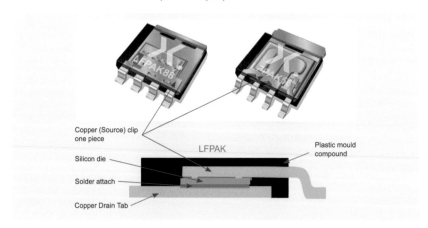

Figure 2 | LFPAK internal structure

Silicon / die: 250 °C. Pure silicon melting temperature is 1,414 °C. However, silicon in the MOSFET is doped and at ~250 ºC there will be thermal activation where current will flow across the PN junction and the MOSFET no longer acts as a switching device – i.e. there is no control over turn-on / turn-off.
Copper clip: melting temperature of copper is 900 °C. This is to highlight the fact

that it can handle very high temperature and not used for any calculation purposes. The criteria used to make sure that the copper in the MOSFET is capable for current handling is explained later in the note.

Solder attach: melting point >300 °C.

Plastic mould compound: Can potentially harden and becomes brittle around 190 °C and above. The composition of the plastic mould compound is carefully selected to withstand high temperature specification.

As shown above, the internal components of the MOSFET are either naturally capable of withstanding temperatures >175 °C or specifically selected to do so.

Limiting the MOSFETs maximum junction temperature T_j to 175 °C is driven by the reliability requirements MOSFETs need to meet. And thus, 175 °C is the temperature limit used by Nexperia for qualification and life test of MOSFETs in line with industry standard.

All automotive power MOSFETs must meet the 175 °C junction temperature specification. Although this requirement is not applicable to non-automotive devices which meet T_j of 150 °C, most of Nexperia industrial MOSFETs are life tested and qualified to 175 °C.

5 Maximum power and maximum current

5.1 Maximum power

With the junction temperature limit set to a maximum of 175 °C, the maximum amount of power allowed in the MOSFET can then be determined.

The key parameters needed to calculate this maximum power allowance are the thermal impedance between the die and the mounting base; $Z_{th(j-mb)}$ and thermal resistance between the die and the mounting base $R_{th(j-mb)}$.

$R_{th(j-mb)}$ is the thermal resistance which means that the thermal response has reached steady state conditions (also referred to as DC conditions).

$Z_{th(j-mb)}$ is the term used to represent thermal impedance in its entirety, steady state as well as transient conditions (more details are given later).

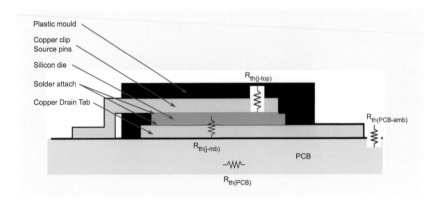

Figure 3 | Thermal resistances inside and outside the MOSFET

Figure 3 illustrates the main thermal paths that exist from the MOSFET silicon die to the external surroundings and ambient environment. The dominant path in dissipating heat from the die is through the MOSFET drain tab and therefore the thermal impedance of most relevance is $Z_{th(j-mb)}$ (also referred to as $R_{th(j-mb)}$).

It is worth pointing out that the source clip in the LFPAK package also provides an important thermal path. Having the right amount of copper in the PCB layout for the source pins is beneficial and should be considered in the design.

The LFPAK thin plastic mould adds another option of dissipating heat from the top of the device should the design consider a heat sink at the top. For more details about thermal performance and recommendations please refer to the application note AN90003 (chapter 9 of this book) - LFPAK MOSFET thermal design.

As previously mentioned all maximum capabilities of the MOSFET are given in reference to $T_{mb} = 25\,°C$.

The maximum power allowance can then be derived from the following formula:

$$P_{(max)} = \frac{T_{j(max)} - T_{(mb)}}{R_{th(j-mb)}} \qquad [1]$$

The junction to mounting base thermal impedance values can be obtained from the graph provided in the data sheet; the parameter used is transient thermal impedance $Z_{th(j-mb)}$.

For references the device used in the application note is PSMNR70-40SSH (LFPAK88 0.7 mΩ, 40 V, standard level) qualified to 175 °C.

Maximum continuous currents in Nexperia LFPAK power MOSFETs

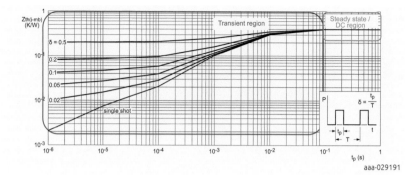

Figure 4 | Transient thermal impedance from junction to mounting base as a function of pulse duration

As can be seen from the graph in Fig. 4 the MOSFET thermal response is similar to an RC network electrical response – hence the thermal models provided on Nexperia support page representing this response are referred to as RC thermals – see the Support tab of the PSMNR70-40SSH product information page. For detailed information about RC thermal models see application note AN11261 (chapter 5 of this book) - Using RC Thermal models.

The curve in the graph showing pulses up to 100 ms is known as the transient condition section (transient region) and the parameter used is $Z_{th(j-mb)}$. It is given in single shot pulse or repeated PWM pulses with various duty cycles. The transient region is relevant to situations such as short circuits, power surges or switching transitions, they tend to be high power for short periods of time. Larger devices normally perform better in this region due to their bigger drain tab areas.

For pulses above 10 ms, as can be seen from the graph the curves start to plateau and will flatten after 100 ms. This section of the graph is referred to as steady state and is given as thermal resistance parameter $R_{th(j-mb)}$.

From 100 ms onwards the MOSFET will transition into thermal stability and is considered in DC state. In this region the thermal impedance reaches its maximum value and the steady state capabilities of the MOSFETs are given against this maximum value.

Note: the time it takes the MOSFET to reach steady state is not necessarily the same for the PCB where the MOSFET is mounted on as the PCB thermal response is slower. Therefore it is important to use the right thermal impedance for each the PCB and the MOSFET when running thermal analysis for a given condition. RC Cauer models found in Nexperia support page allow for PCB RC network to be added if known.

5.2 Maximum continuous drain current

The maximum current a MOSFET can achieve is primarily derived from the maximum power allowance in the MOSFET. When calculating maximum continuous current, the maximum steady state power must be used.

Example:

Device Name: PSMNR70-40SSH
$T_{mb} = 25\,°C$
$T_{j(max)} = 175\,°C$
$R_{th(j-mb)} = (0.4\ K/W\ max)$

Table 1. Thermal characteristics

Symbol	Parameter	Conditions	Min	Typ	Max	Unit
$R_{th(j-mb)}$	thermal resistance from junction to mounting base	Figure 4	-	0.35	0.4	K/W

$$P_{(max)} = \frac{T_{j(max)} - T_{(mb)}}{R_{th(j-mb)}} = \frac{175 - 25}{0.4} = 375\ W \qquad [2]$$

This value for maximum power can be found in data sheet limiting values table:

Table 2. Limiting values
In accordance with the Absolute Maximum Rating System (IEC 60134).

Symbol	Parameter	Conditions	Min	Max	Unit
P_{tot}	total power dissipation	$T_{mb} = 25\,°C$	-	375	W

Using the power formulae:

$$P = I^2 \times R \qquad [3]$$

Where I is the drain current (I_D) and R is the on-state resistance of the MOSFET ($R_{DS(on)}$). I_D can then be calculated as:

$$I_D = \sqrt{\frac{P}{R_{DS(on)}}} \qquad [4]$$

The on-state resistance value that must be used to calculate $I_{D(max)}$, is the MOSFET $R_{DS(on)}$ at T_j max – in this case $R_{DS(on)}$ at $T_j = 175\ °C$.

$$I_{D(max)} = \sqrt{\frac{P_{(max)}}{R_{DS(on)}@175\ °C}} \qquad [5]$$

A factorisation graph is provided in the data sheet for $R_{DS(on)}$ as a function of junction temperature, (see Figure 5). This can be useful to calculate the current for a specific temperature requirement. For PSMNR70-40SSH the $R_{DS(on)}$ multiplication factor for $T_j = 175\ °C$ is 2.19. Note: this graph is based on measured values.

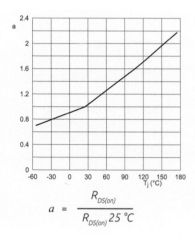

aaa-026897

Figure 5 | Normalized drain-source on-state resistance factor as a function of junction temperature

From the data sheet characteristics table,
Max $R_{DS(on)} = 0.7\ m\Omega$ ($V_{GS} = 10\ V$, $T_j = 25\ °C$):

Table 3. Characteristics

Symbol	Parameter	Conditions	Min	Typ	Max	Unit
Static characteristics						
$R_{DS(on)}$	drain-source on-state resistance	$V_{GS} = 10\ V$; $I_D = 25\ A$; $T_j = 25\ °C$	0.43	0.62	0.7	$m\Omega$
		$V_{GS} = 10\ V$; $I_D = 25\ A$; $T_j = 175\ °C$	0.85	1.23	1.53	$m\Omega$

The resulting $R_{DS(on)}$ at $V_{GS} = 10\ V$, $T_j = 175\ °C = 1.53\ m\Omega$, (2.19 x 0.7 m$\Omega$). This value is also included in the data sheet characteristic table. For further details about MOSFET data sheet parameters please refer to application note AN11158 (chapter

1 of this book) - Understanding power MOSFET data sheet parameters..

$$I_{D(max)} = \sqrt{\frac{P}{R_{DS(on)}}} = \sqrt{\frac{375}{0.00153}} = 495\,A \qquad [6]$$

495 A is considered to be the theoretical capability at $T_j = 175\,°C$. Another term commonly used is silicon capability.

Once the theoretical maximum I_D is established, the next stage is to validate this value through test and verification. This will allow for other limiting factors to be highlighted and considered in finalising and protecting the $I_{D(max)}$ given in the data sheets.

In the case of PSMN70-40SSH, the validated $I_{D(max)}$ @ $T_{mb} = 25\,°C$ is 425 A.

Table 4. Limiting values
In accordance with the Absolute Maximum Rating System (IEC 60134).

Symbol	Parameter	Conditions		Min	Typ	Max	Unit
I_D	drain current	$V_{GS} = 10\,_V$; $T_{mb} = 25\,°C$	[1]	0.43	0.62	0.7	mΩ
		$V_{GS} = 10\,_V$; $T_{mb} = 100\,°C$		-	350	A	mΩ

[1] 425A. Continuous current has been successfully demonstrated during application. Practically, the current will be limited by the PCB, thermal design and operating temperature.

The formulae:

$$I_{D(max)} = \sqrt{\frac{P_{(max)}}{R_{DS(on)}\,@175\,°C}}$$

can also be used for different temperatures. For example $I_{D(max)}$ at 100 °C can be calculated as follows:

$$P_{(max)} = \frac{T_{j(max)} - T_{(mb)}}{R_{th(j\text{-}mb)}} = \frac{175 - 100}{0.4} = 187.5\,W \qquad [7]$$

$$I_{D(max)} = \sqrt{\frac{187}{0.00153}} = 350\,A \qquad [8]$$

The same principle applies across the full operating temperature range. MOSFET data sheets contain a drain current de-rating graph in the limiting values section, see Figure 6.

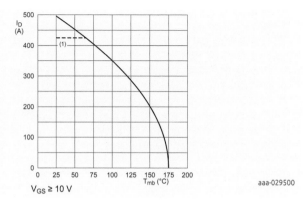

$V_{GS} \geq 10\ V$

aaa-029500

(1) 425 A continuous current has been successfully demonstrated during application tests. Practically the current will be limited by PCB, thermal design and operating temperature.

Figure 6 | Continuous drain current as a function of mounting base temperature

Fig. 6 shows:

- $I_{D(max)}$ for silicon capability @ 175 °C (solid curve)
- $I_{D(max)}$ capped value (dashed line)

As stated in Nexperia data sheets the continuous $I_{D(max)}$ value in the limiting table is not given as a figure verified by design i.e. theoretical, but rather demonstrated through testing. Some of the reasons for capping the continuous $I_{D(max)}$ value at lower limits than the solid curve given in the graph are as follows:

Package limit

- This is normally associated with wire bond MOSFETs.
- Historically old parts (10 years or older) experienced issues with the package - this was due to a combination of:
  1. Wire bond fuse - being a major reason for lowering the current rating
  2. Plastic mould compound.
- This limited $I_{D(max)}$ to 100 A - 120 A, and this legacy approach had been carried on for some devices even if they were clip bond LFPAK and less than 10 years old.
- As MOSFETs capabilities have reached a much higher level than has been possible in the past, it is only appropriate to select the right plastic compound and adapt a more accurate approach so that these new limits are achieved.
- By making the package not the limiting factor Nexperia MOSFETs can operate to their optimum level, giving the designer full advantage of these capabilities.

Test boards

- Test boards are important part in verifying the $I_{D(max)}$ capabilities more so at

Nexperia as they may be the limiting factor – as mentioned previously only $I_{D(max)}$ values that are verified through test are used.
- Improvement have been made in recent years so the right test boards are used to maintain T_{mb} at 25 °C.
  - Note that some MOSFETs vendors state continuous max current as verified by design and some limit the rating to a one second test. Although for R_{th} thermal stability is considered to be reached at one second, (represented by the flat line in Z_{th} graph) and for the MOSFET this is steady state condition. The length of time for max I_D test at Nexperia exceeds 30 seconds continuous.

$T_{j(max)}$ exceeded

- Junction temperature T_j is monitored during continuous I_D testing. Higher I_D values resulting in T_j exceeding 175 °C are not considered.

Silicon limit

- The silicon capability at 175 °C given in the data sheet as the solid curve is the absolute limit. Meaning only the I_D values that <u>PASS</u> the test at the curve level or below are validated. Instances where MOSFETs I_D measure values above the curve can be explained by the fact that most MOSFETs operate at their typical $R_{DS(on)}$ values while the curve only considers the $R_{DS(on)(max)}$ values.

Source pins

- Calculations based on the source pins dimensions i.e. length, width, cross-section area, size, etc., as well as the alloy/copper property are used to make sure the current density and capability of the pins meet the I_D rating.

In summary the final maximum continuous I_D rating is based on the lowest limit met by any of the above criteria.

5.3 Maximum continuous source current

Although I_S has always been given as a separate parameter, its value had historically been linked to I_D. The value of I_S was based on calculation and was either lower than I_D or made the same even if it was calculated to be a higher value. A more accurate approach is to rate the current capabilities for both I_D and I_S separately. This approach is now standard and verification through testing in the same way as explained previously is applied.

Determining the I_S limiting value

As far as the maximum power in the MOSFET is concerned, it is the same power allowance whether it is applied through the MOSFET channels (I_D) or the MOSFET body diode (I_S). Therefore the simple power formulae to use is P = V × I, where V is the body diode voltage drop (V_{SD}) and I is the source-drain current IS. Therefore the power calculated in the previous sections still applies, and in the case of the device example given, P = 375 W.

- The power through the MOSFET channel is $P = I^2 \times R$
- Power through the MOSFET body diode is P = V × I, where V is the diode voltage drop (V_{SD}) and I is the source-drain current IS

The V_{SD} maximum value given in the data sheet characteristics table is 1 V, (see Table 5 below).

Table 5: Characteristics

Symbol	Parameter	Conditions	Min	Typ	Max	Unit
Source-drain diode						
V_{SD}	source-drain voltage	I_S = 25 A; V_{GS} = 0 V; T_j = 25 °C	-	0.75	1	V

In theory I_S should be = 375 A, (I = P/V, P = 375 W, V = 1). In reality though V_{SD} is typically around 0.75 V and this would be the case for more than 90% of all devices. Furthermore, V_{SD} is temperature dependant and the voltage will drop as temperature goes up. It is also true to say that the voltage V_{SD} goes up when current increases, but the heating element (induced by the current as self-heating) has a bigger impact.

The continuous source current that has been measured and is validated in the data sheet for PSMNR70-40SSH is 500 A, see Table 6 below.

Table 6. Limiting values
In accordance with the Absolute Maximum Rating System (IEC 60134).

Symbol	Parameter	Conditions	Min	Max	Unit
Source-drain diode					
I_S	source current	T_{mb} = 25 °C	[1] -	500	A

[1] 500A. Continuous current has been successfully demonstrated during application. Practically, the current will be limited by the PCB, thermal design and operating temperature.

Source-drain characteristic

MOSFET data sheets include a V_{SD} characteristic graph, see Figure 7 below.

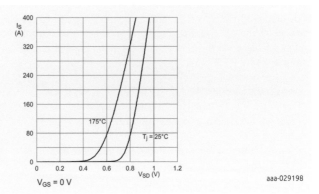

$V_{GS} = 0\ V$

aaa-029198

Figure 7 | Source-drain (diode forward) current as a function of source-drain (diode forward) voltage; typical value

The above graph is obtained by testing the device with pulsed current to avoid self-heating, (which would result in higher values for V_{SD}). In real applications self-heating will most likely occur, as currents lasting more than 100 ms will be sufficient to get R_{th} in steady state region and allow the device to heat up.

To help determine V_{SD} values at higher temperatures Figure 7 includes curves for T_j = 25 °C and for T_j = 175 °C. This shows that the V_{SD} value reduces with increased junction temperature. As can be seen from Figure 7 (T_j = 175 °C curve), with I_S = 400 A, V_{SD} is just over 0.8 V and with power = 375 W this will result in I_S = 440 A. The rating for I_S given in data sheet is = 500 A, this difference can be explained by the following: power of 375 W is based on max R_{th} of 0.4 K/W. However, a typical R_{th} is = 0.35 K/W resulting in power = 428 W. With I_S = 500 A, VSD = 0.85 V.

Note: the I_S value given in the data sheet (in this case 500 A) has been proven through testing and the value is validated.

6 Practical application examples

This section details the function and configuration of power MOSFETs in a basic application circuit. Three key application stages will be discussed - RPP (Reverse Polarity Protection), isolation and load drive. Figure 8 below shows a simplified circuit capturing some basic operations of the different MOSFET configurations.

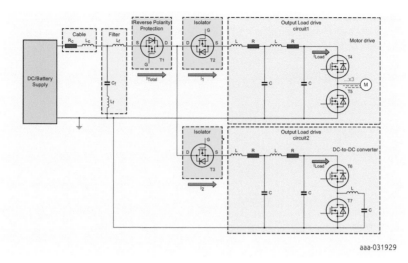

aaa-031929

Figure 8 | Simplified motor drive and DC-to-DC converter application diagram

6.1 Output load drive MOSFETs T4, T5, T6 and T7

The circuits shown in Figure 9 and Figure 10 both show a pair of power MOSFETs implemented as a half-bridge, a common configuration for motor drive (T4 and T5 see Figure 9) and DC-to-DC converters (T6 and T7, see Figure 10) – for details on half-bridge MOSFET switching parameters and performance refer to Nexperia application note AN90011 (chapter 7 of this book) - Half-bridge MOSFET switching and its impact on EMC.

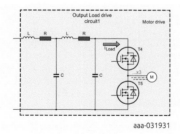

aaa-031931

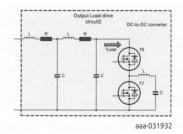

aaa-031932

Figure 9 | Output load drive circuit 1 (motor drive)

Figure 10 | Output load drive circuit 2 (DC-to-DC)

In this example we look at output load drive circuit 1, T4 and T5 in relation to current demand which will be gated by the type of motors driven and the power requirement of the application.

Motor drive application

Parameters profiling a motor can be summarised in Figure 11 below:

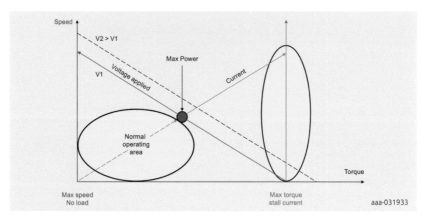

Figure 11 | Motor operation parameters

Normal operating area is where a motor is designed and specified to spend most of its working life. However, it is expected that motors will go through situations of stalled rotation a number of times in their operating life. These stalled motor situations, albeit don't happen on a prolonged periods, are considered part of the a normal operation. Adding to this profile, fault conditions situation such as short circuit where motor drive circuit are expected to recover from, one can appreciate the type of power capabilities that need to be considered in selecting a power MOSFET driving such application. Note: although stall conditions may last few tens or hundreds milliseconds, as explained previously this will be enough to make the MOSFET operate in DC conditions and therefore continuous current capability is key.

6.2 Output isolator MOSFETs T2 and T3

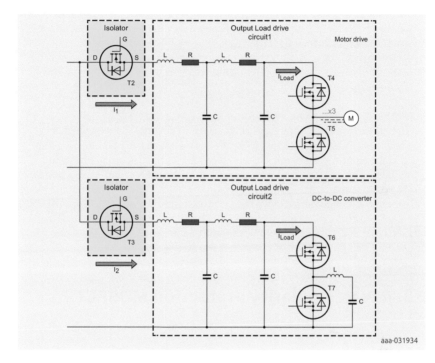

Figure 12 | MOSFETs used as isolators T2 and T3

Some designs may drive two different output loads. A representation of such circuits is given in Figure 12 above. MOSFETs T2 and T3 are used to isolate their respective circuits as they may not need to operate at the same time.

MOSFETs are also used as isolators is designs using the same circuit duplicated to drive one common output. This may be due to redundancy requirement in order to meet a safety standard (usually associated with automotive application to allow continuous operation even in cases of failure – such redundancy circuit is not part of this example here, but the same principle applies).

In such applications particular attention should be given to:

- Current capability in MOSFETs. T2 and T3 need to cater not only for the current needed to drive the loads, but also for the immediate drive circuits current drawn (Figure 12 circuit 1 & circuit 2 respectively).

- Some designs require large capacitors in the drive circuit. The drive circuit itself can be treated as a capacitive load and therefore high inrush current or soft start capabilities are important in the selection of MOSFETs – soft start mode is applied to MOSFET's turn on so that high inrush currents are brought under control and this type of operation requires a MOSFET with strong SOA performance. For SOA related details please see Nexperia application note AN11158 (chapter 1 in this book) - Understanding power MOSFET data sheet parameters.

- Another issue that might result from such large capacitors used in the drive circuits is the current they supply in a case of a fault incident explained as follows: In a case where T3 is off (circuit 2 is disabled) and T2 is ON, if a short circuit occurs in drive circuit 1, charged capacitors from drive circuit 2 can supply very high current to drive circuit 1 through the MOSFET body diode of T3 and through T2 (the same can occur in the opposite direction). In this example it is important to pay attention to I_S capability in a MOSFET

MOSFETs T2 and T3 require strong capabilities in continuous I_D, I_S and depending on implementation of soft start, strong SOA.

6.3 Reverse polarity protection MOSFET T1

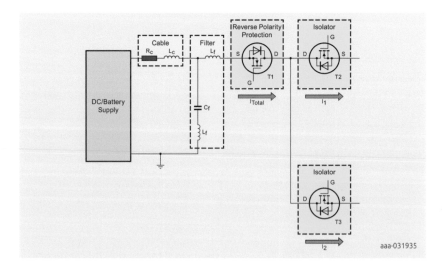

Figure 13 | Reverse polarity protection MOSFET T1

See Figure 13 continuous current capability is of most relevance here as the MOSFET T1 is implemented on the supply line which allows the flow of all the current needed for the whole module on a continuous basis.

It can also be seen that current flows through T1 from the supply regardless of whether the MOSFET is ON or OFF – when MOSFET is OFF it will still conduct through its body diode. As such it is important to pay attention to I_S capability. To avoid current flowing through MOSFET body diode some designs implement two MOSFETs back to back for reverse polarity protection, see Figure 14.

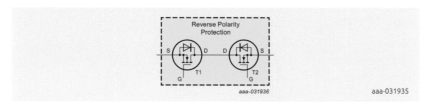

aaa-031935

Figure 14 | Reverse polarity protection using back-to-back MOSFETs

In a back-to-back configuration the other parameter that becomes of relevance is the avalanche performance of the MOSFETs. A situation where a fault condition occurs and T2 turns off as part of a protection mechanism. Due to inductances in the cable and/or the circuit a build-up of a voltage at the drain of T2 might occur and potentially lead to an avalanche event. For details on avalanche topic see Nexperia application note AN10273 (chapter 7 of this book) - Half-bridge MOSFET switching and its impact on EMC.

Multiple MOSFET parameters are highlighted in the application examples given above, all showing the importance of, and the need to use a MOSFET that is capable of handling high continuous current.

7 Tables

8 Figures

LFPAK MOSFET thermal resistance - simulation, test and optimization of PCB layout

Application Note: AN90019

1 Introduction

This chapter explains the parameter thermal resistance from junction to ambient and how it can be reduced by careful PCB layout.

Nexperia MOSFET data sheets contain a parameter $R_{th(j-a)}$ which is the thermal resistance from junction to ambient. This is a guide to how much heat can be dissipated from the device to its surroundings in a typical application. For a surface-mounted device such as an LFPAK MOSFET this is highly dependent on the type of Printed Circuit Board (PCB) on which it is mounted. The type of material, the thickness of copper and the shape of the copper footprint all contribute to $R_{th(j-a)}$.

This application note looks at the structure of an LFPAK MOSFET and the way it is mounted on a PCB. It uses thermal modelling techniques to analyse how heat, generated inside the device, is transferred to its surroundings. Various circuit layouts are considered and tested so that developers can use a value for $R_{th(j-a)}$ that closely reflects practical applications.

2 Definition of thermal resistance $R_{th(j-a)}$

$R_{th(j-a)}$ is the thermal resistance from the active surface of the silicon crystal to the surrounding environment. It is a value that represents the net effect of all the possible series and parallel paths from the semiconductor junction to ambient and includes heat transfer by means such as conduction, convection and radiation. $R_{th(j-a)}$ is defined as the temperature difference between junction and ambient that transfers one watt of power to the environment. It is given by:

$$R_{th(j-a)} = \frac{T_j - T_a}{P} \qquad [1]$$

where $R_{th(j-a)}$ is measured in K/W Tj is the junction temperature (°C)
T_{amb} is the ambient temperature (°C)
P is the heating power dissipated inside the MOSFET (W)

2.1 Test method

The method used to measure $R_{th(j-a)}$ is defined by JEDEC standard 51-1 and 51-2A. The approach is a static implementation, meaning heating power is applied on continuous basis while monitoring the junction temperature. The formula for $R_{th(j-a)}$ shown above can be used once a known power is applied and steady state is reached. The Device Under Test (DUT) is soldered to a FR4 test board and placed in the geometric centre of the test enclosure as shown in Figure 1 and Figure 2. The enclosure comprises a 305 mm cube made from low thermal conductivity materials such as cardboard, polycarbonate, polypropylene, wood, etc.

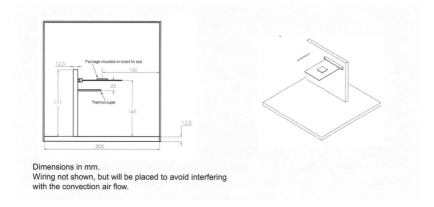

Dimensions in mm.
Wiring not shown, but will be placed to avoid interfering with the convection air flow.

Figure 1 | Side view of the test fixture and enclosure   Figure 2 | Isometric view of the test board and fixture without the enclosure

2.2 Heat transfer in the JEDEC enclosure

Within the JEDEC enclosure, heat is transferred from the DUT to the PCB and surroundings by three basic mechanisms; conduction, convection, and radiation. Conduction is the process by which heat transfers from high temperature regions to low temperature regions that are in contact with each other. Figure 3 shows how heat is transferred from the semiconductor junction to the copper clip and from the clip to the encapsulant. Also, from the junction through the silicon die to the mounting base, and from the mounting base to the PCB.

Convection refers to the heat transfer process caused by displacement of air surrounding the test fixture. The movement is caused by the tendency of hotter and therefore less dense air to rise, and colder, denser air to sink under the influence of gravity, which consequently results in transfer of heat.

Radiation does not depend on contact as heat conduction and convection do. Thermal radiation is when an object loses energy in the form of electromagnetic radiation in the infrared part of the spectrum. In the example shown in Figure 3, heat is radiated from the surfaces of the MOSFET and the PCB into the space inside the box.

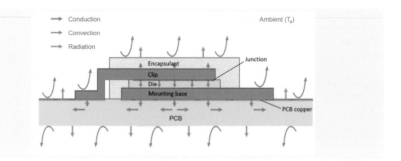

Figure 3 | LFPAK MOSFET - heat transfer model

The measured thermal resistance of a MOSFET, $R_{th(j\text{-}a)}$, depends upon the package size, the material properties and the internal structure of the device. It also depends on the PCB that is used in the test fixture. Modern surface-mount MOSFETs are designed to use the PCB as a heat sink and rely on the copper traces to spread the heat over a large area to assist with cooling.

Nexperia power MOSFET data sheets usually specify two values for $R_{th(j\text{-}a)}$ – one with a minimum footprint that conforms with the JEDEC standard, and another with a 25.4 mm (1") square of 70 μm thick (2 oz) copper on the top surface. See Table 1 also Figure 4 and Figure 5 below.

Table 1 | Thermal characteristics

Symbol	Parameter	Conditions	Min	Typ	Max	Unit
$R_{th(j\text{-}mb)}$	thermal resistance from junction to mounting base		-	0.56	0.63	K/W
$R_{th(j\text{-}a)}$	thermal resistance from junction to ambient	Figure 4	-	50	-	K/W
		Figure 5	-	125	-	K/W

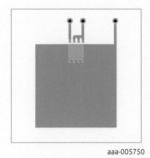

aaa-005750

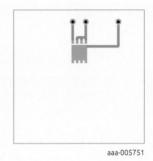

aaa-005751

Figure 4 PCB layout for thermal resistance
junction to ambient 1" square pad,
FR4 Board 2oz copper

Figure 5 PCB layout for thermal resistance
junction to ambient minimum
footprint, FR4 Board 2oz copper

3 MOSFET drain-source current path

Modern power MOSFETs have an on-state resistance in the order of milliohms and surface-mount variants are capable of switching hundreds of amps. In these cases consideration must be given to the Joule heating effect, i.e. induced heat due to current flowing through the conductor, in this case current through the device and the PCB traces.

Figure 6, below, shows the current path through a LFPAK MOSFET. The clip is attached directly to the semiconductor junction and at low current it acts as a heat sink, conducting heat away from the junction to the PCB. At high current, however, it becomes heated by its own resistance and requires cooling by being connected to a cooling surface connected to the source terminal.

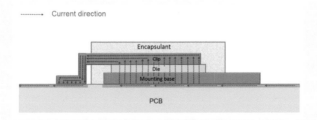

Figure 6 LFPAK package MOSFET current path

4 PCB layout optimization

4.1 PCB trace width calculation

To examine the heating effect of the PCB trace let us consider as an example a Nexperia LFPAK MOSFET; PSMN1R0-30YLD. This has an on-state resistance $R_{DS(on)} = 1$ mΩ ($V_{GS} = 10$ V; $T_j = 25$ °C).

At a typical current of 55 A, the simplified power dissipation, given by I^2R will be 55^2 x 0.001 = 3 W. This power can be dissipated with the appropriate PCB layout applying the right amount of copper to spread the heat.

Many PCB manufacturers websites include a trace width calculation tool based on the IPC-2221 Generic Standard on Printed Board Design. Using an IPC-2221 trace width calculator we can determine the size of trace required to carry 55 A.

Assuming 70 µm (2 oz) thick copper and allowing for manageable 30 °C rise in the trace temperature, Figure 7 shows that a trace almost 20 mm wide is required.

Printed Circuit Board Width Tool

This Javascript web calculator calculates the trace width for printed circuit board conductors for a given current using formulas from IPC-2221 (formerly IPC-D-275).

Inputs:

Current	55	Amps
Thickness	70	um

Optional Inputs:

Temperature Rise	30	Deg C
Ambient Temperature	25	Deg C
Trace Length	10	mm

Results for Internal Layers:

Required Trace Width	50.4	mm
Resistance	0.0000538	Ohms
Voltage Drop	0.00296	Volts
Power Loss	0.163	Watts

Results for External Layers in Air:

Required Trace Width	19.4	mm
Resistance	0.000140	Ohms
Voltage Drop	0.00769	Volts
Power Loss	0.423	Watts

Figure 7 | Example IPC-2221 trace width calculator

4.2 PCB layout simulations

A number of thermal simulations have been carried out using a PSMN1R0-30YLD as an example to find the optimum PCB layout that extracts the maximum amount of heat from the device and therefore gives the lowest possible value for $R_{th(j-a)}$. All the simulations were on a 25.4 mm square of 70 μm thick copper. The MOSFET was fully turned on with a constant current that produced a 3 W power loss in the device.

The investigation examined different positions of the MOSFET within the copper square. It also considered allocating different percentages of the copper square to the source and drain.

Finally, it examined the heating effect of trace width on the temperature of the MOSFET and the consequences for $R_{th(j-a)}$ measurement.

Test layout 1

In Figure 8 the device is mounted on the edge of a 25.4 mm square copper pad. **$R_{th(j-a)}$ = 41.8 K/W** according to the simulation result.

This layout assumes that the main heat transfer path is from the junction, through the silicon die to the mounting base. All of the copper pad is allocated to cooling the mounting base. We see from the thermal profile that very little heat reaches parts of the copper furthest away from the MOSFET and these contribute little to the cooling. The source trace is very hot because of inefficient cooling of the source pins. This is evidently not an optimum solution resulting in a relatively high value for $R_{th(j-a)}$.

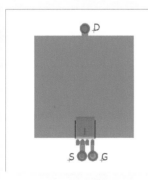
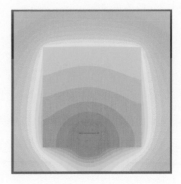

Figure 8 Test layout 1 and surface temperature profile

Test layout 2

The test layout of Figure 9 shows the MOSFET mounted in the middle of the 25.4 mm copper square with the copper area divided equally between source and drain.

The simulation result gives: **$R_{th(j-a)}$ = 39.1 K/W**

Placing the device in the middle of the copper has improved the cooling and reduced the thermal resistance. However, the copper area connected to the drain tab is hotter than that connected to the source pins which suggest that more heat flows through the drain tab. Selecting the proper ratio of source to drain copper is important to obtain the optimum $R_{th(j-a)}$) value.

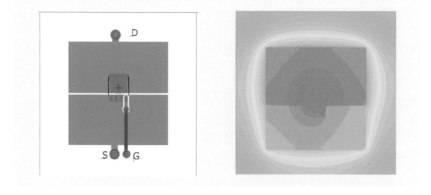

Figure 9 | Test PCB layout 2 and surface temperature profile

Test layouts 3, 4 and 5

In Figure 10, Figure 11and Figure 12 different layouts examine the effect of various trace widths for the source connection.

Layout 3 has the MOSFET located in the centre of the copper pad and the Joule heating effect of the source trace is not considered.

The simulated result gives: **$R_{th(j-a)}$ = 38.6 K/W.**

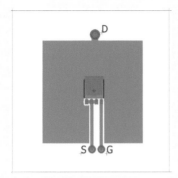 

Figure 10 | Test PCB layout 3 and surface temperature profile

However in a practical working circuit when low $R_{DS(on)}$ MOSFETs are fitted, the drain-source current can reach tens or even hundreds of amperes, and the heat generated in the PCB traces cannot be neglected.

Layout 4 shows what happens when the Joule heating of the source trace is taken into account. In this case the trace width is 0.8 mm. The power loss in the MOSFET is 3 W as before, but the power loss in the trace is 8.8 W. Figure 11 shows the rise in temperature of the source trace which is higher than the die temperature of the MOSFET and is therefore heated significantly.

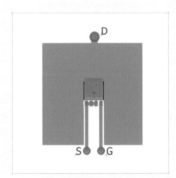 

Figure 11 | Test PCB layout 4 and surface temperature profile

Layout 5 has the source trace increased to 3 mm. The test conditions are the same as in layout 4. This time the power loss in the source trace is reduced to 2.4 W but Figure 12 shows that the temperature still exceeds that of the die.

The simulated result gives: R_{1111}= **56.7 K/W.**

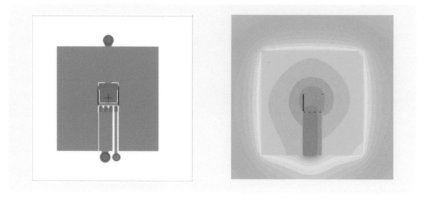

Figure 12 | Test PCB layout 5 and surface temperature profile

We can deduce from test layouts 4 and 5 that in a practical application involving an LFPAK MOSFET careful consideration must be given to trace thickness and width so that the Joule heating of the current path does not contribute to the heating of the MOSFET.

Optimal PCB layout - layout 6

Layout 6, shown in Figure 13, attempts to optimise the copper traces to obtain the lowest possible $R_{th(j-a)}$. Approximately 1/3 of the 25.4 mm copper pad is allocated to the source pins whilst the width of the source trace is a maximum.

The simulation result gives: $R_{th(j-a)}$ = **37.1 K/W.**

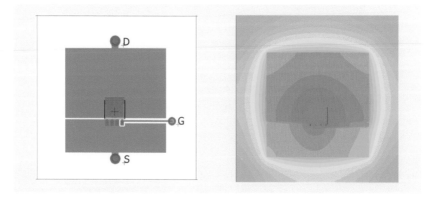

Figure 13 | Test PCB layout 6 and surface temperature profile

5 Conclusion

Nexperia LFPAK MOSFETs are designed to handle high levels of current, 300 A in the case of PSMN1R0-30YLD and in excess of 400 A for packages such as LFPAK88. To take full advantage of the MOSFET's ability to handle these levels of current, designers are faced with the challenge of dissipating the resulting power through the PCB and therefore care must be taken in the design of the layout.

A larger amount of copper and a larger area used under the MOSFET's drain tab will provide better thermal performance and thus better power dissipation. Perhaps less obvious is the PCB layout/ trace for source pins and the importance of the amount/area of copper used. LFPAK packages provide a good thermal path from the junction to the source pins as they use one piece copper-clip (i.e. not two pieces of copper soldered together or copper-ribbon combination). It is therefore very important, for an efficient thermal design to consider a layout with the right amount and area of copper for the source pins.

As shown in this application note the best $R_{th(j-a)}$ can be achieved when this layout approach is applied. Another important factor to consider is the width and thickness necessary for PCB traces providing the electrical connections to the MOSFETs, in order to handle the high currents.

LFPAK MOSFET thermal resistance - simulation, test and optimization of PCB layout

LFPAK vs DPAK thermal performance comparison

Addressing thermal concerns LFPAK88 vs DPAK

Increasing thermal capability in small signal MOSFETs

LFPAK56D taking the heat out of engine management systems

Weighing the benefits of LFPAK

LFPAK88 A very cool customer

Using Nexperia Power MOSFETs to handle high currents up to 380 A

High current, 3 phase BLDC motor drive application using Nexperia LFPAK88 MOSFETs

6 Tables

7 Figures

Chapter 12

H-bridge motor controller design using Nexperia discrete semiconductors and logic ICs

Application Note: TN90002

1 Introduction

An example of a H-bridge motor controller designed with Nexperia discrete and Nexperia logic IC components.

This chapter demonstrates a H-bridge motor controller PCB, built using Nexperia discrete semiconductors and logic ICs.

The H-bridge circuit is a full bridge DC-to-DC converter allowing operation of a brushed DC motor (48 V max, 12 V min, 5 A max). The key feature of this design is that all electronic functions are designed with Nexperia discrete and logic IC components (low cost, no micro-controller or software needed).

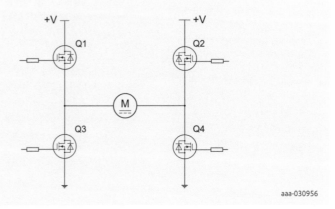

aaa-030956

Figure 1 | Simplified MOSFET H-bridge motor control

The left MOSFETs of the full bridge (Q1 and Q3 in the simplified diagram above) are the switching MOSFETs (see the PCB top view in Figure 26), the right MOSFETs (Q2 and Q4 in the simplified diagram above) select the motor rotation direction:

• right high side MOSFET fully ON = Forward
• right low side MOSFET fully ON = Reverse A switch selects the motor rotation direction.

Jumpers select one of 3 switching frequencies: 7.8 kHz, 15.6 kHz or 31.3 kHz. Two tactile push buttons allow the duty cycle (motor speed) to be increased or decreased. There are 8 steps from 0 to 100% duty cycle. A current limitation protection avoids over current in the motor and MOSFETs (set at approximately 6.5 A).

This H-bridge motor controller PCB allows the user to choose between 3 Nexperia

MOSFET packages (LFPAK33, LFPAK56D or LFPAK56), jumpers are used to connect the MOSFETs chosen by the user.

This chapter describes each of the main functions used in the design.

2 Block diagram and system functionality

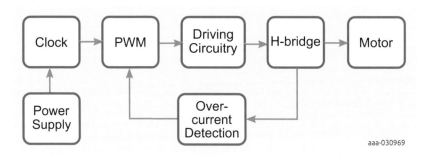

aaa-030969

Figure 2 | H-bridge motor controller block diagram

2.1 Subsystems overview

1. Power Supply
   - Accepts 12 V to 48 V DC input
   - Transient overvoltage protection
   - Reverse polarity protection
   - Buck converter (12 V)
   - Linear regulator (5 V) for logic devices
2. Clock and duty cycle generator
   - 4 MHz crystal oscillator and frequency divider to create 3 different switching frequencies
   - Duty cycle sets by push button inputs to select the duty cycle (0% to 100%)
   - 62.5 kHz output is used to supply the charge pump on the driving circuitry block
3. PWM
   - Reset function to activate other function when V_{CC} 5 V supply is stable
   - Dead-time function and PWM enable (over current protection disabling)
   - Level shifter
   - Direction selection
4. Driver circuit
   - High-side and low-side drivers to drive 4 MOSFETs of the full bridge
   - Charge pump to supply the high-side MOSFETs

5. H-bridge
   - Reservoir and decoupling capacitors
   - Snubber on the left MOSFETs (switching MOSFETs)
   - Jumper to connect the selected MOSFETs
   - Gate drive resistors
   - Low-side current measurement
6. Overcurrent detection
   - Comparator, with voltage reference setting current limit
   - PWM reset function reactivating PWM if fault disappears

3 Subsystem descriptions

3.1 Power supply

The H-bridge motor controller power supply circuit comprises of:
- DC input stage with transient overvoltage and reverse voltage protection
- 12 V output DC-to-DC buck converter stage
- 5 V output linear regulator (for logic ICs) with status LED

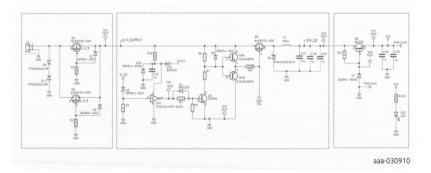

aaa-030910

Figure 3 | Power supply circuit

Transient overvoltage protection

D8 and D17 (PTVS60VS1UTR) are transient voltage suppressor diodes, rated at 60 V, 400 W for a 10/1000 μs current pulse waveform. They protect against positive and negative transients.

Note: These TVS diodes provide protection for transient overvoltage only - not for DC overvoltage.

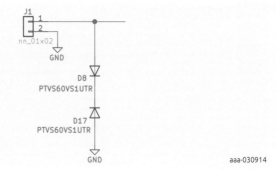

Figure 4 | Transient overvoltage protection

Reverse polarity protection

Two parallel P-channel MOSFETs Q1 and Q2 (BUK6Y33-60P) form the reverse polarity protection.

Q1 and Q2 are biased on through D1 and D2 (BZX84J-B10) respectively when the supply polarity is positive (V_{GS}= -10 V). Q1 and Q2 are off when the supply is negative (V_{GS} = VF = 0.7 V), current cannot flow because the MOSFET body diodes are reverse biased.

This means that if the supply is inverted, no current will flow into the circuit and potentially cause damage.

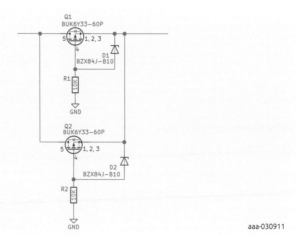

Figure 5 | Reverse polarity protection

H-bridge motor controller design using Nexperia discrete semiconductors and logic ICs

Buck converter (12 V)

The next stage is a switching regulator that outputs 12 V. To start the switching regulator a start- up circuit is used consisting of: Zener diode D18 (BZX84J-B5V6), R10, and C14. This provides a 5 V supply for inverting Schmitt trigger U21 (74HC1G14) before V_{CC} (5 V) is available through D19 (BAS316). U21 can then start the switching regulation.

The buck converter consists of: Q5 (BUK6Y33-60P), Schottky diode D6 (PMEG10030ELP) and inductor L1. The output of the buck converter supplies the 12 V rail.

When the output of U21 is high it turns on Q5 via the NPN transistor Q3 (BC846) and the NPN/ PNP dual transistor pair Q4 (BC846BPN). The voltage on node "V_12" will then increase. When "V_12" reaches 12 V, D3 (BZX84J-B10) is conducting and there is enough voltage on U21 input to force U21 output low. Then Q5 is switched off and the voltage at "V_12" decreases until U21 input is low enough to restart a new cycle.

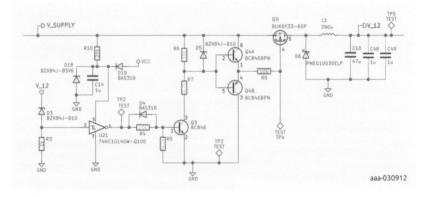

Figure 6 | Buck converter

Linear regulator (5 V) for logic ICs

A linear regulator comprising NPN transistor Q6 (BCP55), Zener diode D7 (BZX84J-B5V6) and R11 provides a regulated V_{CC} (5 V) rail for the logic ICs.

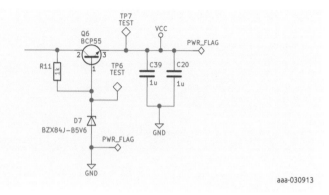

aaa-030913

Figure 7 | Linear regulator

3.2 Clock and duty cycle generator

The Clock circuit comprises of:

- Crystal oscillator and frequency divider
- Duty cycle generator
- Frequency selection jumpers

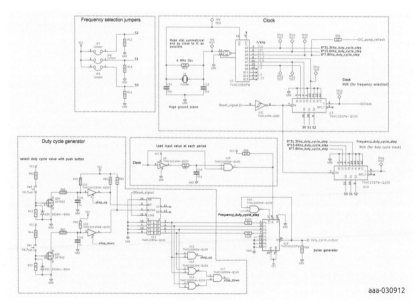

aaa-030912

Figure 8 | Clock, duty cycle and frequency selection

Crystal oscillator and frequency divider

A crystal oscillator is used for accuracy and stability. The oscillator frequency is 4 MHz.

U1 (74HCT4060) is a frequency divider, used to obtain different frequencies from the 4 MHz. It provides outputs at:

- 62.5 kHz to drive the charge pump circuit (see Figure 19)
- 31.3 kHz, 15.6 kHz and 7.8 kHz for the switching frequency (user selectable)

The switching frequency is selected by the multiplexer U3 (74HCT151) according to the jumper settings of JP7, JP8 and JP9.

Note: Only one jumper should be fitted at the same time.

The switching frequency output is labeled "Clock".

A reset signal enables both multiplexer U3 and U19 (see next section for U19 explanation) when V_{CC} is 5 V.

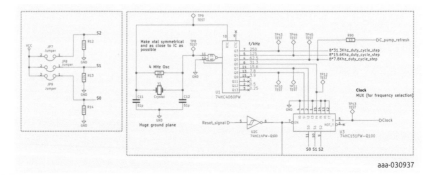

aaa-030937

Figure 9 | Oscillator and frequency divider

Duty cycle generator

Signals with a frequency 8 times higher than the required final switching frequencies are fed to 3 of the inputs of an 8-bit multiplexer IC, U19 (74HCT151). These are labeled "8*Frequency_duty_cycle step".

Jumpers JP7, JP8, JP9 select both the switching frequency "Clock" and at the same time, "Frequency_duty_cycle step" which is a multiple (x8) of the switching frequency.

This higher frequency is used to create 8 duty cycle steps.

"Frequency_duty_cycle step" goes into the clock input of programmable timer U18 (74HC40103PW). U18 uses "Frequency_duty_cycle step" as a clock.

U18 output produce a duty cycle time in "duty_cycle_output" equals to the value read in input (P0 to P3) multiplied by the clock period.

"duty_cycle_output" is the general output of the Clock circuit.

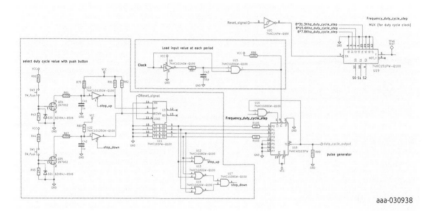

aaa-030938

Figure 10 | Duty cycle

Table 1 | Duty cycle selection

P0 (1)	P1 (2)	P2 (4)	P3 (8)	Duty Cycle
0	0	0	0	0%
1	0	0	0	12.5%
0	1	0	0	25%
1	1	0	0	37.5%
-	-	-	-	-
1	1	1	0	87.5%
0	0	0	1	100%

The signal "Clock" from U3 resets U18 at each new switching period. When reset, U18 will read inputs P0 to P3 and output a duty cycle in "duty_cycle_output" proportional to the settings.

The outputs of a 4-bit synchronous binary up/down counter U11 (74HC193) set the duty cycle value, it is the input of U18. Each time a rising edge appears on the UP input, the output value (Q0 to Q3) increases by 1, each time a rising edge appears on the DOWN input, output value (Q0 to Q3) decreases by 1.

The push buttons SW3 and SW1 with U10 and U22 (74HC1G125) create the rising edges on UP or DOWN input of U11, when the user releases the push button.

When U11 output reaches a maximum count of 9 (8 to 9 transition), (Q0 and Q3 =1), the "stop_up" output of U12 (74HC1G08) is set to 1 and U10 (74HC1G125) is deactivated (high impedance), any further impulses on SW3 can't produce a rising edge on UP input (U11) and the duty cycle reaches a maximum.

When U11 output reaches a minimum of 0 (Q0 to Q3 = 0), U17 (74HC1G08) "stop_down" output is set to 1 and U22 (74HC1G125) is deactivated (high impedance), any further impulses on SW1 can't produce a rising edge on DOWN input (U11) and the duty cycle reaches a minimum (after 0 the next counter value is 15, we need to stop the counter from setting duty cycle to a maximum).

3.3 Pulse Width Modulation

The PWM circuit consists of:

- PWM enable and reset
- Dead-time control
- Level shifting stage
- Direction selection

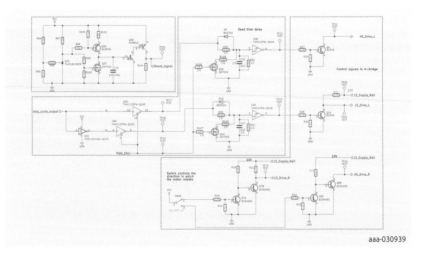

aaa-030939

Figure 11 | PWM, dead-time, level shifting and direction selection

Reset function

The reset function to activate other function when the V_{CC} (5 V) supply is stable.

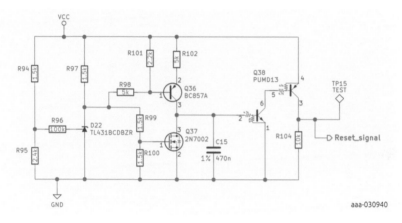

Figure 12 | Reset circuit

When V_{CC} (5 V) reaches approximately 4 V, "Reset_signal" will go high after a delay set by C15. This validates all functions enabled by this signal. This ensures that all logic ICs will start with a clean V_{CC} (5 V).

Adjustable precision shunt regulator D22 (TL431BCDBZR) acts like a comparator. PNP transistor Q36 (BC857A) is a current source charging C15 when the threshold is reached.

MOSFET Q37 (2N7002) discharge C15 when V_{CC} (5 V) is no longer present. The dual NPN/PNP resistor-equipped transistor Q38 (PUMD13) switches "Reset_signal" high when the voltage on C15 (delay setting) reaches a value high enough to turn on the NPN transistor (input, pin 2).

Dead-time function and PWM enable (over current protection disabling)

"duty_cycle_output" is the high side command (a) and "duty_cycle_output" is inverted by U20 (74HC1G14) to create the low side command (1-a).

The duty cycle command is disabled by U6 (74HC125) through its input "PWM_EN" equal to 1 (over current protection switch U6 output in high impedance).

A dead time is controlled by U2 (74HC14) and RC filter. Q39, Q40 (2N7002) force the duty cycle to 0 when "PWM_EN" is 1.

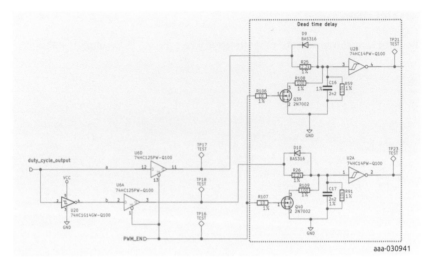

Figure 13 | Dead-time function and PWM enable

Level shifter

Transistors Q9 and Q10 (BC846) interface the 5 V duty cycle signal to the high side and low side drivers (see Section 3.4)

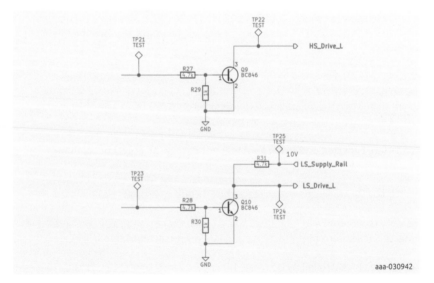

Figure 14 | Level shifter

Direction selection

Switch SW2 selects the motor direction by activating either Q7 or Q8 (BC846BS).

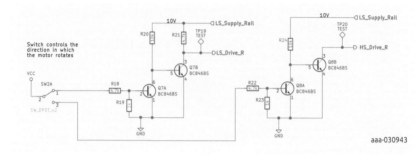

Figure 15 | Direction selection

Q7 or Q8 are fully ON and activate one of the right MOSFETs: high side fully ON or low side fully ON.

3.4 Drive circuit

The drive circuit comprises of high-side and low-side drivers to drive the 4 power MOSFETs that form the full bridge.

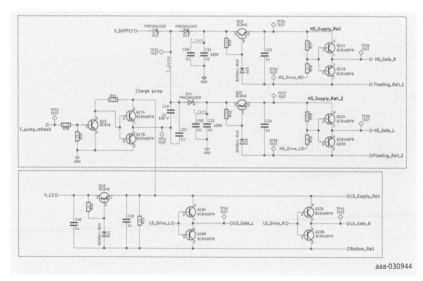

Figure 16 | Driver circuit

High-side and low-side driver

Two high side drivers supplied by the charge pump function and regulated at 9 V:

- Q19 (BC846), D15 (BZX84J-B10), C23, R45, Q21(BC846BPN) driven by "HS_Drive_R" for the right high side
- Q20 (BC846), D16(BZX84J-B10), C24, R46, Q22(BC846BPN) driven by "HS_Drive_L" for the left high side

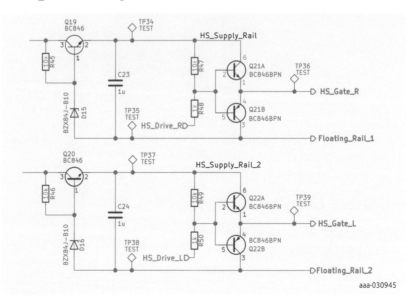

Figure 17 | High side driver circuit

Two Low side drivers supplied by the 12 V from the buck converter and regulated at 9 V

- Q16 (BC846), D11(BZX84J-B10), C18, R40 for the supply:
- Q18(BC846BPN) driven by "LS_Drive_L" for the left low side
- Q23 (BC846BPN) driven by "LS_Drive_R" for the right low side

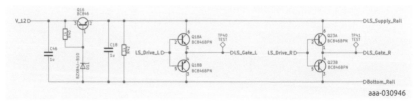

Figure 18 | Low side driver circuit

Charge pump to supply high side MOSFETs

A simple bootstrap function could be used to supply the high side MOSFETs but due to the fact the duty cycle could be 100% there is no time in this configuration to recharge the bootstrap capacitor if the high side MOSFET is fully ON (100% duty cycle) and the low side MOSFET is fully OFF.

The solution is to use a charge pump to supply the high side MOSFETs in every duty cycle configuration.

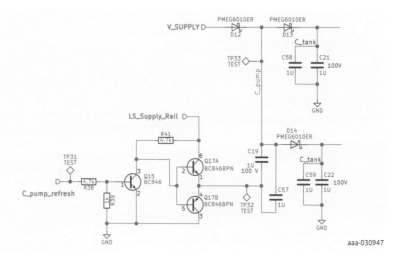

aaa-030947

Figure 19 | Charge pump

"C_pump_refresh" from the clock function (see section Section 3.2) controls Q15 (BC846),

Q17 (BC846BPN) with a frequency of 62.5 kHz, 50% duty cycle. The 9 V regulated from "LS_Supply_Rail" is applied on C19 bottom pin at 62.5 kHz, during 50% of the time, and 0 V during other 50% of the time.

Due to the fact, there is no fast voltage variation across a capacitor, there is always a voltage equals to "V_SUPPLY" across C19 ("V_SUPPLY" is the supply voltage of the H-bridge).

- When the bottom pin of C19 is 0 V, voltage across C19 is "V_SUPPLY".
- When the bottom pin of C19 is 9 V, voltage across C19 is "V_SUPPLY" +9 V. C21 and C22 are the filtering capacitor for the driver input voltage.

3.5 H-bridge

The H-bridge circuit comprises of:

- Power MOSFETs
- Reservoir and decoupling capacitors
- Snubber components
- Low side current measurement

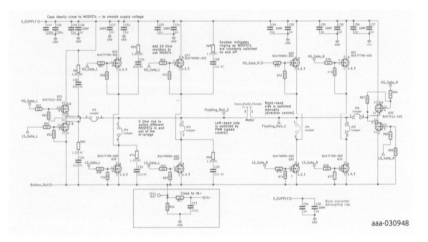

aaa-030948

Figure 20 | H-bridge

Reservoir and decoupling capacitors

Decoupling capacitor (1 μF) and reservoir capacitor (220 μF) are used to filter the "V_SUPPLY".

Snubber on the left MOSFETs (switching MOSFETs)

RC Snubber footprint are implemented on the switching MOSFETs.

An additional RC snubber may be added to further reduce ringing, application note AN11160 (chapter 6 in this book) - Designing RC snubbers gives an explanation about snubber calculation.

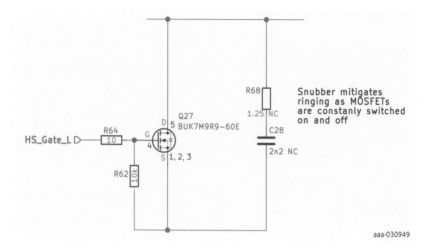

Snubber mitigates ringing as MOSFETs are constanly switched on and off

aaa-030949

Figure 21 | Snubber circuit

Jumper to connect the required MOSFETs

Each MOSFET package is selected by soldering the following jumpers:
- LFPAK33: JP3, JP4
- LFPAK56D: JP1, JP6
- LFPAK56: JP2, JP5
  Note: Solder only the jumpers needed to avoid incorrect operation!

Gate drive resistors

To avoid conflict between the switching MOSFETs gate resistors should be desoldered for those MOSFETs not in use.

Adjust the value of the gate resistor to reduce ringing or modify the switching time. A resistor between gate and source of each MOSFET keeps the MOSFET off when there is no gate voltage applied.

H-bridge motor controller design using Nexperia discrete semiconductors and logic ICs

Low side current measurement

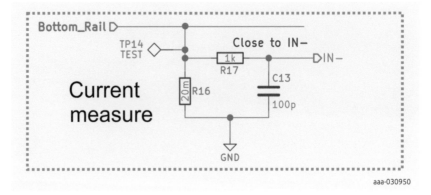

aaa-030950

Figure 22 | Current measurement

A shunt resistor R16 (20 mΩ) measures the current in the H-bridge and provide a voltage proportional to the current to the over current protection input "IN-". A low pass filter R17, C13 filters the signal to avoid false triggering of the current limit circuit due to the noise spike.

3.6 Overcurrent detection

Overcurrent in the motor drive MOSFETs is prevented by comparing the current sense voltage with a reference voltage. In the case of overcurrent the PWM function is reset. The PWM function will be reactivated if the fault disappears.

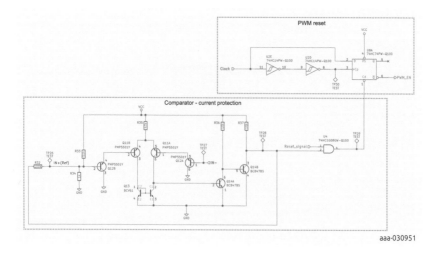

Figure 23 | Overcurrent detection

Comparator, with voltage reference setting current limit

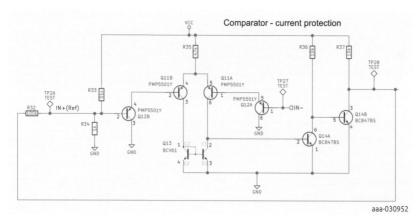

Figure 24 | Comparator, with voltage reference

"IN+" is the maximum current setting input. "IN-" is the current measurement input reference. R35 is a rudimentary current source for the comparator circuit.

Q13 (BCV61) is a current mirror, this means that the polarisation current from R35 is shared equally between the two current paths.

Q11 and Q12 (PMP5501Y) are configured as Darlington pairs to increase the gain to improve the sensitivity of the comparator.

Q11 is a differential pair.
- When IN+ > IN- the output (TP28) is high (no overcurrent)
- When IN+ < IN- the output (TP28) is low (overcurrent)

R33 and R34 set the current limitation, R32 adds hysteresis to avoid transitions due to the noise.

PWM reset

The PWM reset function reactivating the PWM circuit if fault disappears.

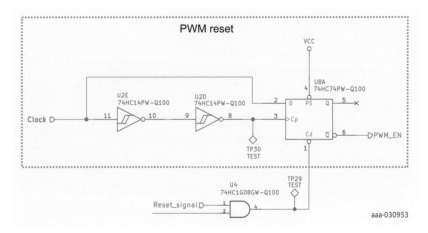

Figure 25 | PWM reset

When there is no overcurrent TP28 is high. "Reset_signal" is high since the V_{CC} (5 V) is supplying the circuit. The output of AND gate U4 (74HC1G08) is high.

The signal "Clock" makes "PWM_EN" output from U8 (74HC74) switch to 0 at the first rising edge and stay at 0. U2 (74HC14) create a delay to have D input high before the rising edge on Cp).

If an overcurrent is detected by the comparator TP28 will switch to 0, TP29 will also switch to 0. Instantaneously "PWM_EN" will switch to 1 and force the duty cycle to be 0 (see section Dead-time function).

When the overcurrent disappears, TP28 and TP29 switch back to 1 and the next rising edge of "Clock" makes "PWM_EN" switch to 0 and the duty cycle is re-enabled.

This allows a cycle by cycle current limit behaviour from the circuit.

4 PCB top view

note: gate resistors R57,R58, R78, R79 and jumpers JP2, JP5 are fitted, selecting the MOSFETs in LFPAK56 package

Figure 26 | H-bridge motor controller PCB top-view

5 Schematics

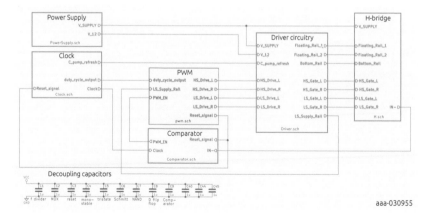

aaa-030955

Figure 27 | Schematics overview

H-bridge motor controller design using Nexperia discrete semiconductors and logic ICs

5.1 Power supply

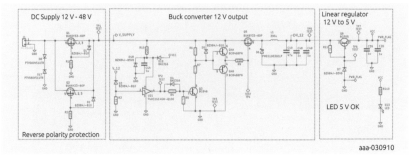

Figure 28 | Power supply schematic

5.2 Clock

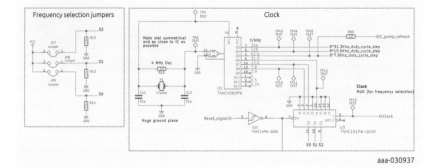

Figure 29 | Clock schematic

5.3 Duty cycle

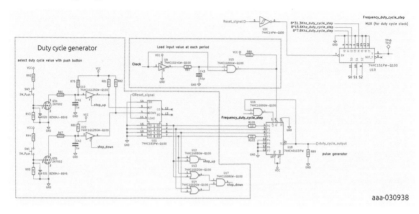

Figure 30 | Duty cycle schematic

5.4 PWM

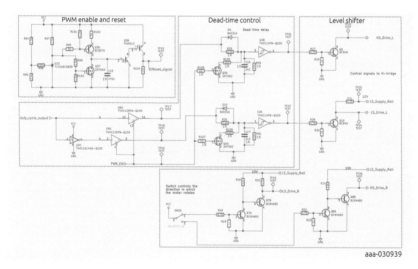

Figure 31 | PWM schematic

5.5 Overcurrent detection

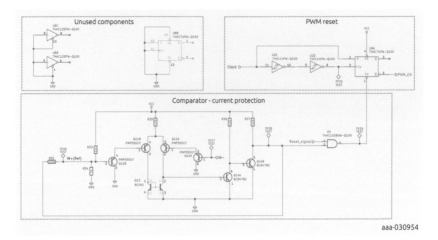

Figure 32 | Overcurrent detection schematic

5.6 H-Bridge

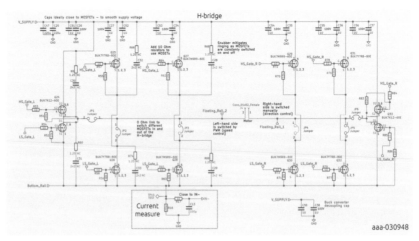

Figure 33 | H-brdige schematic

5.7 Driver circuit

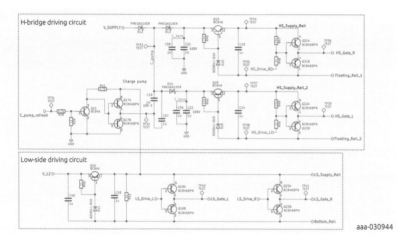

Figure 34 | Driver circuit schematic

6 Bill of materials (Nexperia parts)

Table 2: BOM (Nexperia parts)

Reference	Part number	Description
D1, D2, D3, D5, D11, D15, D16	BZX84J-B10	Single Zener diode 10 V
D4, D9, D10, D19	BAS316	High-speed switching diodes
D6	PMEG10030ELP	100 V, 3 A low leakage current Schottky barrier rectifier
D7, D18, D20, D21	BZX84J-B5V6	Single Zener diodes 5.6 V
D8, D17	PTVS60VS1UTR	High-temperature 400 W Transient Voltage Suppressor
D12, D13, D14	PMEG6010ER	1 A low VF MEGA Schottky barrier rectifier
D22	TL431BCDBZR	Adjustable precision shunt regulator
Q1, Q2, Q5	BUK6Y33-60P	P-channel MOSFET in an LFPAK56 (Power SO8) package 60 V, 33 mΩ
Q3, Q9, Q10, Q15, Q16, Q19, Q20	BC846	65 V, 100 mA NPN general-purpose transistors
Q4, Q17, Q18, Q21, Q22, Q23	BC846BPN	65 V, 100 mA NPN/PNP general-purpose transistor
Q6	BCP55	60 V, 1 A NPN medium power transistor
Q7, Q8	BC846BS	65 V, 100 mA NPN/NPN general-purpose transistor
Q11, Q12	PMP5501Y	PNP/PNP matched double transistors
Q13	BCV61	NPN general-purpose double transistors
Q14	BC847BS	45 V, 100 mA NPN/NPN general-purpose transistor
Q24, Q33	BUK7K12-60E	LFPAK56D, dual N-channel MOSFET

Reference	Part number	Description
Q25, Q26, Q31, Q32	BUK7Y7R8-80E	LFPAK56, N channel MOSFET, 80 V, 7.8 mΩ
Q27, Q28, Q29, Q30	BUK7M9R9-60E	LFPAK33, N channel MOSFET
Q34, Q35, Q37, Q39, Q40	2N7002	60 V, 300 mA N-channel Trench MOSFET
Q36	BC857A	PNP general purpose transistors
Q38	PUMD13	NPN/PNP resistor-equipped transistors; R1 = 4.7 kΩ, R2 = 47 kΩ
U1	74HC4060PW	14-stage binary ripple counter with oscillator
U2	74HC14PW-Q100	Hex inverting Schmitt trigger
U3, U19	74HC151PW-Q100	8-input multiplexer
U4, U12, U17	74HC1G08GW-Q100	2-input AND gate
U6	74HC125PW-Q100	Quad buffer/line driver; 3-state
U8	74HC74PW-Q100	Dual D-type flip-flop with set and reset; positive-edge trigger
U9, U20, U21	74HC1G14GW-Q100	Inverting Schmitt trigger
U10, U22	74HC1G125GW-Q100	Bus buffer/line driver; 3-state
U11	74HC193PW-Q100	Presettable synchronous 4-bit binary up, down counter
U13, U14	74HC1G02GW-Q100	2-input NOR gate
U15, U16	74HC1G00GW-Q100	2-input NAND gate
U18	74HC40103PW	8-bit synchronous binary down counter

7 Bill of materials

Table 3: BOM

Item	Qty	Reference	Value	Footprint	Voltage
1	20	C1, C2, C3, C4, C5, C6, C7, C8, C9, C18, C20, C23, C24, C39, C40, C44, C45, C46, C48, C49	1 µF	Capacitors_SMD: C_1206	
2	1	C10	47 µF	Capacitors_SMD: CP_Elec 6.3 x 5.7	
3	3	C11, C12, C43	51 pF	Capacitors_SMD: C_0805	
4	1	C13	100 pF	Capacitors_SMD: C_0805	
5	3	C14, C41, C42	1 µF	Capacitors_SMD: C_0805	
6	1	C15	470 nF	Capacitors_SMD: C_0805	
7	2	C16, C17	2.2 nF	Capacitors_SMD: C_0805	
8	10	C19, C21, C22, C26, C27, C34, C35, C36, C37, C38	1 µF	Capacitors_SMD: C_1206	100 V
9	2	C25, C47	220 µF	"Capacitors_THT: CP_Radial_D 12.5 mm P	100 V
10	6	C28, C29, C30, C31, C32, C33	* user selected	5.00 mm"	
11	10	C50, C51, C52, C53, C54, C55, C56, C57, C58, C59	1 µF	Capacitors_SMD: C_0805	100 V
12	7	D1, D2, D3, D5, D11, D15, D16	BZX84J-B10	Capacitors_SMD: C_0805	
13	4	D4, D9, D10, D19	BAS316	Diodes_SMD: D_SOD-323 HandSoldering	
14	1	D6	PMEG10030ELP	Diodes_SMD: D_SOD-323 HandSoldering	

Item	Qty	Reference	Value	Footprint	Voltage
15	4	D7, D18, D20, D21	BZX84J-B5V6	Nexperia: SOD128	
16	2	D8, D17	PTVS60VS1UTR	Diodes_SMD: D_SOD-323 HandSoldering	
17	3	D12, D13, D14	PMEG6010ER	Nexperia: D_SOD123W	
18	1	D22	TL431BCDBZR	Nexperia: D_SOD123W	
19	1	D23	LED	TO_SOT_Packages_ SMD: SOT-23	
20	1	J1	Conn_01x02	LEDs: LED_0603 Connectors Phoenix: PhoenixContact_ GMSTBVA-G_ 02 x 7.50 mm Vertical	
21	1	J4	Conn_01x02_ Female	Connectors Phoenix: PhoenixContact_ GMSTBVA-G_ 02 x 7.50 mm Vertical	
22	9	JP1, JP2, JP3, JP4, JP5, JP6, JP7, JP8, JP9	Jumper	Jumpers: SolderJumper-2_P 1.3 mm Open_ TrianglePad 1.0 x 1.5 mm	
23	1	L1	390 μH	Inductors_THT: L_ Radial_D 10.0 mm P 5.00 mm Fastron_07M	
24	4	MK1, MK2, MK3, MK4	Mounting_Hole	Mounting_ Holes:MountingHole 4.3 mm M4	
25	3	Q1, Q2, Q5	BUK6Y33-60P	TO_SOT_Packages_ SMD: SOT-669_LFPAK	
26	7	Q3, Q9, Q10, Q15, Q16, Q19, Q20	BC846	TO_SOT_Packages_ SMD: SOT-23	
27	6	Q4, Q17, Q18, Q21, Q22, Q23	BC846BPN	"TO_SOT_Packages_ SMD: SOT-363_SC-70-6 Handsoldering"	
28	1	Q6	BCP55	TO_SOT_Packages_ SMD: SOT-223 3Lead TabPin2	

Item	Qty	Reference	Value	Footprint	Voltage
29	2	Q7, Q8	BC846BS	"TO_SOT_Packages_SMD: SOT-363_SC-70-6 Handsoldering"	
30	2	Q11, Q12	PMP5501Y	"TO_SOT_Packages_SMD: SOT-363_SC-70-6 Handsoldering"	
31	1	Q13	BCV61	Nexperia: SOT-143B	
32	1	Q14	BC847BS	"TO_SOT_Packages_SMD: SOT-363_SC-70-6 Handsoldering"	
33	2	Q24, Q33	BUK7K12-60E	Nexperia: LFPAK56D	
34	4	Q25, Q26, Q31, Q32	BUK7Y7R8-80E	TO_SOT_Packages_SMD: SOT-669_LFPAK	
35	4	Q27, Q28, Q29, Q30	BUK7M9R9-60E	Nexperia: LFPAK33	
36	5	Q34, Q35, Q37, Q39, Q40	2N7002	TO_SOT_Packages_SMD: SOT-23	
37	1	Q36	BC857A	TO_SOT_Packages_SMD: SOT-23	
38	1	Q38	PUMD13	TO_SOT_Packages_SMD: SOT-363 SC-70-6 Handsoldering	
39	2	R1, R2	10 kΩ	Resistors_SMD: R_1206	
40	14	R3, R11, R17, R19, R23, R29, R30, R34, R39, R40, R42, R48, R50, R87	1 kΩ	Resistors_SMD: R_0805	
41	34	R4, R6, R12, R13, R14, R20, R24, R36, R37, R44, R45, R46, R47, R49, R51, R52, R55, R56, R59, R62, R63, R70, R71, R76, R77, R81, R82, R83, R86, R88, R89, R91, R92, R104	10 kΩ	Resistors_SMD: R_0805	

Item	Qty	Reference	Value	Footprint	Voltage
42	10	R5, R7, R18, R21, R22, R27, R28, R31, R38, R41	4.7 kΩ	Resistors_SMD:R_0805	
43	6	R8, R60, R66, R68, R69, R74	* user selected	Resistors_SMD:R_0805	
44	3	R9, R108, R109	100 Ω	Resistors_SMD: R_0805	
45	1	R10	20 kΩ	Resistors_SMD: R_1206	
46	4	R15, R43, R80, R93	1 MΩ	Resistors_SMD: R_0805	
47	1	R16	20 mΩ	Resistors_SMD: R_2512	
48	3	R25, R26, R101	2.2 kΩ	Resistors_SMD: R_0805	
49	4	R32, R61, R67, R96	100 kΩ	Resistors_SMD: R_0805	
50	1	R33	51 kΩ	Resistors_SMD: R_0805	
51	1	R35	47 kΩ	Resistors_SMD: R_0805	
52	17	R53, R54, R57, R58, R64, R65, R72, R73, R78, R79, R84, R85, R90, R103, R105, R106, R107	10 Ω	Resistors_SMD: R_0805	
53	1	R75	510 kΩ	Resistors_SMD: R_0805	
54	4	R94, R97, R99, R100	1.5 kΩ	Resistors_SMD: R_0805	
55	1	R95	2.4 kΩ	Resistors_SMD: R_0805	
56	2	R98, R102	5 kΩ	Resistors_SMD: R_0805	
57	1	R110	500 Ω	Resistors_SMD: R_0805	

H-bridge motor controller design using Nexperia discrete semiconductors and logic ICs

Item	Qty	Reference	Value	Footprint	Voltage
58	2	SW1, SW3	SW_Push	"Buttons_Switches_SMD: SW_DIP_x1_W 8.61 mm_Slide_LowProfile"	
59	1	SW2	SW_DPDT_x2	Buttons_Switches_THT: SW_CuK_JS202011CQN_DPDT_Straight	
60	1	U1	74HC4060PW	"Housings_SSOP: TSSOP-16 4.4 x 5 mm Pitch 0.65 mm"	
61	1	U2	74HC14PW -Q100	Housings_SSOP: TSSOP-14 4.4 x 5 mm_ Pitch 0.65mm	
62	2	U3, U19	74HC151PW -Q100	"Housings_SSOP: TSSOP-16 4.4 x 5 mm Pitch 0.65 mm"	
63	3	U4, U12, U17	74HC1G08GW -Q100	TO_SOT_Packages_ SMD: SOT-353_SC-70-5	
64	1	U6	74HC125PW -Q100	Housings_SSOP: TSSOP-14 4.4 x 5mm Pitch 0.65 mm	
65	1	U8	74HC74PW -Q100	"Housings_SSOP: TSSOP-14 4.4 x 5 mm Pitch 0.65 mm"	
66	3	U9, U20, U21	74HC1G14GW -Q100	TO_SOT_Packages_ SMD: SOT-353_SC-70-5	
67	2	U10, U22	74HC1G125GW - Q100	TO_SOT_Packages_ SMD: SOT-353_SC-70-5	
68	1	U11	74HC193PW -Q100	Housings_SSOP: TSSOP-16 4.4 x 5mm Pitch 0.65 mm	
69	2	U13, U14	74HC1G14GW -Q100	TO_SOT_Packages_ SMD: SOT-353_SC-70-5	
70	2	U15, U16	74HC1G14GW -Q100	TO_SOT_Packages_ SMD: SOT-353_SC-70-5	

Item	Qty	Reference	Value	Footprint	Voltage
71	1	U18	74HC40103PW	"Housings_SSOP: TSSOP-16 4.4 x 5 mm Pitch 0.65 mm"	
72	1	Y1	Crystal	Crystals: Crystal_SMD_ HC49-SD	

The right package for 12 48 V DC-to-DC conversion

H-bridge DC motor reference design using Nexperia components

8 Tables

H-bridge motor controller design using Nexperia discrete semiconductors and logic ICs

9 Figures

Chapter 13

Power and small-signal MOSFET frequently asked questions and answers

Technical Note: TN00008

1 Introduction

This chapter provides several important questions regarding the use of MOSFETs and the platforms required. Although it is focused on automotive applications, the principles can apply to industrial and consumer applications. It strives to provide clear answers to these questions and the reasoning behind the answers.

This chapter is intended for guidance only. Any specific questions from customers should be discussed with Nexperia power MOSFET application engineers.

2 Gate

2.1 Q: Why is the V_{GS} rating of Trench 6 automotive logic level MOSFETs limited to 10 V and can it be increased beyond 10 V?

A: The V_{GS} rating of 10 V given to Trench 6 logic level MOSFETs is driven by our <1 ppm failure rate targets and was rated to the best industry practices at the time. The ppm failure figures are not given in any data sheet nor are they part of AEC-Q101 qualification. In other words, two devices can both be qualified to AEC-Q101 and still have different ppm failure rate figures.

Methods of defining, characterising and protecting these ratings have improved and there is now a possibility to operate beyond the given rating of 10 V. This will be a function of time, voltage and temperature. For further explanation see below; more details are available in Nexperia application note AN90001 (chapter 2 in this book) - Designing in MOSFETs for safe and reliable gate-drive operation.

Additional information

There are two key words in the above question that are worth expanding on - "rating" and "logic level".

Logic level MOSFETs are primarily intended for applications where the drive voltage is 5 V and thus optimised accordingly. To achieve a fully-on MOSFET and best $R_{DS(on)}$ performance with relatively low gate voltages these MOSFETs will need a thinner gate oxide than standard-level parts which operate with a drive of 10 V V_{GS}. Thinner gate oxides will breakdown at lower voltages and will have a lower rating than standard level devices, (full details are given in AN90001 (chapter 2 in this book) - Designing in MOSFETs for safe and reliable gate-drive operation.

However, there are instances where logic level MOSFETs are chosen for non-logic level applications. For example, in automotive applications where the battery supply voltage can drop to a level where drive circuits need to operate below 6 V. Therefore, MOSFETs must turn ON with lower gate voltages than standard level MOSFETs are capable of. Conversely, the MOSFET gate needs to withstand the nominal battery voltage of approximately 12 V.

Is a logic level MOSFET suitable?

In terms of capability logic level MOSFETs are not expected to suddenly fail as soon as higher voltages are applied. However, applying higher V_{GS} than the maximum rated voltage will compromise the <1 ppm failure rate and therefore Nexperia would not consider including these ratings in data sheets.

Nexperia's methodology of removing defectives and reducing early life failures is achieved through effective screening at production. As a supplier Nexperia is committed to zero defects and high quality levels. Therefore, the ratings may appear lower than our competitors where commitment to quality is possibly not as stringent. Nexperia V_{GS} max ratings are based on applying 100% max (rated) voltage at 175 °C for 1000 hours with failure rate <1 ppm – for more details see: AN90001 (chapter 2 in this book) - Designing in MOSFETs for safe and reliable gate-drive operation.

Designers must consider failure rates figures for logic level MOSFETs when V_{GS} in their data sheets is rated to ±20 V

A model exists at Nexperia for calculating life failure rates with higher gate voltages against temperatures. This information can be provided upon request as a calculated figure and will **only** be given as a guide.

2.2 Q: Why is V_{GS} maximum limit of Trench 9 automotive logic level MOSFETs different to previous generations?

A: The rating is based on meeting AEC-Q101 requirements, as it is with previous generations. However, Nexperia has developed a new testing methodology which ensures <1 ppm failure rates over lifetime at the rated V_{GS}. This has been applied to Trench 9 and its V_{GS} rating is set to meet this new requirement.

Additional information

Detailed explanation can be found in AN90001 (chapter 2 in this book) - Designing in MOSFETs for safe and reliable gate-drive operation..

3 Thermals

3.1 Q: When comparing Z_{th} curves in some data sheets, there appear to be some contradictions. From an R_{th} point of view, the BUK9Y38-100E (Trench generation 6) looks better (lower). However, from a Z_{th} (at less than 100 ms) point of view, the BUK9Y30-75B (Trench generation 3) looks better. The shape of the graphs indicates that a more advanced model or measurement was done on the Trench generation 6 part. Is this assumption correct?

A: The method for setting the Z_{th} curve has changed between the Trench generation 3 parts (2008) and Trench generation 6 (2012). The die size is also different which changes the Z_{th} and R_{th} characteristics.

Additional information

The earlier method used empirical models for Z_{th} (1 µs) and R_{th}, joined by an exponential line.

The latest method uses models for the Z_{th} generated by Computational Fluid Dynamics (CFD) simulation, verified by measurement.

The dies in the 2 parts have different dimensions and therefore they have different Z_{th}.

The plots depicted in Figure 1 compare the data sheet curves for the single shot Z_{th}. There is a good match between the limit lines for both parts. The biggest difference is in the region 1 ms to 20 ms.

The conclusion from this comparison, is that the Trench generation 3 part is designed to work within these Z_{th} limits. The Trench generation 6 part is an excellent alternative that has a very high probability of working satisfactorily.

It is possible to assess how to rate the Trench generation 3 part using the new rules with a more accurate reflection of its true performance. Figure 1 shows the new line in comparison with the two data sheet lines.

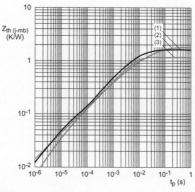

(1) BUK9Y38-100E
(2) BUK9Y30-75B
(3) BUK9Y30-75B (new test method)

aaa-013060

Figure 1 | Comparison of transient thermal impedance

Although there is a difference in the R_{th}, it is probably unimportant. In practice, it is the $R_{th(j\text{-amb})}$ that is the limiting factor for the design. The R_{th} of the Printed-Circuit Board (PCB) that is common to both parts, is dominant.

When considering the old test method with the new one for the BUK9Y30-75B, the other region of difference is below 10 μs.

For pulse duration between 1 μs and 2 μs, the temperature rise (or $Z_{th(j\text{-mb})}$) in the Trench generation 3 part, is only a half of what the original data sheet curve predicted. The importance of this factor depends on the application.

3.2 Q: It is understood that the values for thermal resistance listed in data sheets are based on controlled conditions that do not apply to typical applications. If this understanding is true, how is the proper thermal resistance/junction temperature accurately calculated?

A: This understanding is correct. To ensure reliability of the MOSFET, always limit the maximum junction temperature to 175 °C.

Additional information

It is understood that the typical values for thermal resistance listed in data sheets are based on controlled conditions that do not apply to typical applications.

Device characterization at a junction temperature of 25 °C is the accepted standard in the semiconductor industry. It is also most convenient for users to take measurements at this temperature.

How is the proper thermal resistance calculated?

Only a maximum value of thermal resistance is given on Nexperia MOSFET data sheets. The typical value is significantly less than the maximum. It is understood that thermal cycling can induce an increase in $R_{th(j-mb)}$) over the lifetime of the MOSFET.

A tolerance margin is included in the data sheet maximum $R_{th(j-mb)}$ value which allows for an increase over the lifetime of the MOSFET.

For worst case design analysis, always use the maximum value. Maximum $R_{th(j-mb)}$ given on the data sheet is evaluated from characterization measurements.

Its value is not dependent on temperature or other environmental conditions.

How is junction temperature calculated?

MOSFETs usually operate with a junction temperature greater than 25 °C due to temperature rise caused by the environment and/or power dissipation in the MOSFET.

If MOSFET power dissipation and mounting base temperature (T_{mb}) are known, MOSFET junction temperature can be calculated. Use Equation (1), below to determine T_j.

$$T_j = P \times R_{th(j-mb)} + T_{mb} \qquad [1]$$

SPICE thermal models of MOSFETs provide an excellent means of estimating T_j by simulation. It is particularly useful when MOSFET power dissipation changes with time.

Worked example for a BUK7Y12-40E:

From the data sheet:
Maximum $R_{DS(on)}$ at 25 °C = 12 mΩ

Maximum $R_{DS(on)}$ at 175 °C = 23.6 mΩ
Maximum $R_{th(j-mb)}$ at 2.31 K/W

From the application data:
PWM frequency = 100 Hz
Maximum duty cycle = 50 %
V_{supply} = 14 V
R_{load} = 0.7 Ω
Maximum ambient temperature = 85 °C
Maximum PCB temperature = 100 °C

Calculation based on average power, ignoring any temperature fluctuation due to the power pulsing and also ignoring switching losses at 100 Hz:

Assume that the temperature of the MOSFET is initially 100 °C and its maximum $R_{DS(on)}$ is 18 mΩ. It is midway between 12 mΩ at 25 °C and 24 mΩ at 175 °C.

When conducting, the MOSFETs power dissipation $I^2 \times R_{DS(on)}$ is: 20 x 20 x 0.018 = 7.2 W

The duty cycle is 50 %, so the average power dissipation = 7.2 x 0.5 = 3.6 W. It is assumed that the switching loss at 100 Hz can be ignored.

The rise of the MOSFET junction temperature, above the mounting base is: 2.31 x 3.6 = 8.3 K.

The maximum MOSFET die temperature in this situation is very safe at: 100 + 8.3 = 108.3 °C

To guarantee that the PCB temperature does not rise above 100 °C in an 85 °C ambient, the thermal resistance between PCB and ambient must be: (100 - 85)/3.6 = 4.2 K/W

3.3 Q: What effect does changing the device have on $R_{th(j-a)}$? The customer is trying to achieve ~60 K/W on a dual N channel FET.

A: The customer is trying to achieve a $R_{th(j-amb)}$ = 60 K/W using a dual N channel LFPAK56 (SOT1205).

$R_{th(j-amb)} = R_{th(j-amb)} + R_{th(mb-amb)}$, see Figure 2.

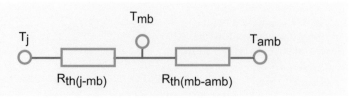

Figure 2 | MOSFET thermal resistance junction to ambient

$R_{th(j-mb)}$ is in Nexperia's control (it is a function of the die size and package design, for example the bigger the die the lower the $R_{th(j-mb)}$). $R_{th(mb-amb)}$ is a function of the PCB design and the thermal management scheme and is not under the control of Nexperia. A very good multilayer FR4 design with thermal vias would be around 30 - 40 K/W.

Worked example for BUK9K6R2-40E and BUK761R6-40E

From the BUK9K6R2-40E data sheet, the $R_{th(j-mb)}$ is 2.21 K/W.

However, the $R_{th(mb-amb)}$ is in the control of the customer, i.e. it depends on the PCB design. Assume the PCB assembly thermal resistance to ambient is 40 K/W.

A. Using a SOT1205 dual LFPAK56 (such as BUK9K6R2-40E)

$R_{th(j-amb)} = R_{th(j-mb)} + R_{th(mb-amb)} = 2.21 + 40 = 42.21$ K/W

B. Using a device with a larger die will result in a lower $R_{th(j-mb)}$. For demonstration purposes a max die D²PAK (BUK761R6-40E) with low $R_{th(j-mb)}$ is used (0.43 K/W).

$R_{th(j-amb)} = R_{th(j-mb)} + R_{th(mb-amb)} = 0.43 + 40 = 40.43$ K/W

You can see that for DC conditions, the effects of changing the die size on the device is swamped by the PCB cooling arrangement, $R_{th(mb-amb)}$, (note that the $R_{th(j-a)}$ of 50 K/W in the data sheet is for a different PCB thermal arrangement).

So transposing this into temperature: $\Delta T = P \times R_{th(j-amb)}$, then for a dissipation of 1 W:

A. 42.21 K/W: if $T_{amb} = 105\ °C$ then $T_j = 105 + 42.21 = 147.21\ °C$
B. 40.43 K/W: if $T_{amb} = 105\ °C$ then $T_j = 105 + 40.43 = 145.43\ °C$

$R_{th(mb-amb)}$ will change due to the package size, this effect is ignored here. The bigger package will result in a lower mounting base to ambient thermal resistance.

In example B above, T_j will probably be a few degrees lower than calculated. Refer to AN90003 (chapter 9 in this book) - LFPAK MOSFET thermal design guide for more detailed information.

To estimate $R_{th(j-amb)}$, bias the body diode of the MOSFET with 1 W on the intended PCB design. Use an infra-red camera or sensor to measure the temperature of the MOSFET plastic body, this is approximately the same temperature as the junction.

3.4 Q: Why is there no $R_{th(j-amb)}$ in the data sheet?

A: The $R_{th(j-amb)}$ is dependent on the PCB design. As MOSFET manufacturers we do not determine this part of the system and the value would be meaningless, therefore. We have provided some examples in (chapter 9 in this book) - LFPAK MOSFET thermal design guide for more detailed information.

3.5 Q: How can I achieve the $R_{th(j-mb)}$ – I try to put the rated power in the device, but the junction is getting too hot?

A: $R_{th(j-mb)}$ tells you the temperature difference between the junction and mounting base for a given power profile. Because of the power dissipation the mounting base to ambient path will also heat up, causing the junction temperature to rise further. The junction to ambient is the full thermal path that needs to be considered and is a function of the PCB design too, please see AN90003 for more details. (chapter 9 in this book) - LFPAK MOSFET thermal design guide for more detailed information.

3.6 Q: Why is there no $R_{th(j-case)}$ in the data sheet?

A: The drain tab (mounting base) and source leads are the two main paths through which a down side cooling package dissipates heat. In fact, contrarily to some through hole packages (like TO-220), SMD packages such as LFPAK and D^{2}PAK get rid of all the heat through the PCB. Hot air rises from the board and envelopes the device lowering the efficiency and thus the efficacy of any heatsink attached to the top of the plastic case. Instead, when a substantial power needs to be dissipated, copper traces, vias and planes are employed in order to lower as much as possible the $R_{th(j-a)}$ of a device.

3.7 Q: Can I measure T_j from T_{case}?

A: Flotherm simulations and measurements carried out using LFPAK56 and variable power dissipation and PCB copper area show how, in steady state conditions, temperature taken on the top center of the case is, within a reasonably low accuracy, very similar to the junction temperature. This result is not due to heat being dissipated from the top of the case but rather from the one coming out of the PCB that increases the temperature of the surrounding air immediately close to the device, up to almost that of the junction.

3.8 Q: Why can an LFPAK88 have higher $R_{th(j-mb)}$ than an LFPAK56E?

A: Conduction is the predominant phenomena regulating heat flow from junction to mounting base. The resulting resistance is inversely proportional to the cross sectional area of the medium through which it propagates (die area) and directly to its thickness (drain tab). Given an LFPAK56E and an LFPAK88 with the same die size the former has lower $R_{th(j-mb)}$ because the thickness of its drain tab is lower. It is worth noting, however, that the thermal path doesn't end here and that the LFPAK88 shows better thermal performances due to its lower $R_{th(j-amb)}$ given by a much larger drain tab.

3.9 Q: Does the LFPAK88 have better or worse thermal impedance than LFPAK56?

A: For a given die size the LFPAK88 shows an overall better transient thermal impedance $Z_{th(j-mb)}$.

Additional information

Referring to Figure 3 we can see a much lower impedance in the region 20 µs to 10 ms. This is due to the larger mounting base of the LFPAK88. The greater volume of copper acts as a heatsink with larger thermal capacitance that allows a faster absorption of heat from the die into the drain tab itself. This is beneficial in short circuit events, inrush current events as well as other high current events.

During steady state the LFPAK56E shows lower thermal resistance $R_{th(j-mb)}$ due to the thinner drain tab (see Section 3.8).

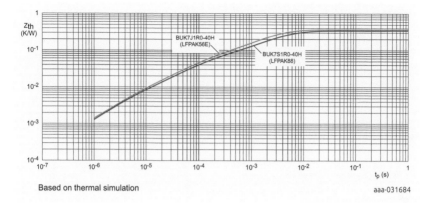

Based on thermal simulation

aaa-031684

Figure 3 | LFPAK88 (BUK7S1R0-40H) and LFPAK56E (BUK7J1R0-40H) transient thermal impedance comparison

4 MOSFET body diode

4.1 Q: How much current can the MOSFET body diode carry?

A: The data sheet states the I_S capability for the diode. The power constraints are the same as for the MOSFET conduction. The diode is an integral part of the MOSFET structure. They are in effect the same size and have the same thermal properties. The MOSFET can carry the same current through the channel or in reverse through the body diode. The maximum steady state current in the diode is dependent on the total allowed power loss for the device. However, the diode current may be different from the channel current because the power dissipation may be different under the 2 modes of operation.

Additional information

The objective is to keep the junction temperature below $T_{j(max)}$ so it is necessary to calculate the diode dissipation. In a DC case, it is simply $I_F \times V_F$. It is equivalent to $V_{SD} \times I_S$ as used in the Nexperia MOSFET data sheet. For a worse case analysis, the max V_F of the data sheet should be used (normally 1.2 V). Where the current is varying but in cyclic manner, the dissipation can be found using Equation (2) below:

$$Power = V_O \times I_{(AV)} + R_S \times I^2_{(RMS)}$$ [2]

where:

$I_{(AV)}$ is the average diode current

$I_{(RMS)}$ is the RMS diode current

R_S is the slope of the I_{SD}/V_{SD} characteristic graph given in data

V_O is typically where the R_S line meets the axis at $I_{SD} = 0$. For a conservative worst case analysis, use 1.2 V.

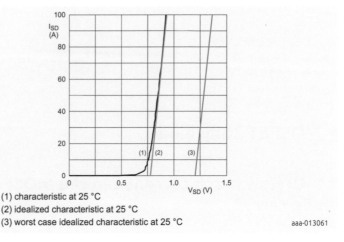

(1) characteristic at 25 °C
(2) idealized characteristic at 25 °C
(3) worst case idealized characteristic at 25 °C

aaa-013061

Figure 4 | Diode characteristics

For transient currents, a simulation using the SPICE model of the diode is useful but care is needed because the model is for a typical part. Once the dissipation is known, standard thermal analysis methods can be used to check that T_j is acceptable.

It can include SPICE simulation using RC thermal models.

4.2 Q: What is the importance of the Q_r parameter?

A: When a MOSFET transitions from diode conduction to blocking state there is an additional loss, called the diode recovery charge (Q_r). The Q_r needs to be factored in the switching loss calculation of the application for accurate analysis. This switching transition also impacts on the EMC performance and needs careful consideration - see AN90011 (chapter 7 in this book) - Half-bridge MOSFET switching and its impact on EMC and TN90003 (chapter 9 in this book) - LFPAK MOSFET thermal design for more details.

Additional information

Q_r is relevant in all half-bridge topologies, for example DC-to-DC convertors or motor control. In both examples the MOSFET's body diode will be conducting in the forward direction before it is required to block voltage in the reverse direction. This change of operation is called diode recovery and takes time (reverse recovery time, t_{rr}) during which charge is stored (diode recovery charge, Q_r). The Q_r adds additional losses to the switching transient.

In addition to switching losses the recovery of the diode is related to the EMC performance of a MOSFET in an application. A fast recovery will cause high voltage spikes and a poorly damped diode will cause voltage and current oscillations after the switching event causing EMI.

5 Safe operating area and linear mode operation

5.1 Q: The current derates with temperature. Is this limit based on power dissipation?

A: The most important factor in current derating or power derating is junction temperature. T_j is a function of power dissipation. Power dissipation is a function of I_D current and on-state resistance ($P = I_D^2 \times R$) when operating in the fully enhanced mode. It is the product of I_D and V_{DS} when operating between on and off states. The $R_{DS(on)}$ of a MOSFET, increases with increase in temperature. Therefore, for a given maximum power dissipation, the maximum current must be derated to match the maximum power dissipation. In Nexperia data sheets, graphs show the continuous drain current and normalized total power dissipation (see Figure 6) as a function of the mounting base temperature. These graphs can be used to determine the derating.

5.2 Q: Is it necessary to de-rate any limit (current, voltage, power etc.) to achieve high reliability?

A: If current, voltage, power, junction temperature, etc. are within Nexperia data sheet limitations, no additional derating is needed. In the data sheet, there is a power derating curve based on junction temperature. Junction temperature (T_j) is one of the most important factors for reliability. Particular care should be taken to extract enough heat from the device to maintain junction or die temperature, below rated values. The device should be operated within the SOA region. It should be de-rated if necessary (see Section 5.3) as recommended in the data sheet and it should be possible to obtain optimum reliability.

5.3 Q: How do I de-rate an SOA graph for temperatures other than 25 °C?

A: As an example, assume that the temperature required is 100 °C, instead of 25 °C. T_j rated is 175 °C for this automotive grade MOSFET. To de-rate when considering the effect of temperature on SOA performance the current must be reduced, (see Figure 5). To determine the new current (at temperature) for a fixed voltage, use the power derating line in Figure 6. For example, power at 100 °C = 50 % of power at 25 °C. Therefore, the 1.0 A line represents 0.5 A at 100 °C etc. It is explained in Application note AN11158 (chapter 1 in this book) - Understanding power MOSFET data sheet parameters. If necessary, the SOA lines for 1 ms, 10 ms etc. can be extended at the same slope to the right.

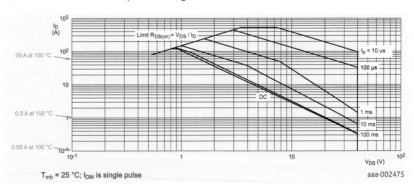

Figure 5 | Example: BUK7Y12-55B SOA curve showing derating for 100 °C

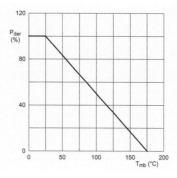

Figure 6 | Normalized total power dissipation as a function of mounting base temperature

$$P_{der} = \frac{P_{tot}}{P_{tot\,(25°C)}} \times 100\%$$

[3]

5.4 Q: Is there a Spirito boundary limit line for linear mode operation?

A: The Spirito region or hot spotting issue with new higher density technologies may have more effect in the linear mode of operation. This effect is evident from the change in gradient in the limit lines for 1 ms, 10 ms and 100 ms at higher V_{DS} values (see Figure 5). The 1 ms, 10 ms, 100 ms and DC lines at higher V_{DS} values emphasize it. The reason is that most newer technologies pack more parallel fundamental cells to share more current in a smaller die (lower $R_{DS(on)}$ per unit area). It leads to an increased thermal coupling between cells. Also, to attain higher current densities, the MOSFETs are designed with higher transconductance or gain ($g_{fs} = I_D/V_{GS}$). It enables them to carry higher currents even at lower V_{GS} values. However $V_{GS(th)}$ (threshold voltage) has a negative temperature coefficient which leads to a higher zero temperature coefficient crossover value. For various reasons, the distribution of temperature in the die is never perfectly uniform. Therefore, when the device is operated for extended periods in linear mode, hot spotting occurs. Due to the shift in threshold voltage, there is a risk of thermal runaway and device destruction where the hotspots form. Because of these reasons, special care should be taken when using trench or planar MOSFETs for linear applications. Ensure that operation remains within the data sheet SOA limits.

5.5 Q: Regarding the SOA curve for the 1 ms and 10 ms curves, there is a bend-down at higher voltages and low currents. Why does this bending disappear for longer and shorter pulse times?

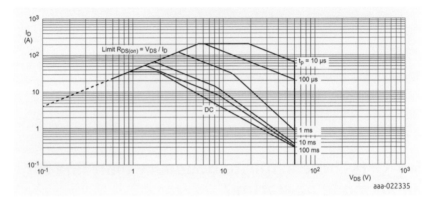

Figure 7 | Safe operating area: continuous and peak drain currents as a function of drain-source voltage

A: The inflexion points on the 1 ms and 10 ms lines represent the points where the 'Spirito' effect starts. At higher I_D, the lines represent constant power (P); at lower I_D, P decreases as I_D decreases. The 100 ms and DC lines are straight, but have higher negative gradients than constant power lines, i.e. power also decreases as I_D decreases. The flat portion of the DC line represents package maximum I_D.

The Spirito effect is a form of electro-thermal instability i.e. uneven die heating leading to hot-spot formation. It happens because $V_{GS(th)}$ has a Negative Temperature Coefficient (NTC) at I_D values below I_{ZTC} (zero temperature coefficient current). The consequence is to reduce MOSFET power dissipation capability in lower I_D zones of the SOA chart.

Measurement at DC, 100 ms, 10 ms and 1 ms establishes SOA capability. The 100 μs and 10 μs lines on this graph are theoretical constant power lines. They are realistic, as the Spirito effect is much less significant at higher currents and shorter pulse periods.

Reliable 100 μs SOA measurement capability has recently been achieved, so future data sheets include 100 μs SOA lines based on measured data. It is now evident that the Spirito effect is apparent at 100 μs. Consequently, from 2016, new

MOSFET releases have a measured 100 µs SOA line in their data sheet SOA graph.

See AN11158 (chapter 1 in this book) - Understanding power MOSFET data sheet parameters for further information.

5.6 Q: How does Nexperia ensure compliance with the SOA curve during series production?

A: The factors influencing the compliance of the MOSFET with the data sheet SOA graph are:

- the uniformity of the MOSFET cells across the active (trench) surface of the die
- the integrity and uniformity of the die attachment (the solder layer between the die bottom (drain) surface and mounting base)

Cell uniformity must be good for the MOSFET to work. However, cell uniformity can never be perfect and there is always some variation between cells.

The integrity of the soldering to attach the die must be good without voids or die tilt. If not, the local (junction to mounting base) thermal impedance varies with location across the die. It gives uneven cooling. Uneven die surface cooling may be due to either or both of the factors stated. However, the consequence is the same i.e. SOA non-compliance with the data sheet graph.

In production, linear mode power pulse tests are used to stress the MOSFET thermally. If the die cooling is not sufficiently uniform, hotspots can form and the device parameters can change more than expected. A decision to reject parts can be made based on the results.

5.7 Q: How can a part be identified when it is designed for linear mode operation?

A: While all Nexperia MOSFETs can be used in linear mode operation, some Nexperia MOSFETs are designed specifically to be used in linear mode. The device description in the data sheet states that the device is suitable for operation in linear mode. To determine the suitability for operation in linear mode, perform a thorough analysis of the SOA graph. This analysis includes derating the SOA graph for junction temperatures above 25 °C. The naming convention indicates that the MOSFET is designed for linear mode applications.

5.8 Q: For parts designed for linear mode operation, are there any restrictions (such as the Spirito boundary)?

A: Even if a MOSFET is intended for use in linear mode applications, the part must not be operated outside its SOA. Post 2010, all Nexperia MOSFETs have a measured SOA characteristic. The limit of linear mode capability on Nexperia parts is shown in the SOA characteristic. As a result, the boundary of what is safe is established via measurement rather than calculation. The Spirito capability limit is shown in the SOA characteristic.

6 Avalanche ruggedness and Unclamped Inductive Switching (UIS)

6.1 Q: Are trench designs susceptible to the UIS issue (parasitic BJT turn-on)?

A: In general - Yes, but Nexperia Trench MOSFETs are designed to suppress this effect. The trench structure, unlike planar, can be very easily designed to suppress parasitic turn on of the BJT. For new Nexperia MOSFET technologies, the failure mechanism is thermal, which represents the limit of achievable UIS performance. Planar (on the left in the diagram) and trench (on the right in the diagram) MOSFET technologies, are shown in Figure 8. In the trench case, a design feature in the source contact effectively short circuits the base-emitter of the parasitic BJT. In older planar technology, the shorting of base to emitter of the parasitic bipolar is not as effective. It is due to the longer path length in the n and p regions.

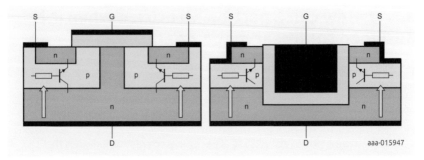

aaa-015947

Figure 8 | Simplified planar and trench technology

6.2 Q: Why are planar designs susceptible to failure during UIS?

A: All MOSFETs are susceptible to failure during UIS. It depends on whether the MOSFET T_j reaches the intrinsic temperature of silicon. Furthermore, if the parasitic BJT is triggered, they can fail even earlier. It is because the BJT can be switched on relatively quickly but is slow to switch off. Current can then crowd in a certain part of the device and failure results. Newer Nexperia trench technologies are less vulnerable to triggering of the BJT than planar designs. See Section 7.1 and the additional information associated with Section 6.3.

6.3 Q: How are parts constructed to minimize failure during UIS?

A: The base emitter path in the silicon design is designed to minimize the risk of triggering the parasitic BJT.

Additional information

There are two strategies employed to prevent triggering of the parasitic BJT:

1. Reduce the avalanche current per cell - To reduce the avalanche current per cell, there must be a higher cell density. It is easily achieved with trench technologies but more difficult with planar devices. If improvements in planar technologies are seen, it is likely that modern fabrication equipment achieves a high enough cell density. Increasing cell density too much, deteriorates linear mode performance (Spirito boundary occurs sooner), so cell density is a trade-off. For this reason, Nexperia has not been as aggressive as other trench MOSFET manufacturers in achieving very high cell densities. The target is to ensure that the thermal limit in UIS is achieved.

2. Ensure that the current flow during avalanche does not flow through the base-emitter region of the BJT. This feature is the significant advantage of trench over planar. The parasitic bipolar is formed between the source of the MOSFET, the body region (i.e. channel) and the epi region (i.e. the drain). If there is enough avalanche current through body junction, there may be enough voltage developed to bias on the BJT leading to device destruction. In Nexperia devices, a modified source contact is used. This contact collects any avalanche current, preventing it from biasing the BJT on.

   For planar devices, strategies include reducing the gain of the BJT by placing high doped implants close to the channel. It is similar to (2) in intention but it is not as effective.

6.4 Q: Is 100 % UIS testing required on MOSFETs?

A: UIS testing is a fundamental part of Nexperia's defect screening procedures. It is applied to all devices. The test is designed to increase the junction temperature to $T_{j(max)}$.

6.5 Q: I have parts not capable of parasitic BJT turn-on. Why?

A: Devices fail at the thermal limit. At the thermal limit, the silicon becomes intrinsic and blocking- junctions cease to exist. It is considered to be the only UIS-related failure mechanism in our devices.

6.6 Q: What is the chart accuracy for avalanche current versus time in avalanche, or energy versus junction temperature?

A: Avalanche current versus time graphs are based on conditions that take a device to $T_{j(max)}$ and therefore, our ruggedness screening covers them. All Nexperia MOSFETs are ruggedness tested during assembly and characterized during development. The graphs are accurate and provide the worst case capability of the device to ensure reliability.

6.7 Q: For energy versus junction temperature charts (if applicable), how is the inductance, maximum current, time in avalanche etc., determined from the chart?

A: A temperature rise model is used, which is shown in AN10273 (chapter 4 in this book) - Power MOSFET single-shot and repetitive avalanche ruggedness rating.

Additional information

Although energy levels for UIS are often quoted on data sheets, a single number can be misleading. Therefore a graph is provided, that outlines conditions that take junction temperature to $T_{j(max)}$. The user must determine the current/time in avalanche based on the particular conditions. Examples are provided in AN10273 (chapter 4 in this book) - Power MOSFET single-shot and repetitive avalanche ruggedness rating.

6.8 Q: Are repetitive avalanche ratings the same as for a single pulse?

A: No. The repetitive avalanche ratings are lower than the single pulse rating. Refer to the product data sheet for the device capability. An example is shown in Figure 9.

Additional information

Repetitive means that the avalanche event is an intended operating condition for the device.

Similarly, single-shot means that the MOSFET is expected to experience an avalanche event as a result of some unintended fault condition. Only 1 fault can occur at a time, the MOSFET must cool to the starting temperature and the junction temperature must not exceed 175 °C. Degradation of device characteristics is likely after a relatively low number of occurrences.

Nexperia shows both single shot and repetitive avalanche capability in the MOSFET data sheet. Generally, the repetitive current is 10 % of the single shot current capability for a given inductor (so the time in avalanche is shorter, see Figure 9 and Section 6.14).

For calculating repetitive avalanche ratings, calculate the starting junction temperature for each avalanche incident independently. The calculations are based on the frequency and duty cycle of avalanche condition and summed over the entire period of expected repeated avalanche.

This topic is discussed in detail in Application note AN10273 - (chapter 4 in this book) - Power MOSFET single-shot and repetitive avalanche ruggedness rating.

6.9 Q: Are there any special failure modes associated with repetitive avalanche?

A: The device can sustain small amounts of damage with each avalanche event and over time they can accumulate to cause significant parametric shifts or device failure. Nexperia has performed research into this area and provides the repetitive ratings in the data sheet. See also Application note (chapter 4 in this book) - Power MOSFET single-shot and repetitive avalanche ruggedness.

6.10 Q: How does the increase in cell density affect avalanche capability of MOSFETs?

A: There are two failure modes: current (parasitic BJT turn-on) and thermal. Cell density has implications for these failure modes.

Additional information

Current - If enough avalanche current flows through a cell, a voltage drop occurs in the p- region of the device as the avalanche current flows to the source contact. This volt drop occurs in the base of a parasitic bipolar device. In this mode, the resistance in the p-region/ base and the avalanche current ($I = V/R$) are important. Once V_{BE} reaches the bipolar switch- on threshold, the MOSFET is destroyed (V_{BE} reduces with temperature). So at higher cell densities, for the same avalanche current, there are more cells and current per cell is reduced. Each individual cell has less current and is less likely to trigger the parasitic device. It means that the total die current, required to cause a device to fail, increases. Additionally, since the cell is smaller, the path through the p-region to the source contact is reduced. It makes it even harder to trigger the parasitic device and again increases the current required to destroy the device.

Thermal - If the avalanche current is such that the parasitic BJT is not triggered, the device heats up. If the avalanche energy is sufficient, the silicon die reaches temperatures at which the device starts to become intrinsic. The blocking-junction no longer exists, resulting in the destruction of the device. It is what is meant when a reference is made regarding failure due to reaching the thermal limit of a device. If the failure mode is thermal, changes in technology cannot improve things significantly. New technologies are generally more robust in avalanche conditions. Note, if a thermal limit is reached, the only solution is to improve the thermal impedance at the device level. Moving to a smaller die can be detrimental.

Summary - New technologies improve the high current avalanche capability of a device due to increased cell density and reduced parasitic NPN base resistance. Lower current, higher energy (i.e. longer duration) avalanche capability is unchanged.

6.11 Q: How many times can a device sustain single avalanche events?

Example - A device has an avalanche event once in two months so how many cycles of such an avalanche frequency can the device sustain? This question relates more to quality and reliability but it is important nonetheless.

A: Refer to Section 6.8 of this chapter. For the answer to this question, refer to Section 2.4.3 of AN11158 (chapter 1 in this book) - Understanding power MOSFET data sheet parameters and all of AN10273 (chapter 4 in this book) - Power MOSFET single-shot and repetitive avalanche ruggedness rating..

Additional information

Keep each avalanche event within the safe limits for repetitive operation specified on the data sheet and T_j below 175 °C. There should be no degradation of the MOSFET characteristics and no impact on MOSFET quality or reliability. There are some applications where MOSFETs are repetitively avalanched (e.g. some engine controllers) and the reliability is good. Although this condition takes V_{DS} beyond the data sheet maximum, the data sheet also specifies a maximum avalanche energy.

Extensive avalanche testing is performed on Nexperia MOSFETs. All the indications are that they are very robust. It is understood that most MOSFETs in automotive applications are likely to experience avalanche conditions at some stage during their lifetime. It could be due to occasional fault conditions or as a consequence of the circuit design (e.g. ABS solenoid valve driver MOSFETs).

6.12 Q: Is it possible for the avalanche current on a device to exceed the package maximum current but not the die maximum current?

A: The current specified in the avalanche graph should not be exceeded. It is restricted to the DC rated current. The device factory test defines the limit which is guaranteed for the device.

6.13 Q: How is the avalanche rating on the body diode obtained (testing or modeling)? If it is tested, how is it tested and what circuit model is used?

A: The avalanche rating is modeled first and the results are then verified by testing to destruction. The test circuit used is similar to the one defined in *JESD24-5*. For SPICE modeling, the reverse diode characteristics can be defined and modeled. By adding an RC thermal model of the Z_{th} characteristic, it is possible to estimate the T_j of the device.

Additional information

The body diode of the MOSFET is not a single circuit element, but a structure distributed throughout the MOSFET. There is a diode element associated with each cell. In behavior terms, it can be represented as a single (Zener) diode in parallel with the single MOSFET (representing the sum of all the cells). The design of the MOSFET determines the avalanche rating. Its representation in the model is based on parameters measured during characterization testing.

The constraints are the same as for the MOSFET conduction. Diodes are an integral part of the MOSFET structure. They are in effect the same size and have the same thermal properties. The objective is to keep the junction temperature below $T_{j(max)}$ so it is necessary to calculate the diode dissipation.

For transient currents, the simulation using the SPICE model of the diode is useful but care is needed because the model is for a typical part.

Once the dissipation is known, standard thermal analysis methods can be used to ensure that T_j is acceptable.

6.14 Q: How is the repetitive avalanche safe operating area derived in the data sheet graph? The repetitive avalanche SOA curve seems to be the same as single-shot $T_j = 170\,°C$.

A: The repetitive line is the line for a start temperature of 170 °C. It is because it predicts a temperature rise of 5 °C which is the maximum permissible rise from any starting temperature, see AN10273 (chapter 4 in this book) - Power MOSFET single-shot and repetitive avalanche ruggedness rating.). It also corresponds to 10 % of the single-shot current using the same inductor value, see Figure 9.

Additional information

The reason it applies to any temperature is because the temperature does not strongly influence the wear-out caused by repetitive avalanche. The strongest influence is the current.

The avalanche current is composed of high energy charge carriers moving through the depletion region. As they pass through, they can collide with the Si structure. There is a chance that a high energy carrier (sometimes called a hot carrier) is produced that collides with the gate oxide causing damage. It is not completely destroyed but it does cause it to wear out, which is observed as parameter variation.

Higher currents mean more electrons, more collisions and more frequent damaging events leading to faster wear-out and lower reliability. The target should be a failure level <0.1 ppm over the full vehicle life. Experiments indicate that if repetitive current is limited to 10 % of single-shot current capability for $T_{j(start)}$ = 25 °C, it results in a T_j increase of 5 °C. There is no significant degradation of the device.

For example: A 15 mH inductor carrying ~19 A gives an avalanche time of ~5 ms. It has a peak temperature rise of 150 °C putting it on the limit line for $T_{j(start)}$ = 25 °C. By reducing the current to 10 % = 1.9 A, t_{AL} reduces to ~500 µs and the temperature rise is 5 °C.

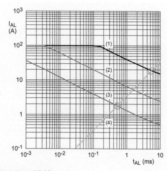

(1) = characteristic at 25 °C
(2) = characteristic at 150 °C
(3) = repetitive characteristic at <170 °C
(4) = inductor characteristic

aaa-013064

Figure 9 | Avalanche safe operating area

7 Capacitive dV/dt issues

7.1 Q: Is there a particular capacitance or charge ratio that should be used to prevent turn-on, or is it circuit dependent?

A: The capacitive dV/dt turn-on is strongly circuit dependent.

If the dV/dt across the MOSFETs drain to source is too high, it may charge C_{GD}, which is the capacitance between drain and gate, inducing a voltage at the gate. The gate voltage depends on the pull-down resistor of the driver based on Equation (4):

$$V_{GS} = R_{driver} \times C_{GD} \times dV/dt \qquad\qquad [4]$$

In some bipolar drive circuits, such as emitter follower derived circuits, the problem is increased. It is because the driver cannot pull the gate down to 0 V and has approximately 0.7 V offset.

It is also important that the driver is referenced to the MOSFET source and not to signal ground, which can be significantly different in voltage.

The ratio of C_{GD} to C_{GS} is a factor but a good drive circuit is the critical factor. Even if a V_{GS} spike is present, it is safe for the MOSFET as long as the dissipation is within thermal limits and MOSFET SOA limits.

7.2 Q: How are parts constructed to minimize this effect?

A: Nexperia MOSFETs are designed with a high threshold at high temperatures and we check V_{GS} threshold at 25 °C is within data sheet limits. Logic level devices are designed and guaranteed to have a minimum threshold voltage >0.5 V even at 175 °C.

Additional information

Maintain a reasonable ratio between C_{GD} and C_{GS}. The gate network structure of the device is designed to have good control of all areas of the die.

7.3 Q: How is dV/dt characterized?

A: It is usually measured in a half-bridge test circuit. It is a measure of the device dV/dt during body diode reverse recovery. This data is not normally published in the data sheet. This dV/dt is in practice the highest dV/dt the device experiences.

Additional information

Failure due to dV/dt is not something seen in modern low-voltage MOSFETs however, dV/ dt is normally characterized for Nexperia MOSFETs. The failure mode is that the capacitive current resulting from dV/dt, triggers the parasitic BJT. However, as the voltages are low (dV/dt is more an issue > 600 V) a current/charge high enough to trigger the parasitic BJT cannot be generated.

7.4 Q: What diode or other parameters are important to assess susceptibility? For example, maximum dV/dt and maximum I_F.

A: High dV/dt can induce glitches onto the gate of the MOSFET. A snubber can help to reduce dV/dt and the magnitude of the V_{DS} spike if significant. The ratio of C_{oss} at low V_{DS} compared to C_{oss} value at high V_{DS} is an indicator of the non-linearity of C_{oss}. A very high ratio can indicate that the device can generate a high dV/dt. Gate driver circuit design can reduce the gate glitch, see Section 7.1. The ratio of Q_{GD} to Q_{GS} and the gate threshold voltage can be used to indicate the susceptibility of the device to gate glitches.

7.5 Q: Is trench technology sensitive to this phenomenon?

A: In theory, all MOSFETs are.

Additional information

dV/dt induced turn-on of the parasitic bipolar transistor is not known as an issue in low voltage Nexperia MOSFETs. If UIS parasitic turn-on is solved, then dV/dt induced turn-on is also solved. Refer to Section 6.1 and Section 6.3 for more information.

7.6 Q: Does a soft recovery body diode give lower dV/dt and if so, how is it designed and fabricated into the part?

A: Soft recovery does reduce the dV/dt. Although dV/dt is not an issue for the MOSFET, a lower dV/dt is better for EMI, voltage spikes and crosstalk. The design and manufacture is very specialized, involving proprietary information.

7.7 Q: How does temperature influence this sensitivity to dV/dt and why?

A: At high temperatures, it is easier to trigger a parasitic bipolar as its V_{BE} reduces. But if the BJT is effectively shorted out and current diverted away from it, as discussed in Section 6.1, then it is not an issue.

7.8 Q: Can Nexperia provide R_B, C_{DB}, V_{BE} saturation values in the parasitic BJT model, as shown in Figure 11?

A: These values are required to be able to calculate Equation 6. The aim is to obtain a dV/dt value to check if parasitic BJT turns on, leading to device failure. It is impossible to measure the characteristics of the parasitic bipolar transistor as its terminals cannot be accessed independently of the MOSFET terminals. A parasitic bipolar transistor is always created when a MOSFET is fabricated. Referring to Figure 10 it can be seen that there are two current paths which could cause MOSFET problems. Current I_1 flows via C_{GD} and depending on C_{GS} and R_G it can cause the MOSFET to switch on momentarily. It is often referred to as a gate glitch. Current I_2 flows via C_{DB} and R_B which can potentially switch on the parasitic BJT.

Additional information

$$V_{GS} = I_1 \times R_G = R_G \times C_{GD} \times dV/dt \qquad [5]$$

$$V_{BE} = I_2 \times R_B = R_B \times C_{DB} \times dV/dt \qquad [6]$$

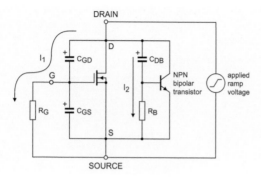

Figure 10 | Power MOSFET showing two possible mechanisms for dV/dt induced turn-on

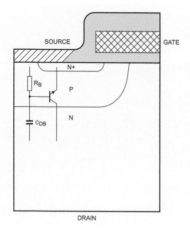

Figure 11 | Physical origin of the parasitic BJT components that may cause dV/dt induced turn-on

Additional information

Early lateral MOSFETs (structure shown in Figure 11), were susceptible to failure caused by the turn-on of this parasitic transistor.

Modern power MOSFETs have greater cell density meaning the current per cell is reduce and the voltage across R_B is lowered. In addition, the geometry of each individual cell is smaller compared to previous generations making R_B shorter in length and therefore a lower value of resistance. Both these greatly improving the immunity of modern trench MOSFETs (structure shown in Fig. 12) to dV/dt latch-up.

In application tests we see dV/dt values in the order of 1 – 10 V/ns for T6 and T9 technology when switched quickly using a high current gate driver with low gate resistance.

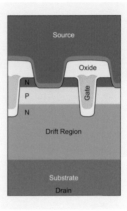

aaa-013075

Figure 12 | Trench generation 6 structure

7.9 Q: In a half-bridge configuration one MOSFET is driven off, and the second MOSFET begins to turn on. The first MOSFET that should be off is turning back on again causing cross conduction and an over-current peak. What could be the cause? See Figure 13 for phenomena.

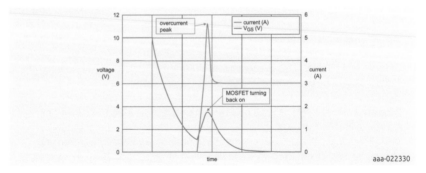

aaa-022330

Figure 13 | Blue V$_{GS}$ trace shows gate bounce and the red current waveform spiking when gate bounce occurs

A: It is sometimes referred to as gate bounce. MOSFETs have internal stray capacitances coupling all three terminals and the gate is floating. The capacitors are inherent to the internal structure of a MOSFET, see Figure 14.

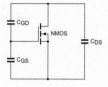

aaa-022333

Figure 14 | MOSFET Schematic representing the internal capacitances

C_{GD} and C_{GS} form a capacitive potential divider. When a voltage appears across the drain and source of the MOSFET, it couples to the gate and causes the internal gate source capacitor to charge. If the voltage on the gate increases beyond the MOSFET's threshold voltage, it starts to turn back on which can cause cross conduction. The ratio of the capacitances C_{GD} and C_{GS} determines the severity of this effect.

Additional information

Figure 15 shows a simplified circuit that can exhibit this behavior. It could be a synchronous buck regulator or one leg of a 3-phase inverter. In both cases, the load is inductive. A current source represents the inductive element in this circuit.

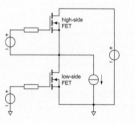

aaa-022334

Figure 15 | Simplified schematic of a MOSFET half-bridge. The high-side and low-side MOSFETs are switched antiphase to each other

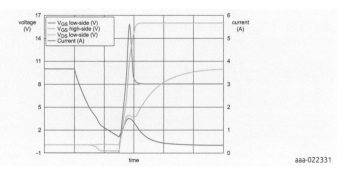

Figure 16 | Waveforms showing the full detail of the gate bounce phenomenon

The waveforms in Figure 16 show the critical part of the applications operation when the current commutates from one MOSFET to the other. In this instance, the high-side MOSFET is being switched on as the low-side one switches off. Current flows from the switch node. Note the low- side MOSFET behaves as a diode when it is switched off. This behavior is similar when current flows into the switch node. In this case, the high-side device becomes the synchronous rectifier. Referencing the waveforms in Figure 16, the blue low-side V_{GS} trace begins to drop and the low-side MOSFET turns off. The green low-side V_{DS} trace going negative indicates that it has switched off. The low-side MOSFET body diode begins to conduct the inductive current and there is a V_F drop of approximately 0.7 V. The high-side MOSFET begins to turn on to a point where it conducts all of the load current. The low-side diode turns off and the low-side V_{DS} can now increase to the supply voltage. However, as the V_{DS} rises, the dV/dt is coupled back to the low-side gate through C_{GD}. The blue low-side V_{GS} trace begins to increase again. In this example, the gate voltage rises sufficiently above the threshold voltage so that it is now turned back on again. Both high-side and low-side MOSFETs are on simultaneously. The current rapidly increases due to the short circuit across the supply as indicated by the red current trace.

There are several factors that influence this behavior, the most dominant of which is the gate resistor. If the gate resistor is set to a level where the gate driver cannot sink the capacitively coupled current, it must feed into the C_{GS}. It causes the gate source voltage to rise as can be seen in Figure 16.

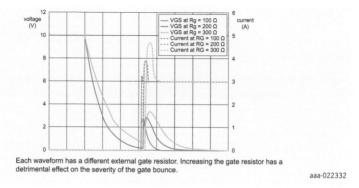

Each waveform has a different external gate resistor. Increasing the gate resistor has a detrimental effect on the severity of the gate bounce.

aaa-022332

Figure 17 | Effect of R_G on V_{GS}, and shoot-through current

It is good practice to keep the external gate resistor as low as possible. In reality, there is a limit to how low this value can be, due to EMC considerations. Good design practices can be employed to improve EMC while maintaining a low enough value of gate resistor to prevent gate bounce. Simple alternatives to increasing the gate resistor include adding extra capacitors external to the MOSFET between gate and source, located close to the MOSFET connections. It helps with radiated emissions without affecting the gate turn off waveforms as much.

Other key factors include the MOSFETs threshold voltage (V_{th}). The lower V_{th} is, the more enhanced a MOSFET is for a given gate bounce voltage. It therefore increases the severity of the cross conduction. Vth is also temperature dependent. It reduces as die temperature increases, further compounding the severity.

7.10 Q: Does the BUK9Y29-40E fulfill the following requirements?

Table 1: Turn on/off delay, rise time and fall time requirements

Symbol	Parameter	Conditions	Min	Typ	Max	Unit
$t_{d(on)} + t_r$	turn on delay time + rise time combined	$T_{amb} = 25\ °C$; $V_{DS} = 30\ V$; $V_{GS} = 5\ V$; $R = 50$; $R_{G(ext)} = 5\ \Omega$	8	13	18	ns
$t_{d(off)} + t_f$	turn off delay time + fall time combined	$T_{amb} = 25\ °C$; $V_{DS} = 30\ V$; $V_{GS} = 5\ V$; $R_L = 50\ \Omega$; $R_{G(ext)} = 5\ \Omega$	9	14	19	ns

A: Typical values of $t_{d(on)}$, tr, $t_{d(off)}$, and t_F are given in the BUK9Y29-40E data sheet:

Table 2: Turn on/off delays, rise time and fall time BUK9Y29-40E specifications

Symbol	Parameter	Conditions	Min	Typ	Max	Unit
$t_{d(on)}$	turn on delay time	$T_{amb} = 25\ °C$; $V_{DS} = 30\ V$; $V_{GS} = 5\ V$; $R_L = 5\ Ω$; $R_{G(ext)} = 5\ Ω$	-	6	-	ns
t_r	rise time	$T_{amb} = 25\ °C$; $V_{DS} = 30\ V$; $V_{GS} = 5\ V$; $R_L = 5\ Ω$; $R_{G(ext)} = 5\ Ω$	-	7	-	ns
$t_{d(off)}$	turn off delay time	$T_{amb} = 25\ °C$; $V_{DS} = 30\ V$; $V_{GS} = 5\ V$; $R_L = 5\ Ω$; $R_{G(ext)} = 5\ Ω$	-	9	-	ns
t_F	fall time	$T_{amb} = 25\ °C$; $V_{DS} = 30\ V$; $V_{GS} = 5\ V$; $R_L = 5\ Ω$; $R_{G(ext)} = 5\ Ω$	-	5	-	ns

$t_{d(on)} + t_r$ must be between 8 ns and 18 ns. For the BUK9Y29-40E, this value is typically 13 ns.

$t_{d(off)} + t_F$ must be between 9 ns and 19 ns. For the BUK7Y29-40E, this value is typically 14 ns.

Minimum and maximum values for $t_{d(on)}$, t_r, $t_{d(off)}$, and t_F are not stated in Nexperia MOSFET data sheets. It is because accurate and repeatable measurements of these parameters, particularly t_r and t_F, very much depend on the test environment.

Even measurement probe positioning is critical because stray inductances, capacitances and coupling fields change when the probe is moved (unavoidable).

A good worst case estimate tolerance on these parameters is ±50 %, however these parameters have only a very small effect on MOSFET dynamic operation.

The typical BUK9Y29-40E fulfills these requirements, but if these parameters are slightly different, the consequences to the circuit switching performance are not significant. In the parametric test, a 50 Ω load resistor and 5 Ω external gate resistor are used. It is very unlikely that these values are the same as the values used in the application.

Gate drive characteristics, MOSFET capacitances and the nature of the load circuit have much more profound effects on the dynamic switching behavior of the MOSFET. Specifically, its power loss, efficiency and EMC performance.

8 Package and mounting

8.1 Q: On the drawing for the power SO8/LF-PAK56 common footprint, there are no vias on the exposed pad. Are the addition of vias advised and, if so, which diameter?

A: If improved thermal resistance is required, vias can be added to the footprint. The effect of adding vias is discussed in Section 3.5 of AN90003 (chapter 9 in this book) - LFPAK MOSFET thermal design guide.

Additional information

Nexperia has used 0.8 mm successfully but it does not mean that other sizes would not work. The vias should be pre-filled with solder and hot air leveled, to give a flat surface, before the devices are placed.

If the vias are not pre-filled, there is a chance that the solder under the part is drawn into the vias, which may result in voids.

The extra process steps on the PCB and the potential problems mean that vias should not be used unless they are needed. Consult the manufacturing process engineers regarding surface mount and soldering process issues.

8.2 Q: How are devices tested for HV isolation tests? An application is tested at approximately 1 kV for HV isolation testing across various terminals and a significant value is seen across the MOSFET. Are there tests that perform HV isolation analysis and, if so, what are they?

A: We do not perform any HV isolation tests on any automotive MOSFETs or specify any HV isolation parameter in our data sheets. Insulation testing is only applicable to TO-220F packages (Nexperia SOT186A)

Additional information

HV isolation is specified for MOSFETs with insulated drain tabs or in modules with isolated bases. The test voltage applied in the Nexperia factory is 2.45 kV for 0.4 seconds (V_{rms} at 50 Hz).

8.3 Q: The efficiency of my DC-to-DC converter exceeds my requirements. Can I use smaller, higher $R_{DS(on)}$ MOSFETs to save money?

Environmental conditions: 4-layer FR4 board at 105 °C ambient temperature.

A: Although it is possible to reduce efficiency, other factors become the constraints.

Additional information

The dominating factor is likely to be the temperature allowed at the solder joint between the MOSFET and the PCB. It is unlikely that 125 °C may be exceeded with FR4. If the dissipation is 2 W, the thermal resistance of the path from the MOSFET mounting base to ambient must be <10 K/W.

(125 °C - 105 °C)/2 W = 10 K/W.

Some special arrangements are required to achieve this figure. However the customer has indicated an allowed dissipation of 2 W so they may have some more information about their system indicating that it is achievable.

If dissipation is increased to 5 W, the temperature at the mounting base reaches 155 °C which is probably not allowed. The alternative would be to improve the thermal resistance to <4 K/W, which is extremely challenging.

An indication as to what can be achieved, is given in AN90003 (chapter 9 in this book) - LFPAK MOSFET thermal design guide.

The junction temperature of the MOSFET has not yet been mentioned. It is because it is only a few degrees higher than the mounting base. For example, consider an application for an LFPAK56 device, such as BUK7Y7R6-40E. The thermal resistance is 1.58 K/W. So for 2 W, the T_j would be 128.2 °C. For 5 W, it would be 133 °C (assuming T_{mb} can be held to 125 °C). Both of these values are well below the $T_{j(max)}$ of the MOSFET which is 175 °C. So in summary, the limiting factor of what can be done with dissipation is the PCB and its thermal path to ambient, not the MOSFET.

8.4 Q: What is the position of Nexperia on using Pb free solder for internal soldering (die attach, clip attach)?

A: Nexperia is a member of the DA5 working group. It is a project consortium comprising Nexperia, Bosch, Infineon, and ST. The goal is to find new solder materials or alternative die attach methods which do not use lead. The European directive 2011/65/Eu exemption (RoHS), allows the use of lead in high melting point solders until 2016. So far, no reliable and cost effective alternative process has been developed, especially where the requirements of AEC-Q101 are considered. An extension to the expiry date of this exemption was applied for in January 2015 by representatives of the electronics industry, including the DA5 working group.

The End of Life Vehicle (ELV) Directive (2000/53/EG) also applies. A similar extension to the Pb free exemption was applied for by the DA5 group in November 2013. It is expected that if approved, this directive allows the use of Pb based solders until 2018 at the earliest. It has been requested that the EU aligns the Pb free exemption between the ELV directive and the RoHS directive.

9 SPICE models

9.1 Q: Is there is a large difference between the data sheet and the SPICE model behavior and in particular, the gate charge characteristics?

A: There is a strong similarity between the data sheet characteristics and the Nexperia SPICE models at 25 °C. It is especially true for transfer curve, $R_{DS(on)}$, diode characteristic, and gate charge. The SPICE model also accounts for the package parasitic resistances and inductances.

Additional information

In PWM circuits, the SPICE model gives quite a good similarity to the behavior of the real device. The SPICE model can therefore be used to give a good indication of the switching losses at turn-on and turn-off, as well as the conduction losses.

The SPICE model is only correct at 25 °C, the $R_{DS(on)}$ versus temperature characteristic can be used to estimate conduction losses at higher temperatures. Switching losses are known not to change significantly with temperature.

The SPICE model also reflects a typical device according to the data sheet characteristics.

The method of creating models has been continuously improved over time. The latest model creation process used for Trench generation 6 devices and newer technologies results in models which closely match measured device behavior.

9.2 Q: Why does the SPICE model not match the data sheet?

A: The SPICE models provided by Nexperia are generated from measurements performed on a sample of devices. Several parameters such as transfer characteristics, output characteristics and gate charge are used. Values for parasitic package impedances and the data sheet maximum $R_{DS(on)}$ value are combined to produce a model that emulates the behavior of the sample MOSFETs.

- It is important to note that the SPICE models generated by Nexperia:
    - represent typical parts that can be found within the production distribution.
    - are set close to the maximum $R_{DS(on)}$ of the part without adversely affecting the other model parameters.
    - are only valid for $T_j = 25\ °C$.

Customers wishing to do design validation using a SPICE model, are advised to proceed with caution given the information provided above. Nexperia encourages designers to perform Monte Carlo simulations and use tolerance stacks in their simulation design. These factors permit part to part variation of their whole system to be accounted for.

Nexperia can advise on what reasonable levels of tolerance on key parameters for the MOSFET would be.

10 MOSFET silicon technology

10.1 Q: What is drift engineering?

A: Drift engineering is optimizing of the drift region between the bottom of the trench and the epi/ substrate interface (light green area). The drift region supports most of the drain-source voltage in the off state. The purpose of drift engineering is to reduce the resistance of the drift region while maintaining the drain-source breakdown voltage $V_{(BR)DSS}$ capability (see Figure 18).

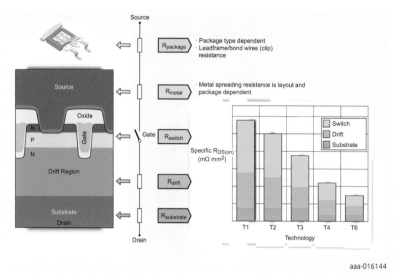

aaa-016144

Figure 18 | Resistance in power MOSFETs

10.2 Q: What is obtained from reduced cell pitch?

A: Reduced cell pitch generally results in lower resistance and higher capacitance. The goal of each new generation of MOSFET technology is to reduce $R_{DS(on)}$ without a large increase in capacitance that usually accompanies reduced cell pitch. Reduced cell pitch also reduces SOA capability (linear mode operation) but improves avalanche capability.

10.3 Q: What is obtained from a shorter channel?

A: Shorter channel gives a lower $R_{DS(on)}$ and a lower C_{GS} capacitance simultaneously. It has higher leakage current and the transfer curve (I_D versus V_{GS} characteristic) becomes more dependent on V_{DS}. It is also observed in the output characteristics.

10.4 Q: What is obtained from thick bottom oxide?

A: Thick bottom oxide refers to gate oxide at the bottom of the trench (see Figure 16). It is made thicker than the gate oxide at the side of the trench. It acts as a thicker dielectric between the gate and the drain resulting in a much lower C_{GD} value.

11 Supply and availability

11.1 Q: What statements can be made concerning the long-term availability of previous generations of TrenchMOS parts?

A: Nexperia continues to supply older products where the volumes of manufacture are economically viable. The sales price margin is commercially viable and there are no manufacturing reasons which prevent manufacture.

A Discontinuation of Delivery (DoD) document notifies key customers (including distributors), when a part is planned to be withdrawn. It allows customers to make arrangements to buy sufficient products for future requirements and if necessary qualify alternative products.

12 EMC and ESD

12.1 Q: I have EMC issues, what can I do?

A: We have a detailed appliaction note on this subject, AN90011 (chapter 7 in this book) - Half-bridge MOSFET switching and its impact on EMC , please refer to this for any EMC related concerns.

12.2 Q: What parameters affect the ESD tolerance and how much does it vary for a particular device?

A: The key parameters are the gate oxide breakdown voltage and the gate input capacitance (C_{iss}). JESD22-A114 specifies the ESD Human Body Model test arrangement and results assessment criteria.

Additional information

The main ESD failure mechanism for any MOSFET is due to breakdown of the gate oxide. The point where the oxide is thinnest will be where failure is most likely to occur.

For Nexperia MOSFETs, factors which affect the thickness are:

- Gate rating: usually standard level or logic level (note that other gate oxide ratings are available from Nexperia)
- Technology used: gate oxide thickness will vary according to the technology used. Check with Nexperia for details of the oxide thickness or rating if this is critical information

The gate oxide is most sensitive between the gate and source. The gate to drain path (typically the gate oxide at the bottom of the trench and semiconductor junction in series) offers a higher capability.

There are 6 combinations of applying an ESD pulse to a MOSFET:

Table 3: ESD test pulses pin combinations

Pin ESD pulse applied to	Pin(s) grounded	Pin floating
G	S	D
G	S, D	-
D	G	S
D	G, S	-
S	D	G
S	D, G	-

The ESD pulse can be positive or negative for each condition. The simplified capacitance model for the MOSFET shown in Figure 19 below is key to understanding how the gate oxide can be damaged by extreme voltage

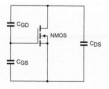

aaa-022333

Figure 19 | MOSFET schematic representing the internal capacitances

The worst-case condition is always by applying the pulse to the gate pin with the source pin grounded and the drain pin floating. This has been verified by experiment. In the case of the pulse being applied between gate and source with the drain floating, the capacitance of the device is minimised, see Figure 20 below. Grounding the drain, for example, would increase the gate – source capacitance, so it becomes more difficult to damage the oxide.

Note that the body diode acts to protect the drain pin of the device: if drain goes negative due to ESD pulse on the drain, then diode conducts. The body diode is capable of handling high current, much higher than due to ESD pulses so is not damaged by ESD. If the drain goes positive, then the diode will avalanche and easily absorb the ESD energy (like a TVS).

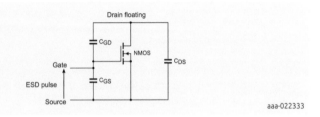

aaa-022333

Figure 20 | MOSFET schematic representing the internal capacitances

12.3 Q: How can gate-source ESD rating be estimated?

A: This formula estimates the ESD capability:

$$V_{esd} \text{ (HBM)} = 16 \times V_{GS(max)} \times C_{iss} \text{ (nF)}$$

Additional information

The simplest approximation for ESD is to assume that the device fails when C_{iss} is charged to the breakdown voltage of the gate oxide ($V_{BR(ox)}$). As a conservative estimate $V_{BR(ox)}$ is approximately 1.6 times the V_{GS} rating as per the limiting values section in the data sheet.

Figure 21 shows the ESD test setup, once ESD test has completed then the voltage across both capacitors is the same and total charge is conserved. At the last surviving voltage, then voltage across the capacitors is as follows:

$$V_{esd} \times C_{esd} = V_{BR(ox)} \times C_{esd} + V_{BR(ox)} \times C_{iss}$$
$$V_{esd} = V_{BR(ox)} \times (C_{iss}/C_{esd} + 1)$$

$$V_{esd} = 10 \times V_{BR(ox)} \times C_{iss}$$
$$V_{esd} = 16 \times V_{GS(max)} \times C_{iss}$$

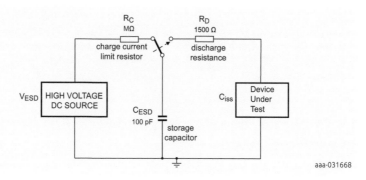

Figure 21 | Test circuit for ESD testing (human body model)

12.4 Q: Does relationship between C_{iss} and ESD rating change by trench generation?

Yes. As per Section 12.3 the ESD rating relies upon C_{iss} and gate oxide breakdown voltage. As Nexperia improves technology and the levels of quality and reliability also improve new generations tend to have stronger gate oxides. However as we improve our switching figure of merit ($Q_G \times R_{DS(on)}$), now for the same $R_{DS(on)}$ new technologies will have lower C_{iss} and therefore lower ESD rating.

12.5 Q: Why are Nexperia power MOSFETs not ESD protected on the chip by gate-source protection networks?

In order to effectively screen MOSFETs with weak gate oxide and achieve <1 ppm quality levels, Nexperia uses special test techniques which involve accurately measuring the gate-source leakage behavior. Adding ESD protection networks means that it becomes very difficult to measure the gate-source leakage characteristics of the gate oxide because the ESD protection network will have a significantly higher leakage current. This means we cannot screen out weaker oxides and will result in a higher field failure rates. Furthermore, adding protection networks results in higher production costs. ESD protection networks are therefore only used where necessary.

Generally, for larger MOSFETs with good gate oxide quality and relatively high C_{iss}

there is no need for ESD protection, as long as these are being mounted onto a PCB in a controlled ESD environment. For special applications where the MOSFET would be subjected directly to ESD in a finished product such as a lithium ion battery module or a power or signal port then on-chip ESD protection may be required to meet IEC 61000-4-2 or other ESD test specifications. Some very small MOSFETs from Nexperia may require on chip ESD protection networks in order to allow handling (such as NX3008NBKW), even in well controlled manufacturing environments.

13 Leakage, breakdown and MOSFET characteristics

13.1 Q: How does drain current (I_{DSS}) vary with respect to temperature?

A: The fundamental relationship between drain leakage current and temperature is exponential in form. The data sheet gives maximum values of I_{DSS} at $T_j = 25\,°C$ and $175\,°C$. This example is specific to Nexperia Trench generation 2 technology but the same principles can be applied for other Nexperia technology. An exponential fit to these points provides the plot of Figure 22. It is also in line with some testing which is performed during the development of new MOSFET technologies.

Figure 23 is the same curve, plotted with a log scale for I_{DSS} to ease reading the value of 20 µA at 50 °C. These values are for a V_{DS} at the rated voltage. Reducing voltage reduces leakage current. Note that Figure 22 and Figure 23 are not in the device data sheets.

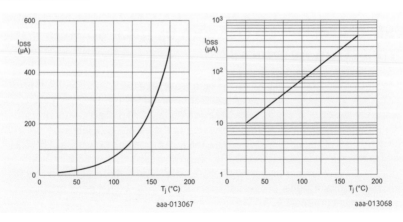

Figure 22 | I_{DSS} as a function of temperature, linear axes

Figure 23 | I_{DSS} as a function of temperature, log - linear axes

13.2 Q: What is the relationship between breakdown voltage $V_{(BR)DSS}$ at $I_D = 250\ \mu A$) and drain leakage current (I_{DSS})? Both state the same V_{DSS} value but the drain current is different.

A: Although these two parameters reference the voltage rating of the part, they look at different characteristics of the product. Drain leakage current (I_{DSS}) is the current which flows when V_{DS} equal to the rated voltage is applied. The test checks that the current is below the limit.

The breakdown voltage of a device $V_{(BR)DSS}$ is the V_{DS} required to cause a drain current of 250 µA to flow. In practice it is slightly higher than the rated voltage of the device and the actual voltage varies for the same nominal type due to manufacturing variations. The minimum $V_{(BR)DSS}$ stated in the data sheet is the rated voltage. Breakdown voltage looks at the characteristic of the part when it is in avalanche. The mechanisms causing leakage current and avalanche current are different.

13.3 Q: Is the standard level gate device BUK7Y28-75B guaranteed to work with a 7 V gate drive at -40 °C for 25 A?

A: Nexperia has a high degree of confidence that this scenario would be OK even in the worst case. However, it cannot be 100 % guaranteed by a production test at 25 °C.

Referring to Figure 24, the typical gate threshold voltage $V_{GS(th)}$ is 3 V. It rises to approximately 3.5 V at -55 °C (i.e. a rise of approximately 0.5 V). The highest $V_{GS(th)}$ rises from approximately 4 V to 4.5 V (again, approximately 0.5 V). So in the worst case at -55 °C, the threshold voltage shifts by 1.5 V from the typical 25 °C value.

Looking at Figure 25, it would shift the gate drive curve from 7.0 V to 5.5 V for a worst case device (1.5 V shift).

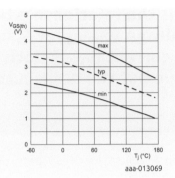

Figure 24 | Gate threshold voltage $V_{GS(th)}$ as a function of temperature

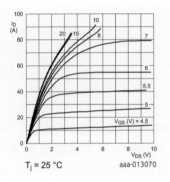

Figure 25 | Drain current as a function of drain-source voltage: typical values

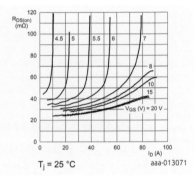

Figure 26 | Drain-source on-state resistance as a function of drain current: typical values

The 5.5 V drive curve allows more than 25 A and is still in the linear $R_{DS(on)}$ region of the output characteristic.

The $R_{DS(on)}$ values for the 5.5 V characteristic at 25 A in Figure 26 is pessimistic for operation at -40 °C. It uses the 25 °C $R_{DS(on)}$ curves, and the carrier mobility increases with lower temperatures making the $R_{DS(on)}$ better. The threshold voltage increase has already been accounted for.

It explains why a 7 V gate drive at -40 °C would be OK for this particular standard level gate device (BUK7Y28-75B). The same principles can be applied to other Nexperia devices. However, the customer must judge whether there is adequate margin in the design, as the result may be slightly different from what is observed.

13.4 Q: What is the lowest voltage $V_{(BR)DSS}$ to be expected at -40 °C for a 40 V device using Trench generation 6?

A: The following principle could be applied to any Nexperia MOSFET technology at any breakdown voltage rating. In the data sheet, the values for minimum drain-source breakdown voltages are specified at -55 °C and 25 °C. The correlation between $V_{(BR)DSS}$ and temperature is approximately linear over this range. Therefore, a straight line can be plotted at Temperature (-55 °C and 25 °C) versus $V_{(BR)DSS}$ (at -55 °C and 25 °C).

For example: a 40 V Trench generation 6 part, has a $V_{(BR)DSS}$ at -55 °C of 36 V and 40 V at 25 °C. Using linear interpolation, gives a $V_{(BR)DSS}$ of 36.75 V at -40 °C.

13.5 Q: What factors affect the value of drain current according to the transfer characteristic graph for BUK9275-55A, especially over the V_{GS} range of 2.2 V to 3.0 V?

A: The answer to this question is not simple - there are several factors which would affect the I_D value.

1. The graph depicted in Figure 27 is typical. The BUK9275-55A MOSFET has a distribution of parameter values within the production tolerance limits. The graph is only intended to illustrate how I_D, V_{DS} and V_{GS} are related when the MOSFET is operating for a particular V_{DS} condition. $V_{GS(th)}$ has a significant influence on the characteristic of a particular device. Temperature is also a major factor. The limiting values and characteristics listed in the data sheet should be used for circuit design.
2. Junction temperature T_j strongly affects the I_D / V_{GS} characteristic. The graph in Figure 27 is for $T_j = 25$ °C and $T_j = 175$ °C. The same graph for the same part with $T_j = -55$ °C, would be very different. The mode of operation preferred by the customer is with V_{GS} in the range 2.2 V to 3 V in the saturation region before full enhancement. In this mode, the MOSFET power dissipation is likely to be significant. As a result, the junction temperature may be high. Figure 22 demonstrates how I_D changes with T_j for a given V_{GS} value.
3. A dashed vertical red line on the graph is shown at $V_{GS} = 2.2$ V. If T_j increases from 25 °C to 175 °C, I_D approximately doubles (from approximately 1 A to 2 A). However, at $V_{GS} = 2.8$ V (dashed vertical green line), the same junction temperature change has no effect on I_D. At $V_{GS} > 2.8$ V, an increase in T_j results in a decrease in I_D.

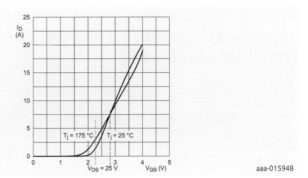

Figure 27 | Transfer characteristics: drain current as a function of gate-source voltage - typical values

It is clear that the relationship between the MOSFET parameters is complex and their relationship with the thermal environment is also complex.

13.6 Q: Can Nexperia provide C_{GD}, C_{GS} and C_{DS} numerical values for T_j = -55 °C and T_j = +175 °C (at V_{GS} = 0 V, V_{DS} = 16 V)? If it is impossible to test, a theoretical one is also acceptable. A graph is provided in Figure 23, but it is for T_j = +25 °C.

A: Unfortunately, Nexperia cannot supply values for these capacitances at the extremes of the MOSFET operating temperature range requested. It is due to the limitations of our parametric test equipment. However, we can comment on how these capacitances vary with temperature and the MOSFET terminal voltages.

C_{iss} is the input capacitance formed by the parallel combination of C_{GS} and C_{GD}, and

C_{GS} dominates. C_{GS} is formed across the gate oxide so it does not vary significantly with temperature or the MOSFET terminal voltages. As C_{GS} depends on gate oxide thickness and other defined die feature dimensions, it should not vary much between samples.

C_{rss} is the reverse transfer capacitance which is essentially the gate-drain capacitance (C_{GD}). It is formed across the MOSFET body diode depletion layer. This layer becomes thicker, as the reverse voltage (V_{DS}) across it increases. C_{rss} increases as V_{DS} decreases. C_{rss} has a greater variability than C_{iss} because it depends on the body diode depletion layer.

C_oss is the output capacitance formed by the parallel combination of C_{DS} and C_{GD}. The drain- source capacitance (C_{DS}) also dominates this capacitance. It varies with V_{DS} in a similar way to C_{rss} varying with V_{DS} and it has similar variability to C_{rss} for the same reasons.

These relationships are illustrated on the data sheet graph depicted by Figure 28. It has been observed that switching losses only slightly increase at $T_{j(max)}$, in the order of 10 %, since the capacitances only marginally change. Other factors can influence switching behavior, especially where the gate driver current capability changes significantly with temperature. The depletion layer thickness varies in proportion to the square root of the absolute temperature in K and it affects C_{rss} and C_{oss}.

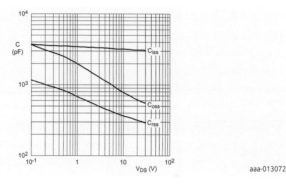

aaa-013072

Figure 28 | Input, output and reverse transfer capacitances as a function of drain-source voltage: typical values, $V_{DS} = 0$ V

13.7 Q: Can Nexperia provide the minimum V_{GS} threshold values for T_j from -55 °C to +175 °C? A graph is already in the data sheet. However, the numerical data of minimum values in the range of -55°C to +175 °C are required for a standard level gate threshold.

A: Worst case values of minimum and maximum $V_{GS(th)}$ should be used for design purposes. They are given in the data sheet Characteristics (see Table 4).

Additional information

Table 4: Characteristics
Voltages are referenced to GND (ground = 0 V).

Symbol	Parameter	Conditions	Min	Typ	Max	Unit
$V_{GS(th)}$	gate-source threshold voltage	$I_D = 1$ mA; $V_{DS} = V_{GS}$; $T_j = 25$ °C	2.4	3	4	V
		$I_D = 1$ mA; $V_{DS} = V_{GS}$; $T_j = -55$ °C	-	-	4.5	V
		$I_D = 1$ mA; $V_{DS} = V_{GS}$; $T_j = 175$ °C	1	-	-	V

These values are guaranteed worst case values. In this case, the 175 °C minimum $V_{GS(th)}$ is not less than 1 V. The -55 °C $V_{GS(th)}$ is not greater than 4.5 V.

13.8. Q: Can Nexperia provide the inherent R_G component value with T_j from -55 °C to +175 °C?

A: The measured R_G value is in the range of 1 Ω to 3 Ω and it does not vary significantly with temperature. In our general MOSFET characterization, it is presently not possible to test R_G over the temperature range.

Additional information

In a circuit such as the 3-phase motor drive circuit, switching speed is not usually critically important. The PWM frequency is usually moderate (<50 kHz). However, to mitigate emissions due to high dV/dt, the circuit designer often deliberately slows the switching of the MOSFET.

A low value (10 Ω) fixed resistor connected between the gate driver output and the MOSFET gate helps to stabilize the gate driver voltage and damp out any voltage transients or oscillations.

Often, even higher external gate driver resistor values are chosen to slow down the gate driver and reduce the EMI effects of the MOSFET switching.

13.9 Q: How is the maximum permissible drain current estimated, at the point of $V_{DS} = 0.1$ V, from the SOA curve of the BUK9K12-60E shown in Figure 24? Some manufacturers describe down to the V_{DS} value in their SOA curves.

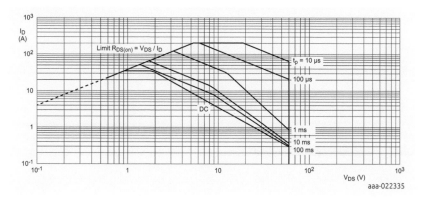

Figure 29 | Safe operating area: continuous and peak drain currents as a function of drain-source voltage

A: The minimum current that is expected at a V_{DS} of 0.1 V can be calculated from the maximum (175 °C) $R_{DS(on)}$ value (26 mΩ):

Table 5: $R_{DS(on)}$ values

Symbol	Parameter	Conditions	Min	Typ	Max	Unit
$R_{DS(on)}$	drain-source on-state resistance	$V_{GS} = 5$ V; $I_D = 15$ A; $T_j = 25$ °C	-	9.5	11.5	mΩ
		$V_{GS} = 5$ V; $I_D = 15$ A; $T_j = 175$ °C	-	21.5	26	mΩ

The drain current that flows with these conditions is 0.1/0.026 = 3.846 A. The maximum die temperature is the critical factor. Do not allow it to exceed 175 °C.

However, if the $R_{DS(on)}$ is not at the top limit of the value range or the die temperature is lower, it is lower. As a result, the corresponding drain current is proportionately higher.

From Table 5 the maximum $R_{DS(on)}$ is 11.5 mΩ at $T_{mb} = 25$ °C. The maximum die temperature is likely to be higher than 25 °C in most applications.

If the mounting base temperature is maintained at 100 °C or less, the (fully ON) MOSFET can safely carry a continuous current up to 35 A, (see Table 6).

Table 6: I_D values

Symbol	Parameter	Conditions	Min	Typ	Max	Unit
I_D	drain current	$T_{mb} = 25\ °C; V_{GS} = 5\ V$	-	-	35	A
		$T_{mb} = 100\ °C; V_{GS} = 5\ V$	-	-	35	A

The (fully ON) MOSFET can also sustain a current pulse of 204 A for a period up to 10 µs, (see Table 7).

Table 7: I_{DM} values

Symbol	Parameter	Conditions	Min	Typ	Max	Unit
I_{DM}	peak drain current	$T_{mb} = 25\ °C; t_p \leq 10\ µs$	-	-	204	A

13.10 Q: Is the BUK7K52-60E drain current specified individually for each (FET1 and FET2) or as a total of 15.4 A?

Table 8: Drain specifications

Symbol	Parameter	Conditions	Min	Typ	Max	Unit
V_{DS}	drain-source voltage	$T_j \geq 25\ °C; T_j \leq 175\ °C$	-	-	60	V
I_D	drain current	$V_{GS} = 10\ V; T_{mb} = 25\ °C$	-	-	15.4	A
P_{tot}	total power dissipation	$T_{mb} = 25\ °C$	-	-	32	W

A: The ratings given on the data sheet are for each individual MOSFET in this device, (see Table 8).

Although there are two MOSFETs housed within the package, they are fully electrically isolated from each other.

However, as the MOSFETs share a common package, there is a small amount of thermal coupling between the two MOSFET dies through the plastic package material. The heat generated by the power dissipated in one MOSFET increases the temperature of the other, even though the other may not be dissipating power. In an application, there is also an external thermal coupling path via the PCB to which the device is mounted. In practice, it is the main thermal coupling mechanism between the two dies.

To guarantee long-term reliability, it is very important that the junction temperature of either of the dies is never allowed to exceed 175 °C.

The individual MOSFET mounting bases are the main exit routes for heat generated in the dies. In practice, the mounting bases are soldered to copper pads on a Printed-Circuit Board (PCB). They provide the electrical connections to the MOSFET drains and heat sinking. Both MOSFETs in the package should operate at their rated power/current when their mounting bases are maintained at 25 °C. However, it is very difficult to achieve in practice and de-rating must be done in most cases.

Example:

Using a BUK7K52-60E for two MOSFETs in a half-bridge, driving an inductive load.

Assumptions:

MOSFETs conduct alternately, never together.

Switching losses are neglected.

PCB material is standard FR4.

Standard FR4 PCB material has a maximum operating temperature of 125 °C, although special higher temperature materials are available.

The maximum temperature of the MOSFET mounting bases is limited to 125 °C by appropriate PCB cooling. The maximum de-rated power that can be dissipated in one MOSFET is:
32/3 = 10.67 W.

Hence, the temperature rise of the die above the temperature of its mounting base is: 10.67 (W) × 4.68 (K/W) = 49.9 K.

Therefore, the maximum die temperature is 125 + 49.9 = 174.9 °C, which is marginally safe.

Worst case $R_{DS(on)}$ at T_j = 175 °C = 101 mΩ.

Maximum allowed current = $\sqrt{(P/R_{DS(on)})}$ = 10.28 A.

> **Note:** This calculation is a theoretical example. The PCB cooling required to maintain a 125 °C mounting base temperature with 10.67 W power dissipation would be very difficult to achieve in practice.

13.11 Q: How does V plateau shift with temperature and process variation?

Data from a T9 MOSFET family device BUK7J1R4-40H is considered but the principle can be applied to T6 devices also. The plateau voltage in the gate charge characteristic is the horizontal portion of the graph (Figure 30) and is related to the transfer characteristic (Figure 31).

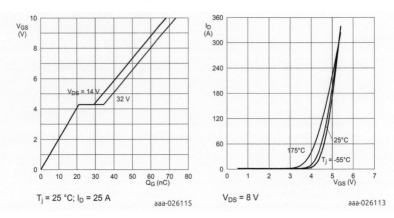

Figure 30 | Gate-source voltage as a function of gate charge; typical values

Figure 31| Transfer characteristics; drain current as a function of gate-source voltage; typical values

The plateau voltage is around 4.25 V typical for a current of 25 A. This corresponds to the value in the transfer curve, also for a typical device. So at -55 °C then the plateau voltage will be 4.35 V and at 175 °C it will be 3.9 V for a typical device.

> **Note:** transconductance reduces with increasing temperature, so the device will switch a little slower and switching losses will increase.

When considering a "worst case" device then the spread in gate threshold $V_{GS(th)}$ needs to be considered. It is assumed that the gain (transconductance) of the device is not affected by the same process related reasons which affect $V_{GS(th)}$. The transfer curve for a typical device would be shifted along the V_{GS} axis according to the delta in the $V_{GS(th)}$ (Figure 32).

The plateau voltage at the 25 A test condition would be 3.65 V for minimum $V_{GS(th)}$ and 4.85 V maximum $V_{GS(th)}$.

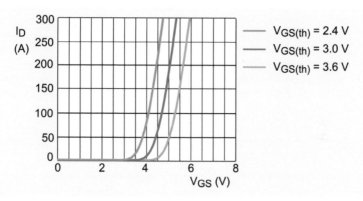

Figure 32 | Transfer characteristic at 25 °C

13.12 Q: What is the current which each device can conduct and how does this relate to the device power rating for the SOT1205 device?

A. Consider a specific example such as BUK9K52-60E. The data sheet shows the following capability:

Table 9: Quick reference data; BUK9K52-60E

Symbol	Parameter	Conditions	Min	Typ	Max	Unit
V_{DS}	drain-source voltage	$T_j \geq 25$ °C; $T_j \leq 175$ °C	-	-	60	V
I_D	drain current	$V_{GS} = 5$ V; $T_{mb} = 25$ °C	-	-	16	A
P_{tot}	total power dissipation	$T_{mb} = 25$ °C	-	-	32	W

The key point is the P_{tot} of 32 W. This is per die at data sheet conditions which assume that the mounting base is maintained at 25 °C. The maximum DC current allowed in each device would be 16.04 A, based on $R_{DS(on)}$ of 124.3 mΩ ($V_{GS}= 5$ V) at 175 °C.

$$I_{DC} = \sqrt{(P/R)}$$
$$I_{DC} = \sqrt{(32/0.1243)} = 16.04\ A$$

If both devices in the package are considered then the total power dissipation when both mounting bases are maintained at 25 °C is 32 W x 2 = 64 W. This only applies when the mounting bases of the devices are maintained at 25 °C (using an infinite heatsink). The power capability will decrease as the mounting base temperatures increase such that T_j does not exceed 175 °C. Consequently the current will decrease as shown in the graph Figure 33 of I_D vs T_{mb}, if the mounting base is maintained at a different temperature such as 125 °C, the current rating would be 9.26 A.

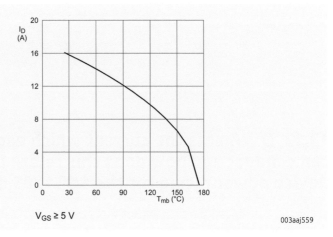

$V_{GS} \geq 5\ V$

003aaj559

Figure 33 | Continuous drain current as a function of mounting base temperature

In practice it is not a realistic condition to mount the device on an infinite heatsink, the device might be mounted on a PCB with $R_{th(mb-amb)}$ = 50 °C / W. In which case how can the steady state current capability be calculated?

The diagram in Figure 34 below shows a simplified thermal model from the junction of each die to ambient. It is assumed that there is good coupling on the substrate such as a PCB between the devices (usually the case but not always) and that there is minimal coupling between the devices within the package (this is >100 °C / W).

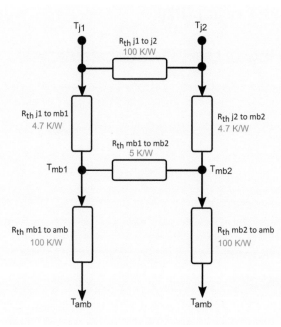

Figure 34 | Dual MOSFET thermal configuration

If the ambient temperature is 25 °C then the maximum total package power dissipation would be 2.87 W assuming the power is shared equally between the two dies.

$P \times 100 + P \times 4.7 = T\Delta = 150\ °C$
$\therefore\ P = 1.433\ W\ per\ die$

This corresponds to a maximum current of 3.40 A in each device simultaneously.

$I_{DC} = \sqrt{(PIR)}$
$I_{DC}\ \sqrt{(1.433/0.\ 1243)} = 3.40\ A$

This will result in a mounting base temperature of 168.2 °C. This is above the typical transition temperature for the PCB of 125 °C. The simplified thermal resistance model can be used to calculate the power based on the actual conditions and requirements. For highly accurate calculations, computational fluid dynamics simulations or calibrated measurements should be conducted.

14 MOSFET reliability

14.1 Q: How is the FIT-rate calculated?

A: FIT (Failure In Time) is commonly used to express component reliability. It is defined as the number of failures occurring in 1×10^9 hours (1 billion hours).

At any elapsed time (t), the reliability (R) of a group of operating semiconductors is:

$R(t) = (n_o - n_f)/n_o$

Where:

n_o is the original sample size and nf is the number of failures after time t.

Over the standard time of 10^9 hours, it approximates to $F = (1/n_o)*(n_f/t)*10^9$.

Accelerated testing

A major factor in determining the reliability of a semiconductor is the total stress applied by the application. Operating temperature results from ambient temperature and the heat due to power dissipation. It is the most important applied operating stress where a product is otherwise generally operated within its ratings.
The Arrhenius equation is used to model the effect of temperature on component failure rate:

$Acceleration\ factor = e(Ea/k)(1/T1 - 1/T2)$ [7]

Where:

Ea = activation energy (eV)

k = Boltzmann constant (8.60×10^{-5} eV / K)

T1 = operating temperature (°C)

T2 = reliability test temperature (K referenced to absolute zero)

Accelerated testing makes components perform at high levels of (thermal) stress. The results are then extrapolated to convert short life under severe conditions into

the expected life under normal conditions.
Under accelerated life test conditions:

$$F = (nf/n0 \times A \times t) \times 109\,FITs \qquad [8]$$

Time t is now equal to A × t, where A is the acceleration factor.

Based on the life-test results for an example part, the FIT data provided in Table 10 has been calculated. Note that an adjustment is made to the number of failures based on Poissons probability distribution. It is used to indicate the number of failures expected in a larger sample depending on the confidence level. It is described in JEDEC JEP122F Section 5.18.1.4 and in numerous other references.

Table 10: Calculated FIT data

Test name	High Temperature Reverse Bias (HTRB) + High Temperature Gate Bias (HTGB) + High Temperature Storage Bias (HTSL)				
Test temperature	175	°C			
Number of device hours	35,051,000				
Number of observed failures	0				
Confidence level	90	%			
Activation energy	0.7	eV			
Failure rate					**Unit**
Failure rate at	125	°C	at 90 % confidence =	6.725	FIT
Failure rate at	85	°C	at 90 % confidence =	0.688	FIT
Failure rate at	55	°C	at 90 % confidence =	0.086	FIT
Failure rate at	25	°C	at 90 % confidence =	0.0007	FIT
MTBF					**Unit**
Mean time before failure at	125	°C	at 90 % confidence =	1.49 × 108	hour
Mean time before failure at	85	°C	at 90 % confidence =	1.45 × 109	hour
Mean time before failure at	55	°C	at 90 % confidence =	1.16 × 1010	hour
Mean time before failure at	25	°C	at 90 % confidence =	1.40 × 1011	hour

15 References

1. AN11158 — Understanding power MOSFET data sheet parameters

2. AN10273 — Power MOSFET single-shot and repetitive avalanche ruggedness rating

3. AN90003 — LFPAK MOSFET thermal design guide

4. AN11160 — Designing RC snubbers

5. AN90001 — Designing in MOSFETs for safe and reliable gate-drive operation

16 Tables

17 Figures

Power and small-signal MOSFET frequently asked questions and answers

Chapter 14

Leakage of small-signal MOSFETs

Application Note: AN90009

1 Introduction

Description of current leakage behavior for small-signal MOSFETs. Examples for typical gate- source and drain-source leakage of MOSFETs is shown. Distinguish between ESD protected and unprotected devices.

Device current leakage is an important factor for the energy consumption of a circuit application. This is especially true for mobile electronic devices such as smart phones, tablets, wearables or medical devices as the off-state current leakage may influence battery life and therefore operation time. The scope of this application note is the current leakage description of a small-signal trench MOSFET in different pin configurations.

2 Leakage currents

The following chapters are related to the pin configurations drain-source (D-S) and gate-source (G-S) as illustrated in Figure 1 below.

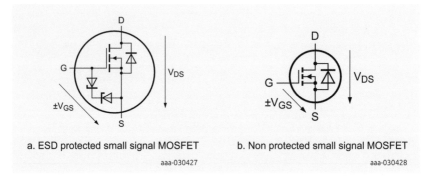

a. ESD protected small signal MOSFET   b. Non protected small signal MOSFET

aaa-030427   aaa-030428

Figure 1 | Illustrated pin configuration for device leakage

For gate-source leakage it is important to distinguish between ESD protected MOSFETs and non- protected ones. Due to the presence of additional ESD protection circuit the V_{GS} to I_{GS} leakage characteristic of such a device is different while the drain-source characteristic is independent from this constructional feature.

2.1 Drain-source leakage

For an enhancement mode MOSFET in the off-state ($V_{GS} = 0$ V), the drain-source leakage is given by a p-n junction diode in reverse direction. In the ideal case this is given by the rectifier equation:

$$I = IS\ [exp\,(qV/kT) - 1] \approx IS \quad (V < 0, -V << kT/q)$$ [1]

Where V is the applied voltage, q the electronic charge, k the Boltzmann constant and T the absolute temperature. $V > 0$ represents the diode in reverse direction with a remaining I_S, (the so called saturation current):

$$I_s = q \cdot A \left(\sqrt{\frac{D_p}{\tau_p}\frac{n_i^2}{N_D}} + \sqrt{\frac{D_n}{\tau_n}\frac{n_i^2}{N_A}} \right)$$ [2]

with the cross-section area A, the diffusion coefficients of holes and electrons D_p, D_n, the donor and acceptor concentrations N_D, N_A, the intrinsic carrier concentration ni and the carrier lifetime of holes and electrons τ_p.

It can be seen that the ideal description of the leakage is independent from the applied voltage. The leakage increases with the cross section area A and therefore the channel width which is proportional to the Xtal size if the same technology is used. The larger the Xtal the higher the leakage.

In practice an additional current is added to the ideal saturation current which is increased at higher reverse voltage applied. (Moll, 1958) Reasons for this component are:

- Surface leakage and inversion layers
- Body defects
- Generation and recombination

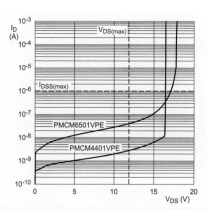

Figure 2 | Drain-source I_D leakage current as a function of drain-source voltage for PMCM4401VPE and PMCM6501VPE at T_j = 25 °C

The drain-source leakage as a function of drain-source voltage is given by Figure 2. Both types have a specified maximum voltage of 12 V with a safety margin up to the breakdown voltage of approximately 17 V when avalanche occurs. Specified maximum value for I_{DSS} leakage at maximum drain source voltage specified is 1 µA however in reality for small-signal MOSFET this current is significantly below this standardized limit. Due to the larger chip size by a factor of 2.3 the PMCM6501VPE has an increased leakage which is related to the higher channel width described in equation (2). Even for the larger chip the real leakage is more than one order of magnitude away from the specification limit.

The saturation current I_S is temperature dependent. In case of silicon the recombination and generation of carriers is increased above room temperature leading to increased leakage. This relation is given as example for PMCM4401VNE in the figure below:

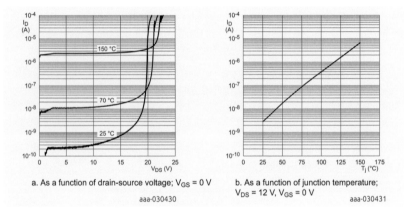

a. As a function of drain-source voltage; V_{GS} = 0 V

aaa-030430

b. As a function of junction temperature; V_{DS} = 12 V, V_{GS} = 0 V

aaa-030431

Figure 3 | Drain-source leakage current of PMCM4401VNE

2.2 Gate to Source leakage

An unprotected MOSFET has an electrically isolated gate with very small leakage from gate to source while a protected MOSFET shows the typical leakage curve of a bidirectional Zener diode. Figure 4 below shows the gate-source leakage current of the ESD protected BSS138BK and the unprotected BSS138P. Both types are specified with a maximum gate to source voltage of 20 V. Channel width and gate oxide are equal.

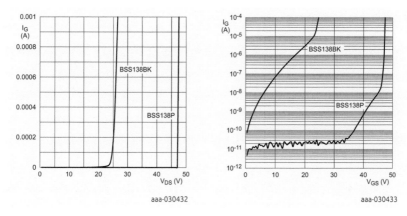

Figure 4 | Gate-source leakage current of ESD protected BSS138BK and non protected BSS138P

It can be seen that where minimizing gate-source leakage is essential an unprotected MOSFET gives the best choice over a wide voltage range. The Zener diode of a protected device is a trade-off between ESD protection and device gate-source leakage. It is designed in a way that the clamping voltage is lower than the oxide breakdown voltage to protect the ESD most vulnerable part of the MOSFET and higher than the specification to keep the leakage at a minimum over specified range. Due to the poly-crystalline construction of the Zener diode the leakage below breakdown voltage is still higher compared to a single crystal diode. The gate leakage temperature dependency for the Zener diode is similar to a silicon p-n junction. The following figure shows an increase in leakage for higher temperature. The leakage of an un-protected MOSFET remains almost constant in the same temperature range.

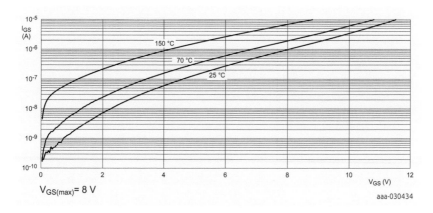

Figure 5 | Gate-source leakage current of an ESD protected MOSFET at different junction temperatures

3 Applications

Normally, when selecting a MOSFET for an application, the typical selection criteria are things like V_{DS} voltage, $R_{DS(on)}$, gate threshold voltage and so on. With the ongoing trend towards battery driven and even energy harvesting based applications, other performance criteria such as leakage start to be become more important.

There are several use-case scenarios where ultra-low leakage of a MOSFET is a key parameter and one of the first things a designer looks at when selecting the component.

3.1 Load switch

When powering an application from a finite power source such as a battery, designers often implement so called low power modes of operation. Most modern microcontrollers feature several levels of low power operational modes. Nevertheless, to get the lowest possible application standby power, the best way is still to simply power everything down while leaving a small fraction of the circuit powered up to handle detection for waking back up. The whole application operates then in a PWM mode of operation. It is powered off most of the time, while only waking up periodically.

The common method to implement this powering-up and down is to use a load-switch that (dis)connects the circuit power from the battery. Many load-switch IC solutions exist, often offering additional features such a current limit, in-rush limit and more. Still, the simplest way to implement a load-switch function is to use a MOSFET. Refer to Figure 6. Here we see a high-side switch implemented with a P-channel MOSFET.

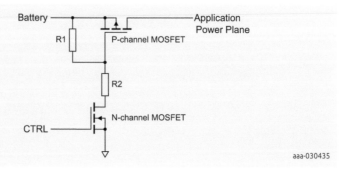

Figure 6 | Load-switch using MOSFETs

One of the nice "side-effects" of using a MOSFET for this function is that the leakage current can be very low. Clearly when implementing a switch to turn some circuit completely off, you would want that switch to be as high Ohmic as possible, i.e. the leakage current between source and drain should approximate zero as much as possible.

Per Figure 6 a separate N-channel MOSFET is often used to control the P-channel MOSFET. A high level on the gate of the N-channel MOSFET will pull the gate of the P-channel MOSFET low and turn it on (connecting battery to the application power plane). Here we see another important leakage path, the one from the control drive line via the gate of the N-channel to either Source or Drain. For optimal application standby time an N-channel MOSFET with very low gate leakage is required. Resistors R1 and R2 are used to further optimize leakage levels. Their values are a trade-off between lowest leakage levels obtainable, V_{GS} switch levels reachable and switching speed of the load-switch circuit.

3.2 General purpose logic

For those applications that require the absolute lowest leakage, it may actually be better to implement basic logic functionality (such as gates) using discrete MOSFETs. While not very commonplace, this is sometimes required in applications using energy harvesting as their only source of power.

The exact circuit implementation dictates what is required, but refer to Figure 7, where a basic discretely build inverter is shown (simplified). Clearly, for lowest possible system level leakage, gate-source and drain-source leakage are important here.

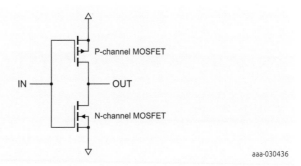

aaa-030436

Figure 7 | Inverter using MOSFETs (simplified)

4 Selecting a low leakage MOSFET

The data as shown in this note elaborates on the (physical) background of leakage in MOSFETs. To help with selecting the right product for low leakage applications, we can summarize this as follows:

- As the drain-source voltage across the MOSFET gets closer to the maximum specified V_{DS} there is a risk of significantly increased channel leakage. Hence the need to stay away from the maximum specified V_{DS}
- At higher temperatures, leakage goes up significantly and not the same for all MOSFETs. Low threshold parts will see a bigger increase
- With rising temperature, leakage increases. Leakage will increase faster in low $V_{GS(th)}$ devices
- Gate protection structures cause an increase to gate leakage.

Combining all of the above, we can argue that the highest chance for lowest possible leakage is to select a device that:

1. Has a max V_{DS} that is at least twice as high the highest V_{DS} that will be seen in the application
2. Has the highest acceptable $V_{GS(th)}$ to help minimize leakage increases at higher temperature
3. Does not have protection on the gate. While not ideal for ESD sensitivity, an unprotected gate will help keep gate leakage down, especially at elevated temperatures
4. Has the highest acceptable $R_{DS(on)}$. While not 100% accurate, if we assume the same process for two different devices, the type with the lower $R_{DS(on)}$ has a larger die size, and hence will show a (minimally) higher leakage.

In all cases Nexperia can only guarantee the limit as per specification.

5 Nexperia low leakage MOSFET portfolio

The market shows a large and growing interest in MOSFETs with a low leakage specification for I_{DSS} and I_{GSS} due to an increasing number of battery-driven applications in the market such as wearables, Bluetooth trackers, wireless measurement devices, computing accessories, e-metering and smoke detectors. In applications that are required to have a long battery life time, although driven by a small coin-cell, every additional leakage current has to be avoided.

Nexperia introduced a low leakage MOSFET portfolio depicted in Table 1 below. The space saving leadless packages DFN1006-3, DFN1006B-3 and DFN1010B-6 have been chosen to support compact board designs. The height of DFN1006-3 is

0.48 mm, DFN1006B-3 and DFN1010B-6 have a reduced height of 0.37 mm only. In DFN1006 single FETs as 20 V P-channel and N-channel version are available. The DFN1010 variants are dual-FETs containing a dual N-channel, a dual P-channel or a complementary pair. Using the complementary PMCXB900UEL allows for a very compact load switch, with the topology of a high-side switch shown in Figure 6. For small battery-driven applications, the load currents are normally not very high so that an $R_{DS(on)}$ of about 1 - 2 Ohms is fully sufficient.

Table 1: Low leakage current MOSFET portfolio

Type name	Polarity	V_{DS}	V_{GS}	I_D	$R_{DS(on)}$ @ V_{GS} = 4.5 V	$R_{DS(on)}$ @ V_{GS} = 2.5 V	$R_{DS(on)}$ @ V_{GS} =1.8 V	Package
		(V)	(V)	(A)	(mΩ)	(mΩ)	(mΩ)	
PMZ600UNEL	N	20	8	0.6	470	620	845	DFN1006-3
PMZB600UNEL	N	20	8	0.6	470	620	845	DFN1006B-3
PMZ950UPEL	P	20	8	0.5	1020	1270	1700	DFN1006-3
PMZB950UPEL	P	20	8	0.5	1020	1270	1700	DFN1006B-6
PMDXB600UNEL	dual N	20	8	0.6	470	620	845	DFN1006B-6
PMDXB950UPEL	dual P	20	8	0.5	1020	1270	1700	DFN1006B-6
PMCXB900UEL	N	20	8	0.6	470	620	845	DFN1006B-6
	P	20	8	0.5	1020	1270	1700	DFN1006B-6

The maximum leakage for the drain -source path is reduced from 1 µA down to 25 nA specified for V_{DS} equal 5 V. The gate-source leakage limit is lowered from 10 µA to 50 nA for a gate voltage of 1.8 V.

Table 2: Comparison of maximum leakage current ratings between standard and low leakage MOSFETs

	Standard type	Low leakage type
$I_{DSS(max)}$	1 µA	25 nA @ V_{DS} = 5 V
$I_{DSS(max)}$	10 µA	50 nA @ V_{DS} = 1.8 V

6 References

Moll, J. L. (1958). The Evolution of the Theory for the Voltage-Current Characteristic of P-N Junctions. Proceedings of the IRE (Volume:46 , Issue: 6), 1076 - 1082.

7 Tables

8 Figures

Chapter 15

DC-to-DC conversion with small-signal MOSFETs

Application Note: AN11119

1 Introduction

This chapter explores different methods of DC-to-DC conversion.
It contains several examples of DC-to-DC down-converters using small-signal MOSFETs.

In modern electronic designs various supply voltages need to be generated. In most cases power supply provides one or a few different DC voltages. These voltages need to be converted to another voltage for several functional units in the application. Voltage conversion can work in both directions: it can be step up or step down.

Using linear voltage regulators for voltage conversion was common, even if a voltage had to be reduced significantly or if the load currents were high. Because linear voltage regulator works as a controlled series resistor, a lot of energy is dissipated thermally.

Due to the environmental requirement to improve energy efficiency of electronic equipment, switch mode power supplies are replacing linear voltage regulators. In switch mode power supplies, energy is stored in the magnetic field of inductors or as a charge in capacitors. Ohmic loss of energy has to be avoided as much as possible.

Newly developed electronic components for implementation of switches, such as modern MOSFETs, support design of highly efficient power supplies. Although fully integrated solutions are available, applications with external switching stages are widely used due to flexibility and cost reasons.

2 DC-to-DC conversion methods

2.1 DC-to-DC down-converter

Figure 6 shows the circuit diagram of a simple DC-to-DC down-converter. In contrast to a linear regulator, this circuit would have 100 % efficiency in case of ideal components application. In practice, there are losses in switching transistor because the on-resistance is not equal to 0 Ω and also because transistor needs switching time, which introduces switching losses. Other components add losses too. Inductor has an ohmic resistance from the wire of the windings and magnetic core adds losses too. Magnetic core losses result from the change of the magnetic field which causes motion of small magnetic domains. The bigger the hysteresis of the core material, the bigger are these losses. Eddy currents cause further loss in the magnetic core of an inductor. Changing magnetic fields can induce circulating loops of current which heat up the ferromagnetic material. For high frequency switching, the current in the wire no longer uses the whole cross-section, instead it concentrates closer to the surface. This is a well-known skin effect which leads to higher ohmic losses.

Also the output capacitor has a residual resistance that leads to energy losses and a temperature increase. Finally, the diode introduces forward voltage losses and reverse current losses. These mechanisms and facts reduce the energy efficiency of DC-to-DC converters from 75 % to 98 % in real life conditions.

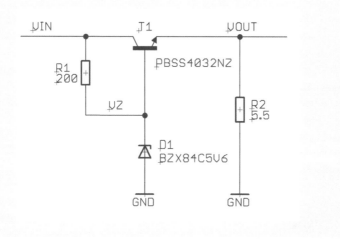

Figure 6 | Simple DC-to-DC down-converter

The P-channel FET Q1 works as high-side switch. When the FET is switched on, the current in the inductor L1 increases with a linear $\Delta I_L = (t_{on}/L_1) \times (V_{IN} \cdot V_{OUT})$, curve V_{OUT} is constant.

When the switch is opened, the current continuously flows via the path of the diode D1. The cathode of D1 is negative with the forward voltage VF against ground. The current decreases linearly. C2 buffers the output voltage. The bigger it is, the smaller the ripple will be.

Figure 7 depicts a SPICE simulation. The high-side switch is implemented with NX2301P P-channel FET. It works at the voltage supply V1. The inductance of the inductor is chosen to 68 µH, the output voltage is filtered with 10 µF capacitor. PMEG2010AEH Schottky diode is selected as a free-wheeling diode. To control NX2301P, a N-channel driver FET is implemented, which is switched from a square wave generator with 3.3 V high level (V2). In this example, the switching frequency is 100 kHz. A load resistor of 10 Ω is connected to the output.

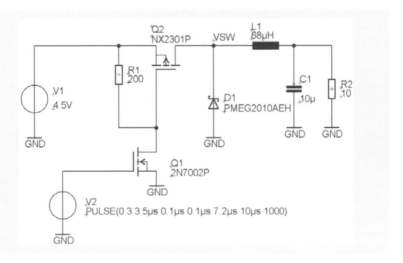

Figure 7 | SPICE simulation diagram for a simple DC-to-DC down-converter using NX2301P as high-side switch and PMEG2010AEH as low-side Schottky diode.

Figure 8 shows simulation result. The current I_{L1} which flows through the inductor shows a linear increase while Q1 is switched on. The voltage at SW node V_{SW} nearly equals to the input voltage. When Q1 is switched off, the current through the inductor decreases. The signal SW changes to a negative voltage of about 300 mV, which is the forward voltage of the Schottky diode. The output current is the average of the triangle shaped waveform and is about 330 mA. The output voltage V_{OUT} is stable at roughly 3.25 V.

In the abovementioned example, the current flows through the inductance for the whole period of the switching cycle. This mode is called continuous mode of a DC-to-DC converter. Below is a calculation of output voltage. The voltage at an inductor is:

$$V_L = L \times (dI_L / dt) \qquad\qquad [6]$$

or

$$V_L = L \times (\Delta I_L / \Delta t) \qquad\qquad [7]$$

so

$$\Delta I_L = V_L / L \times \Delta t \qquad\qquad [8]$$

The stored energy in an inductor is:

$$E = L / 2 \times I^2 \qquad [9]$$

For the Stationary mode while switch is closed, the energy increase in the inductor must be identical to the energy loss while switch is open.

Neglecting $R_{DS(on)}$ losses in the switch and the forward voltage of the diode, we get the formula for ΔI_L:

$$\Delta I_L = (V_{IN} - V_{OUT}) \times t_{on} = V_{OUT} \times t_{off} \qquad [10]$$

$$V_{OUT}/V_{IN} = t_{on}/(t_{on} + t_{off}) = t_{on}/T \qquad [11]$$

where T is cycle time and the duty cycle D is:

$$D = t_{on}/T \qquad [12]$$

$$V_{OUT} = V_{IN} \times D \qquad [13]$$

In our example:

$$V_{OUT} = 4,5\ V \times (7,2/10) = 3,24\ V \qquad [14]$$

If the duty cycle is 1 as a corner case, the switch is always closed and the output voltage equals the input voltage. If the duty cycle is smaller than 1, the output voltage is reduced by factor D.

The ripple of the current is:

$$\Delta I_L = (V_{IN} - V_{OUT})/L \times t_{on} \qquad [15]$$

In our example:

$$\Delta I_L = (4,5\ V - 3,24\ V)/68\ \mu H \times 7,2\ \mu s = 133\ mA \qquad [16]$$

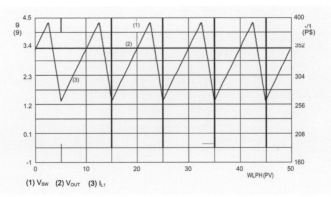

(1) V$_{SW}$ (2) V$_{OUT}$ (3) I$_{L1}$

Figure 8 | Curves of the current through L 1, SW node voltage and output voltage

If the load current is increased in the continuous mode, the output voltage stays constant (ideal components) . This means that duty cycle for the switch does not need to be changed to a significant extent from a DC-to-DC controller IC as long as the converter runs in the continuous mode. There is a current limit where the continuous mode is left. A relevant equation is below:

$$\Delta I_L = 2 \times I_{L(average)} = 2 \times I_{load} \qquad [17]$$

If curve 3 in Figure 8 moves down by decreasing the output current until the x-axis is touched, the limit of the continuous mode is reached. From this point onward the duty cycle has to be reduced in order to keep the same output voltage.

If non-continuous mode is reached, the voltage curve of SW node of the circuit changes significantly. Normally there is roughly a square wave between V$_{IN}$ and −V$_F$. If the current through the inductance reaches 0 A, the voltage at the diode changes from forward direction to reverse. The diode blocks the output capacitor, which is charged to V$_{OUT}$ from being discharged via L1 (Q1 is still closed). After the current through L1 went down to zero, SW node shows an oscillation supported by the resonance circuit of L1 and C$_{OUT}$. Figure 9 shows this typical behavior. Circuit on Figure 7 was modified by reducing the inductance of L1 to 6.8 μH for this experiment. This leads to a higher current ripple, and a non-continuous mode.

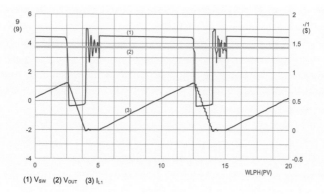

(1) V_{SW} (2) V_{OUT} (3) I_{L1}

Figure 9 | Converter in a non-continuous condition, current curve of I_L reaches the x-axis at 0 A, curve of SW node jumps from $-V_F$ to an oscillation around V_{OUT}

Figure 10 shows a change in the down-converter topology to improve efficiency of the simple circuit. The Schottky diode generates forward voltage losses for the time period when high-side switch is opened. A MOSFET can replace a diode. The low-side switch needs to be turned on when the upper FET is switched off. The controller has to take care that there is never an overlap of the on-states of both transistors in this case the switching stage would create a short circuit with a significant current peak, high losses and risk to damage the FETs. Because every MOSFET contains a body-diode from the source to the drain, the circuit would in principle work even if Q2 is never switched on. In this case, the body-diode of Q2 would work like a Schottky diode in the simple topology on Figure 6. Therefore the turn-on time of Q2 is not very critical. If Q2 switches on after Q1 is closed, the body diode conducts the current from L1.

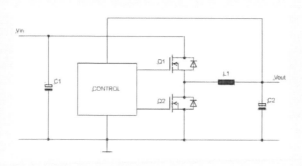

Figure 10 | Synchronous DC-to-DC down-converter (FETs including body-diodes)

2.2 DC-to-DC up-converter

In the previous chapter, inductor-based DC-to-DC down conversion was discussed. With a small change in the topology, the down-converter can be changed into an up-converter. Figure 11 shows the topology of a simple DC-to-DC up-converter. If the low-side switch FET Q1 is closed, the current in the inductance increases:

$$\Delta I_L = V_{IN} \times t_{on} \tag{18}$$

The diode D1 is driven in reverse mode because the anode is connected to the ground and the cathode is connected to the positive voltage V_{OUT} at C2. If the switch is closed, the current IL continues to flow through D1 into the output. If the converter runs in a stationary mode, we can calculate:

$$\Delta I_L = V_{IN}/L \times t_{on} = (V_{OUT} - V_{IN})/L \times t_{off} \tag{19}$$

$$V_{IN} \times t_{on} = (V_{OUT} - V_{IN}) \times t_{off} \tag{20}$$

$$V_{OUT} = V_{IN} \times (t_{on}/t_{off} + 1) \tag{21}$$

where the duty cycle is:

$$D = t_{on} / T \tag{22}$$

$$T = t_{on} + t_{off} \tag{23}$$

$$V_{OUT} = V_{IN} \times (t_{on} + t_{off}) / t_{off} = V_{IN} \times T / (T - t_{on})$$
$$= V_{IN} \times 1 / (1 - t_{on}/T) \tag{24}$$
$$= V_{IN} \times 1 / (1 - D)$$

The corner cases of the equation show that for D = 0, which means that the transistor is never switched on, $V_{OUT} = V_{IN}$. It makes sense to consider lossless components. Lossless means a diode with no forward voltage and an inductance without an ohmic resistance of the windings and the additional loss mechanisms discussed in the previous chapter. If D gets close to 1, the output voltage increases rapidly. This is critical for safe operation because high duty cycle can result in very high voltages at the FETs drain.

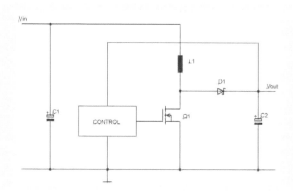

Figure 11 | Simple DC-to-DC up-converter

Figure 12 shows SPICE simulation. The low-side switch is implemented with PMV20XN N-channel MOSFET in SOT23 package and PMEG2010AEH Schottky diode. The converter is switched with 100 kHz signal control signal with a duty cycle of 0.5.

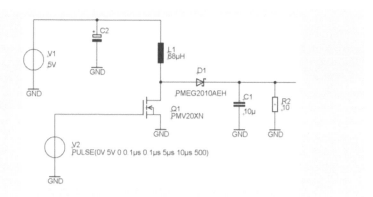

Figure 12 | SPICE simulation diagram for a simple DC-to-DC up-converter example with PMV20XN N-channel FET and PMEG2010AEH Schottky diode

Figure 13 shows simulation results. Curve 2 represents output voltage. For ideal components, the output voltage would be twice as high as the input due to the duty cycle of 0.5. In practice, the forward voltage of the diode reduces the output voltage. Curve 1 shows drain voltage VD of the N-channel FET. It switches between ground level and $V_{D(max)}$ and equals:

$$V_{D(max)} = V_{IN} \times 1/(1-D) + V_F \qquad\qquad [24]$$

In the simulated case with the duty cycle D = 0.5,

$$V_{D(max)} = 2 \times V_{IN} + V_F \qquad [25]$$

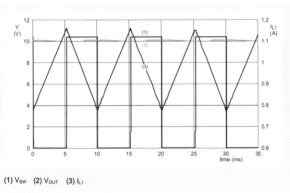

(1) V_{SW} (2) V_{OUT} (3) I_{L1}

Figure 13 | Simulation results, simple up-converter

Similar to DC-to-DC down-converter, energy efficiency of the up-converter also can be improved if the Schottky diode is replaced by a FET, which switches on for the correct phase in the switching cycle. Figure 14 shows the topology of synchronous DC-to-DC up-converter.

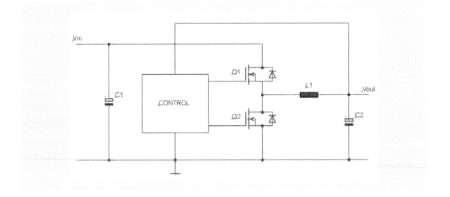

Figure 14 | Synchronous DC-to-DC down-converter

2.2.1 DC-to-DC up- and down-converter

If two topologies of the DC-to-DC down-converter and up-converter are combined as shown on Figure 15, the output voltage can either be reduced or boosted in relation to the input voltage. The MOSFET switches need to be controlled in a proper way to allow the conversion in both directions. Q3 and Q4 can switch similarly to the DC-to-DC down-converter shown on Figure 10. In addition, Q2 must be switched on constantly to connect the inductor to the output capacitor. For the up-conversion mode, MOSFETs Q2 and Q1 work as the switching stage, as described for the synchronous up-converter on Figure 14. The MOSFET Q3 is constantly switched on to connect the inductor to the input supply voltage in this case.

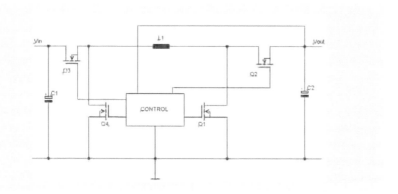

Figure 15 | Up-down converter

3 Medium power DC-to-DC down-converter using small-signal MOSFETs

3.1 DC-to-DC down-converter application board

Figure 16 shows an application Printed-Circuit Board (PCB) with Nexperia small-signal MOSFETs implemented in a DC-to-DC step-down converter. Nexperia offers small-signal MOSFETs in small SMD packages such as SOT457, SOT23, SOT223 and DFN2020MD-6 (SOT1220). Many of these MOSFETs provide very low $R_{DS(on)}$ together with a good switching performance.

The topology of the application board on Figure 16 is a synchronous down-converter same as in Section 2.3.1. The circuit contains a controller LTC3851 of Linear Technology Corporation. Two N-channel MOSFETs build switching stage. The high-side switch connects the node with the inductor to the input supply. Therefore, it is necessary to have a control voltage available that is higher than the input voltage itself. This extra voltage for the control of the gate of the upper MOSFET is generated with a charge pump. The capacitor C25 is connected to the SW node, the switched output and via Schottky diode to a stabilized voltage

INTVCC (pin 12). INTVCC is provided by an internal 5 V LDO. The capacitor is charged via the diode when the low-side switch is turned on. In this case, one side of C25 is connected to ground. If Q2 is turned off and Q1 is switched on, the charged capacitor gets connected to VIN. At the pin BOOST (pin 14) a voltage of V_{IN} + INTVCC – V_F (forward voltage of the diode) can be measured. This boosted voltage can drive the high-side switch properly. Low current Schottky diodes are sufficient for the charge pump (for example, BAT54J, 1PS76SB40 or 1PS76SB21). These diodes are supplied in the SMD packages like SOD323F and SOD323.

The LTC3851 controller contains a 0.8 V precision reference voltage for the output voltage regulation. The output of the down-converter is fed back to the pin FB. A resistor divider formed by R41 + R39 and R38 adjusts the output voltage.The equation for the output voltage is:

$$V_{OUT} = 0,8\ V \times (1 + (R41 + R39)/R38\ ) \hspace{3cm} [26]$$

The controller works with a constant frequency. As described in Section 2.3.1, the output voltage of DC-to-DC down-converter can be controlled rather easily for higher currents, but low current conditions are more ambitious for the control. The duty cycle needs to be changed significantly or the controller can change to a different control mode like burst operation. For the LTC3851 there are three options: forced continuous operation, burst mode operation and a pulse-skip mode.

Burst mode operation gives better efficiency, but more ripple and a higher ElectroMagnetic Interference (EMI) level. The best mode depends on the specification and requirements of the end application.

The switching frequency can be programmed in a range from 250 kHz to 750 kHz. The resistor R30 determines the frequency. Alternatively the controller can synchronize the internal oscillator to an external clock source (MODE/PLLIN, pin 1). In this mode an RC network needs to be connected to pin 2 (FREQ), which serves as PLL loop filter.

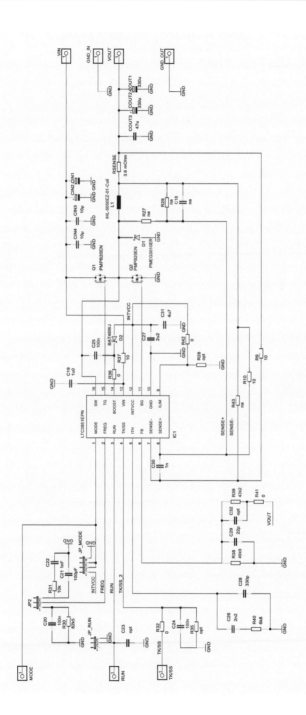

Figure 16 | Circuit diagram for reference application of DC-to-DC down-converter with Nexperia small-signal MOSFET PMN15UN and LTC3851 as controller

3.2 Small-signal MOSFETs suitable for DC-to-DC conversion

DC-to-DC converters can be found in many applications. Topology of step-down converter controller with an external FET stage are often implemented in computing and consumer applications. Modern concepts with latest generation SOC (System-on-Chip) solutions require many separate supply voltages. These can be processors on motherboards, in notebooks and tablet PCs, on core chips of LCD-TV or a set-top box.

The power requirements range from more than hundred watts down to a few watts. In desktop PCs, DC-to-DC converter can be found on the motherboard which provide a current capability of up to 100 A and an output power of up to 130 W. MOSFETs in switching stages are Loss-Free Package (LFPAK) types and to a growing extent Quad Flat-pack No-lead (QFN) 5 × 6 packages. For net- and notebooks the power requirements are smaller. The power consumption ranges from 18 W to 55 W. The switching MOSFETs are mainly SO-8 and QFN 3 × 3 types. In consumer applications such as LCD-TVs and set-top boxes as well as in low-power netbooks or tablet PCs, power requirements from 7 W to 15 W can be found.

For medium power range small-signal MOSFETs can replace SO-8 versions nowadays in smaller packages like QFN 3 × 3, but also in QFN 2 × 2 or SOT457.

3.3 Dimensioning aspects for the inductor and output capacitor

In order to reach a desired current ripple, choose carefully inductance of the inductor used in the down-converter. With a bigger current ripple, the output voltage shows a larger ripple. The ripple increases the smaller the inductance becomes and the higher the input voltage is. Furthermore it increases if the switching frequency is reduced.

ΔI_L can be calculated:

$$\Delta I_L = V_{IN}/L \times t_{on} = V_{OUT}/L \times t_{off} \qquad [27]$$

with:

$$T = t_{on} + t_{off} = 1/f \qquad [28]$$

we get:

$$\Delta I_L = (V_{OUT}/L) \times (1 - V_{OUT}/V_{IN}) \times 1/f \qquad [29]$$

this means:

$$L = (V_{OUT}/\Delta I_L) \times (1 - V_{OUT}/V_{IN}) \times 1/f \qquad [30]$$

For the corner case in which circuit runs at the limit of the continuous mode, current goes down exactly to zero before it increases again and we get simple relation:

$$\Delta I_L = 2 \times I_{average} \qquad [31]$$

Putting equation 32 into the formula for ΔI_L:

$$L = V_{OUT} \times (1 - V_{OUT}/V_{IN})/2 \times I_{average} \times f \qquad [32]$$

In practice, the ripple current ΔI_L is about 30 % of the maximum current, as a rule of thumb.

The ripple of the output voltage does not depend on the chosen inductance and the ΔI_L only, but also on the capacitance of the output capacitor. The bigger the capacitor, the smaller the ripple is. Figure 17 shows the waveform of the current into the capacitor. For a lossless capacitor, there is basic equation:

$$Vc = \frac{1}{C} \times \int_{t0}^{t2} Ic \times dt \qquad [33]$$

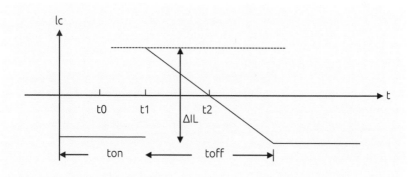

Figure 17 | Capacitor current I_C versus time

For t0 to t1:

$$I_C = \Delta I_L/t_{on} \times t \qquad [34]$$

and for t1 to t2

$$I_C = \Delta I_L / t_{off} \times t \tag{35}$$

the integral formula for the capacitor ripple voltage can be written as:

$$V_{Cpeak} = \frac{1}{C} \int_0^{\frac{ton}{2}} \left(\frac{\Delta I_L}{t_{on}}\right) t \, dt + \frac{1}{C} \int_0^{\frac{toff}{2}} \left(\frac{\Delta I_L}{t_{off}}\right) \cdot t \, dt \tag{36}$$

With:

$$T = t_{on} + t_{off} = 1/f \tag{37}$$

the result is:

$$V_{C\_ripple} = \Delta I_L / (C \times 8 \times f) \tag{38}$$

For real capacitors take into account an Equivalent Series Resistance (ESR). So we get an equation:

$$V_{C\_ripple} = \Delta I_L \times (ESR + 1/(8 \times f \times C_{out})) \tag{39}$$

3.4 MOSFET losses calculation

For MOSFETs used as switches consider two loss processes. One is the ohmic loss caused by the residual on-state resistor $R_{DS(on)}$. The second loss process happens at the switching transients. Because FETs are not ideal switches that can change from off- to on-state or reverse without a small turn-over time.

The $R_{DS(on)}$ losses are also called I^2R-losses and they can be calculated:

$$P_{up\_side\_switch} = D \times (I_{OUT})^2 \times (1 + \delta) \times R_{DS(on)} = V_{OUT} / V_{IN} \times (I_{OUT})^2 \times (1 + \delta) \times R_{DS(on)} \tag{40}$$

with duty cycle:

$$D = t_{on} / T \tag{41}$$

The term $1+\delta$ contains the temperature dependency of $R_{DS(on)}$ of a MOSFET. δ has typically a value of:

$$\delta = (0,005/°C) \times (T_j - 25°C) \tag{42}$$

For the low side switch, there is a similar formula. Because synchronous FET is conducting while the high-side switch is closed, the I^2R looses can be calculated with the equation:

$$P_{low\_side\_switch} = (1 - D) \times (I_{OUT})2 \times (1 + \delta) \times R_{DS(on)} =$$
$$1 - (V_{OUT}/V_{IN}) \times (I_{OUT})^2 \times (1 + \delta) \times R_{DS(on)} \qquad [43]$$

Regarding the transition losses, only the high-side switch suffers from this mechanism. The reason is that the implemented free-wheeling diode (D1 on Figure 16) is getting conductive. It reduces the voltage over the synchronous FET to its small forward voltage V_F. If the circuit does not contain a free-wheeling diode, the situation is different: losses of the body diode need to be added to the $R_{DS(on)}$ losses of the FET. In general, efficiency suffers from the higher V_F and reverse recovery time of the body diode if there is no free-wheeling Schottky diode implemented.

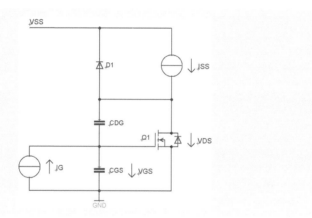

Figure 18 | Diagram for switching behavior tests for MOSFET

Figure 18 shows a test circuit for the switching behavior of a MOSFET. The parasitic capacitors from the gate to the source C_{GS} and from the drain to the gate C_{DG} are depicted explicitly. Current source I_G controlls gate. At the drain another current source is connected towards V_{SS} with a free-wheeling diode in parallel. As long as the FET is closed, the current flows through this diode.

Figure 19 shows how the switching-on process looks like. If the current source I_G is switched on, voltage at C_{GS} rises with a linear curve until gate-source threshold voltage $V_{GS(th)}$ is reached. At this time a drain current starts to flow. This means that the FET remains in the off-state during the time period t0.

During t1 the drain current increases. Also the gate voltage increases until $V_{GS(pl)}$ is reached. $V_{GS(pl)}$ is commonly known as plateau voltage of a MOSFET. It is normally not explicitly mentioned in data sheets, but it can be derived from the diagram gate charge versus gate-source voltage which can be found in detailed data sheets. After the time period t0 and t1, the charge is $Q0 = V_{pl} \times (C_{GS} + C_{DS})$.

In the next time period t2, the drain voltage decreases and gate-source voltage V_{GS} stays constant at $V_{GS(pl)}$. C_{DS} gets charged in the reverse direction with the charge Q1 which is:

$$Q1 = V_{SS} \times C_{DS} \tag{44}$$

C_{DS} is similar to the Miller capacitance known from bipolar transistors and has a significant impact on the switching performance of a MOSFET.

During t3 the gate voltage increases again until the current source is stopped where the desired maximum gate voltage is reached. The $R_{DS(on)}$ of the FET is reduced further. The gate driver provides an additional charge Q2, which is:

$$Q2 = (V_{GS(t4)} - V_{GS(pl)}) \times (C_{GS} + C_{DS}) \tag{45}$$

The total charge follows the equation: $Q_G = Q0 + Q1 + Q2$

This charge can easily exceed 100 nC for a power MOSFET. With the equation:

$$I_G = Q_G/t_s \tag{46}$$

the gate current can be calculated to achieve a switching time t_s. Therefore, if small transition times are desired, in order to keep the switching losses small, apply powerful drivers to control MOSFETs.

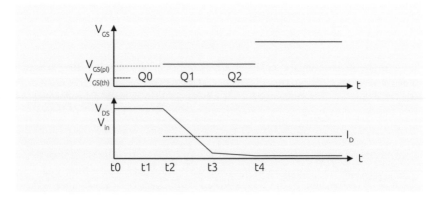

Figure 19 | Turn-on process for MOSFET, V_{GS}, V_{DS} and I_D curves

During the time t1, there is the full input voltage at the FET while drain current I_D increases. In the next time section t2, I_D is constant while drain-source voltage V_{DS}

decreases. The major switching losses occur during these two time periods in the switching process. Rather small losses during t3 are neglected. During t3 $R_{DS(on)}$ falls to the minimum value that is reached when the final V_{GS} voltage is reached.

Switching losses during turn-on occur in the time period t1 and t2. The most dominant time is t2 where the gate voltage of the MOSFET remains at the plateau voltage $V_{(pl)}$. The losses can be calculated as:

$$P_{SW(on)} = V_{IN} \times I/2 \times (t3 + t1) \times 1/T \qquad [47]$$

with the switching frequency of converter: $f_{SW} = 1/T$

Turn-off behavior of a MOSFET is similar to the turn-on process. Total switching losses can be summarized as:

$$P_{SW} = V_{IN} \times 1/T \times (I_{min}/2 \times t_{on} + I_{max}/2 \times t_{off}) \qquad [48]$$

Switching time depends on the current drive capabilities of the driver device and the gate resistance of the FET. If we assume an identical drive current for turn-on and turn-off event, switching time equals: $t_{SW} = Q_G/I_{drive}$

For the LTC3851 t_{SW} can be estimated roughly as follows. R_{drive} is about 2 Ω for the controller. The relevant voltage is driver voltage INTVCC – $V_{(th)}$, so we get:

$$t_{SW} = Q_G \times R_{drive}/(V_{drive} - V_{GS(th)})$$

4 Figures

Chapter 16

Load switches for mobile and computing

Application Note: AN90017

1 Types of load switches

This chapter presents simple load switches in mobile and computing applications

There are several reasons why a circuit or subsystem is required to be disconnected from the power supply by means of a load switch. A very simple and very common reason is, that it helps saving power. An unpowered subsystem may not consume power due to leakage or standby currents. In portable electronic devices, load switches can be used to prevent damage from electrical surges, incorrect battery insertion, and other damaging events that can enter through the power source.

Before diving deeper into the key parameters, let's look at the different types of load switches, first. A high-side load switch connects or disconnects a power source to a load. The switch is controlled by an external enable signal. High-side switches source current to a load. Low-side switches connect or disconnect the load to ground, thus sinking current from the load.

A load switch can be easily implemented with a MOSFET pass transistor. The MOSFET passes current from the power source to the load and is turned on or off via a control signal. Providing the control signal to the MOSFET, a gate-drive circuit connects to the MOSFET's gate to switch the MOSFET on or off.

1.1 P-channel MOSFET load switch

Using a P-channel MOSFET a high-side load switch can be implemented by connecting the input voltage to the MOSFET source and the load to the MOSFET drain, see Figure 1. Pulling the gate low will enable the current flowing into the load.

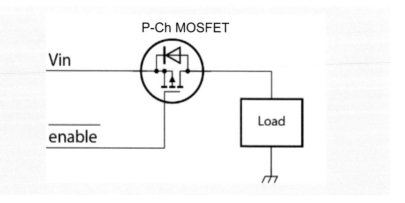

Figure 1 | P-channel MOSFET load switch

1.2 N-channel MOSFET load switches

N-channel MOSFETs have lower ON resistance values than P-channel devices of the same size. However, to get the lower resistance values, a high voltage is needed to drive a MOSFET's gate in the implementation of a high-side load switch using an N-channel MOSFET, see Figure 2. A voltage higher than the input voltage V_{in} has to be provided for proper gate drive otherwise the MOSFET would not turn on entirely but run in linear mode with high power losses.

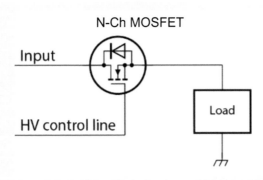

Figure 2 | N-channel MOSFET load switch with high voltage control line

If a high enough voltage to drive the gate is not available, a charge-pump circuit can be used to increase the drive voltage applied to the MOSFET's gate, see Figure 3. While this increases the complexity of the circuit, it is rewarded with the lower ON resistance of the N-Channel MOSFET. However a charge-pump circuit will dissipate some power so that in very energy critical applications that may stay most of the time in stand-by mode, a P-Channel topology can be more efficient.

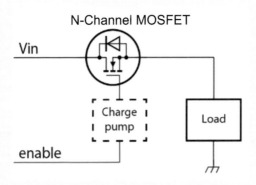

Figure 3 | N-channel MOSFET load switch with high voltage control line

Without high voltage or additional circuitry, the N-channel MOSFET can be used in a low-side load switch. This implementation of a low side load switch is shown in Figure 4. A downside of the low-side load switch is the slight lifting of the ground potential of the load. This needs to be considered especially if the load has communication lines with external components.

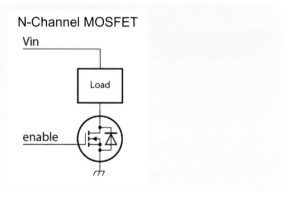

Figure 4 | N-channel MOSFET low-side load switch

More advanced load switch features include reverse voltage protection, reverse current protection. This can be implemented with MOSFETs in common-drain or common-source configuration as shown in the next section

1.3 Reverse current protected load switches

Load switches based on a single MOSFET topology can block current in one direction only. As MOSFETs have an inherent body diode they act like a diode in off-state if driven reverse. In some applications it is required to be able to block current flow in both directions.

Applications, that need blocking of reverse currents are e.g battery driven applications, where discharge of the battery shall be prevented for fault conditions like a short at the charger connector side or in case of electrical failure causing leakage in connected cables and AC adapters.

A common way to block reverse currents is by applying diodes. However, this function can be realized far more efficiently with MOSFET load switches. In order to achieve blocking for both current directions, two MOSFETs have to be put in series with reverse polarity to each other. In this case one of the body diodes can block current flow if not both FETs are turned on. This approach allows to create two alternative topologies of back-drive protected load switches. Either the drain contacts or the source contacts can be connected.

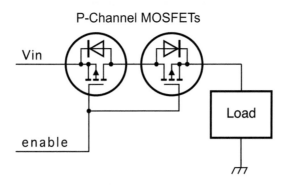

Figure 5 | Reverse current protected common drain load-switch

Control of the back-drive protected load switches can be done with separate gate drive or connected gates. The common drain topology, see Figure 5 has the advantage for a semiconductor component that the drain contact is located towards the substrate side. So, the common drain can be attached directly to the lead frame with a good thermal path into the PCB. For mobile applications often CSP packages can be found. Here the source and gate contacts are facing down to the PCB whereas a drain contact needs an additional down contact. If there is no need to make the drain accessible necessarily. In this case a CSP design becomes very space efficient because no chip area needs to be sacrificed for down connections of drain.

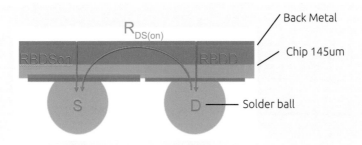

Figure 6 | Turn-on resistance ($R_{DS(on)}$) of a single CSP MOSFET

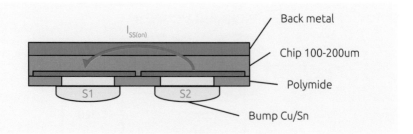

Figure 7 | Turn-on resistance ($R_{DS(on)}$) of a common-drain CSP MOSFET

The common source topology requires an access to the source connection between the MOSFETs. The gate has to be discharged after a turn on, see Figure 8. This does not work without access to this node if the common sources might float.

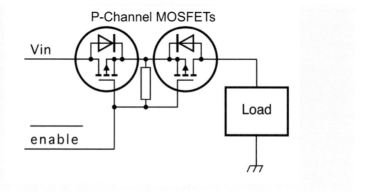

Figure 8 | Reverse current protected common source load-switch

1.4 Reverse polarity protection and supply OR-ing

In cases where no switching of the load is needed a single MOSFET can be used for reverse polarity protection only, Figure 9. The MOSFET can replace simple diodes e.g. in supply OR-ing applications this has the advantage of a lower voltage drop across the MOSFET compared to the voltage drop across the diode.

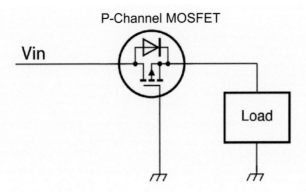

Figure 9 | Reverse current and reverse polarity protection with a P-Ch MOSFET

Another important application of back-drive load-switches is power OR-ing, see Figure 10. If a circuit is able to be powered by one of several power supplies then current flow back into a non-selected supply has to be avoided.

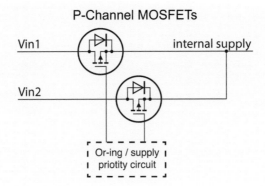

Figure 10 | Power supply OR-ing with P-Channel MOSFETs

2 Important parameters

Important key parameters of a load switch are the turn-on resistance ($R_{DS(on)}$) of the MOSFET that connects between the voltage input and voltage output pins, the maximum current $I_{D(max)}$ that the transistor withstand, and the maximum voltage $V_{DS(max)}$ that the circuit can withstand. The lower the turn-on resistance, the lower the power dissipation of the transistor and the lower the voltage drop from input to output.

While $R_{DS(on)}$, $I_{D(max)}$, and $V_{DS(max)}$ are parameters of the MOSFET, the maximum voltage drop and the maximum power dissipation of a loadswitch can be calculate for a given current I with the formulas below.

$V_{drop} = I * R_{DS(on)(max}$

$P = I * V_{drop} = I^2 * R_{DS(on)(max}$

Today's MOSFETs typically have turn-on resistance values in the tens of milliohms, so, for example, if the load switch has an ON resistance of 50 milliohms and controls a 200 mA load, the MOSFET dissipates just 2 mW when ON, and has an input-to-output voltage drop of 10 mV. Even a peak current of 1 A would only cause a voltage drop of 50 mV and peak power dissipation of 50 mW.

As load switch circuits are active whenever the power is on and are thus designed to have low leakage currents, see Nexperia Application note AN90009 (chapter 14 in this book) - Leakage of small-signal MOSFETs.

3 Figures

Chapter 17

Level shifting techniques in I²C-bus design

Application Note: AN10441

1 Introduction

Logic level shifting may be required when interfacing legacy devices with newer devices that use a smaller geometry process. For bidirectional bus systems like the I²C-bus, such a level shifter must also be bidirectional, without the need of a direction control signal. The simplest way to solve this problem is by connecting a discrete MOSFET to each bus line.

Present technology processes for integrated circuits with clearances of 0.5 μm and less limit the maximum supply voltage and consequently the logic levels for the digital I/O signals. To interface these lower voltage circuits with existing 5 V devices, a level shifter is needed. For bidirectional bus systems like the I2C-bus, such a level shifter must also be bidirectional, without the need of a direction control signal. The simplest way to solve this problem is by connecting a discrete MOSFET to each bus line.

2 Bidirectional level shifter for Fast-mode and Standard-mode I²C-bus systems

In spite of its surprising simplicity, such a solution not only fulfils the requirement of bidirectional level shifting without a direction control signal, it also:

- Isolates a powered-down bus section from the rest of the bus system

- Protects the 'lower voltage' side against high voltage spikes from the 'higher-voltage' side.

The bidirectional level shifter can be used for both Standard-mode (up to100 kbit/s) or in Fast-mode (up to 400 kbit/s) I²C-bus systems. It is not intended for Hs-mode systems, which may have a bridge with a level shifting possibility.

2.1 Connecting devices with different logic levels

Different voltage devices could be connected to the same bus by using pull-up resistors to the supply voltage line. Although this is the simplest solution, the lower voltage devices must be 5 V tolerant, which can make them more expensive to manufacture. By using a bidirectional level shifter, however, it is possible to interconnect two sections of an I²C-bus system, with each section having a different supply voltage and different logic levels. Such a configuration is shown in Figure 1. The left 'low-voltage' section has pull-up resistors and devices connected to a 3.3 V supply voltage; the right 'high-voltage' section has pull-up resistors and devices connected to a 5 V supply voltage. The devices of each section have I/Os with supply voltage related logic input levels and an open-drain output configuration.

The level shifter for each bus line is identical and consists of one discrete N-channel enhancement MOSFET; TR1 for the serial data line SDA and TR2 for the serial clock line SCL. The gates (g) have to be connected to the lowest supply voltage V_{DD1}, the sources (s) to the bus lines of the 'lower-voltage' section, and the drains (d) to the bus lines of the 'higher-voltage' section. Many MOSFETs have the substrate internally connected with its source, if this is not the case, an external connection should be made. Each MOSFET has an integral diode (n-p junction) between the drain and substrate.

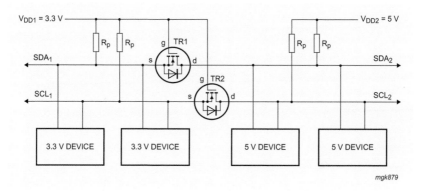

Figure 1 | Bidirectional level shifter circuit connecting two different voltage sections in an I2C-bus system

2.1.1 Operation of the level shifter

The following three states should be considered during the operation of the level shifter:

1. No device is pulling down the bus line. The bus line of the 'lower-voltage' section is pulled up by its pull-up resistors R_p to 3.3 V. The gate and the source of the MOSFET are both at 3.3 V, so its V_{GS} is below the threshold voltage and the MOSFET is not conducting. This allows the bus line at the 'higher-voltage' section to be pulled up by its pull-up resistor R_p to 5 V. So the bus lines of both sections are HIGH, but at a different voltage level.

2. A 3.3 V device pulls down the bus line to a LOW level. The source of the MOSFET also becomes LOW, while the gate stays at 3.3 V. V_{GS} rises above

the threshold and the MOSFET starts to conduct. The bus line of the 'higher-voltage' section is then also pulled down to a LOW level by the 3.3 V device via the conducting MOSFET. So the bus lines of both sections go LOW to the same voltage level.

3. A 5 V device pulls down the bus line to a LOW level. The drain-substrate diode of the MOSFET the 'lower-voltage' section is pulled down until V_{GS} passes the threshold and the MOSFET starts to conduct. The bus line of the 'lower-voltage' section is then further pulled down to a LOW level by the 5 V device via the conducting MOSFET. So the bus lines of both sections go LOW to the same voltage level.

The three states show that the logic levels are transferred in both directions of the bus system, independent of the driving section. State 1 performs the level shift function. States 2 and 3 perform a 'wired-AND' function between the bus lines of both sections as required by the I2C-bus specification.

Supply voltages other than 3.3 V for V_{DD1} and 5 V for V_{DD2} can also be applied, e.g., 2 V for V_{DD1} and 10 V for V_{DD2} is feasible. In normal operation V_{DD2} must be equal to or higher than V_{DD1} (V_{DD2} is allowed to fall below V_{DD1} during switching power on/off).

3 Figures

Chapter 18

Understanding Power GaN FET data sheet parameters

Application Note: AN90005

1 Introduction

This chapter explains the content of Nexperia Power GaN FET data sheets. Nomenclature, pinning and key parameters are detailed.

The chapter details the data sheet for the GAN063-650WSA GaN FET device from Nexperia. Visit the product information page on Nexperia.com to download the latest version of the full data sheet.

2 Nomenclature

The device name (type number) is shown at the top of the data sheet. The name contains some important information about the device. In the below example for GAN063-650WSA, the maximum on-state resistance and the limiting drain-source voltage are specified, together with letter codes indicating the package, the mounting base electrical connection and the technology generation.

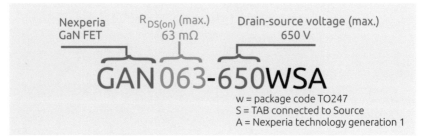

Figure 1 | GaN FET Nomenclature

3 Pinning information

Table 1: Pinning information

Pin	Symbol	Description	Simplified outline	Graphic symbol
1	G	gate		
2	S	source		
3	D	drain		
mb	S	mounting base; connected to source	TO-247 (SOT429)	aaa-028116

The Nexperia GAN063-650WSA is packaged in a TO247 (SOT429) package with a source tab. The traditional TO-247 provides excellent heat transfer, and therefore excellent power-handling capability.

mounting base
connected to source

aaa-029292

Note: the pin functions are different from a standard MOSFET: pin 1 is the gate, pin 2 is the source and pin 3 is the drain.

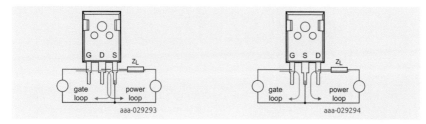

Figure 2 | Conventional pin assignment   **Figure 3** | Nexperia pin assignment

Using pin 2 as the source pin allows the circuit designer to keep the gate loop and the power loop separate. This facilitates a very clean design and greatly reduces or eliminates cross coupling. The PCB design can be optimised to take advantage of this feature.

4 Two-chip, integrated, normally-off power switch

The full graphic symbol of a GaN FET is shown in the pinning information section of the data sheet. Note that the symbol includes two devices:

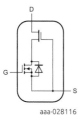

aaa-028116

- Low-voltage Si MOSFET with a p-n body diode

- High-voltage GaN FET without a p-n body diode

The full graphic symbol shows that the device is a two chip integrated switch. Functionally the switch is normally off. Internally the device is built with two chips. The high-voltage GaN HEMT or FET is normally on, which is the type most naturally made with GaN, and is combined with a high performance normally-off Si MOSFET specifically developed to complement the GaN HEMT. The two chips are integrated with absolute minimum inductance between them.

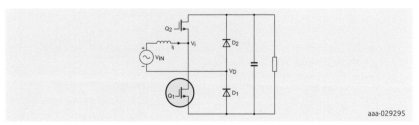

aaa-029295

Figure 4 | Simplified GaN FET symbol

In circuit schematics where just the basic switching function is important, a simple N-channel FET symbol is used to represent the complete, integrated switch (see Q1 circled in red above). When you see the simple symbol, understand that it represents this two-chip integrated combination.

5 GaN FET limiting values

The limiting values table provides the range of operating conditions allowed for the GaN FET. The conditions are defined in accordance with the *Absolute Maximum Rating System* (IEC 60134).

Operation outside of these conditions is not guaranteed, so it is recommended that these values are never exceeded. Doing so risks immediate device failure or reduced lifetime of the GaN FET. To calculate how the limiting values change with temperature de-rating curves are provided.

The limiting values table for the GAN063-650WSA is given as an example of a standard limiting values table, in Table 2.

Table 2: Limiting values

In accordance with the Absolute Maximum Rating System (IEC 60134).

Symbol	Parameter	Conditions	Min	Max	Unit
V_{DS}	drain-source voltage	-55 °C ≤ T_j ≤ 175 °C	-	650	V
V_{TDS}	transient drain to source voltage	pulsed; t_p = 1 µs; δ_{factor} = 0.01	-	800	V
V_{GS}	gate-source voltage		-20	20	V
P_{tot}	total power dissipation	T_{mb} = 25 °C; Figure 8	-	143	W
I_D	drain current	V_{GS} = 10 V; T_{mb} = 25 °C	-	34.5	A
		V_{GS} = 10 V; T_{mb} = 100 °C	-	24.4	A
I_{DM}	peak drain current	pulsed; t_p ≤ 10 µs; T_{mb} = 25°C	-	150	A
T_{stg}	storage temperature		-55	150	°C
T_j	junction temperature		-55	175	°C
$T_{sld(M)}$	peak soldering temperature		-	260	°C
Source-drain diode					
I_S	source current	T_{mb} = 25 °C; V_{GS} = 0 V	-	34.5	A
I_{SM}	peak source current	pulsed; t_p ≤ 10 µs; T_{mb} = 25 °C	-	150	A

5.1 Drain source voltage , V_{DS}

In accordance with the Absolute Maximum Rating System (IEC 60134).

Symbol	Parameter	Conditions	Min	Max	Unit
V_{DS}	drain-source voltage	-55 °C ≤ T_j ≤ 175 °C	-	650	V
V_{TDS}	transient drain to source voltage	pulsed; t_p = 1 µs; δ_{factor} = 0.01	-	800	V

This 650 V rating is the maximum value that will give you the desired product life. GaN FETs do not have an avalanche breakdown mechanism. The Nexperia GaN FET does not typically show any significant leakage current until a V_{DS} well beyond 800 V is reached. So there is an extra margin in V_{DS} before excess leakage occurs. If the GaN FET is subjected to a sufficiently high voltage, well beyond the specified maximum, then because there is no clamping mechanism damage and failure will occur. Since GaN FETs do not have an avalanche breakdown mechanism they are immune to cosmic radiation and so no further derating is required.

- V_{DS} is the maximum voltage the device is guaranteed to block between drain and source terminals in the off-state. V_{DS} is a DC rating
- V_{DS} is not limited by avalanche breakdown; the rating can be applied over the entire operating range of -55 °C to 175 °C in contrast to the V_{DS} for a Si MOSFET which must be de-rated below 25 °C

5.2 Transient drain-source voltage, V_{TDS}

In accordance with the Absolute Maximum Rating System (IEC 60134).

Symbol	Parameter	Conditions	Min	Max	Unit
V_{DS}	drain-source voltage	-55 °C ≤ T_j ≤ 175 °C	-	650	V
V_{TDS}	transient drain to source voltage	pulsed; t_p = 1 µs; δfactor = 0.01	-	800	V

V_{TDS} is the **Maximum** repetitive transient voltage the device is guaranteed to block between drain and source in the off state. This transient rating, applies over the entire operating temperature range.

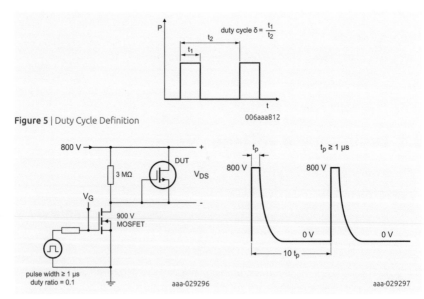

Figure 5 | Duty Cycle Definition

Figure 6 | V_{TDS} test circuit

Figure 7 | V_{TDS} waveform

5.3 Gate source voltage, VGS and total power dissipation, P_{tot}

In accordance with the Absolute Maximum Rating System (IEC 60134).

Symbol	Parameter	Conditions	Min	Max	Unit
V_{DS}	drain-source voltage	-55 °C ≤ T_j ≤ 175 °C	-	650	V
V_{TDS}	transient drain to source voltage	pulsed; t_p = 1 μs; δfactor = 0.01	-	800	V
V_{GS}	gate-source voltage		-20	20	V
P_{tot}	total power dissipation	T_{mb} = 25 °C; Figure 8	-	143	W

V_{GS}
Maximum voltage the device is guaranteed to block between the gate and source terminals. This is a DC rating, and applies over the entire operating temperature range.

P_{tot}
P_{tot} is the Total Power dissipation is the maximum for a device with a mounting base temperature of 25 °C.

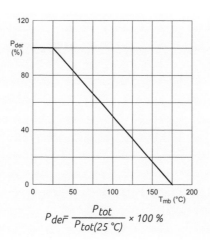

$$P_{der} = \frac{P_{tot}}{P_{tot(25\,°C)}} \times 100\,\%$$

03aa16

Figure 8 | Normalised total power dissipation as a function of mounting base temperature

Power dissipation is calculated as that which would take the device to the maximum allowed junction temperature while keeping the mounting base at 25 °C.

5.4 Continuous and pulsed currents, I_D, I_{DM}, I_S and I_{SM}

In accordance with the Absolute Maximum Rating System (IEC 60134).

Symbol	Parameter	Conditions	Min	Max	Unit
V_{DS}	drain-source voltage	-55 °C ≤ T_j ≤ 175 °C	-	650	V
V_{TDS}	transient drain to source voltage	pulsed; t_p = 1 µs; $^\delta$factor = 0.01	-	800	V
V_{GS}	gate-source voltage		-20	20	V
P_{tot}	total power dissipation	T_{mb} = 25 °C; Figure 8	-	143	W
I_D	drain current	V_{GS} = 10 V; T_{mb} = 25 °C	-	34.5	A
		V_{GS} = 10 V; T_{mb} = 100 °C	-	24.4	A
I_{DM}	peak drain current	pulsed; t_p ≤ 10 µs; T_{mb} = 25ºC	-	150	A
T_{stg}	storage temperature		-55	150	°C
T_j	junction temperature		-55	175	°C
$T_{sld(M)}$	peak soldering temperature		-	260	°C
Source-drain diode					
I_S	source current	T_{mb} = 25 °C; V_{GS} = 0 V	-	34.5	A
I_{SM}	peak source current	pulsed; t_p ≤ 10 µs; T_{mb} = 25 °C	-	150	A

The 25 °C current ratings are the same for both current directions (I_D and I_S).

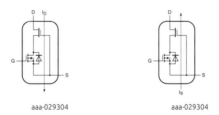

aaa-029304   aaa-029304

The maximum current at any T_{mb} is the current which increases T_j to the maximum allowed temperature (175 °C).

6 GaN FET static characteristics

These are the device parameters that explain how the GaN FET behaves in it normal operating conditions

6.1 Gate-source threshold voltage, $V_{GS(th)}$

Symbol	Parameter	Conditions		Min	Typ	Max	Unit
Static characteristics							
$V_{GS(th)}$	gate-source threshold voltage	$I_D = 1$ mA; $V_{DS}=V_{GS}$; $T_j = 25$ °C		3.4	3.9	4.5	V
		$I_D = 1$ mA; $V_{DS}=V_{GS}$; $T_j = 175$ °C; Fig. 9		2.2	-	-	V
		$I_D = 1$ mA; $V_{DS}=V_{GS}$; $T_j = -55$ °C; Fig. 9		-	-	5.2	V
I_{DSS}	drain leakage current	$V_{DS} = 650$ V; $V_{GS} = 0$ V; $T_j = 25$ °C		-	2	25	µA
		$V_{DS} = 650$ V; $V_{GS} = 0$ V; $T_j = 175$ °C		-	25	-	µA
I_{GSS}	gate leakage current	$V_{GS} = -20$ V; $V_{DS} = 0$ V; $T_j = 25$ °C		-	10	100	nA
		$V_{GS} = 20$ V; $V_{DS} = 0$ V; $T_j = 25$ °C		-	10	100	nA

Gate-source threshold voltage for the GaN FET device is the gate-source threshold voltage of the Si MOSFET. This gate threshold is 3.9 V typically, with a negative temperature co-efficient.

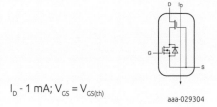

$I_D - 1$ mA; $V_{GS} = V_{GS(th)}$

aaa-029304

Figure 9 | GaN FET gate-source threshold voltage

6.2 Drain-source on-state resistance, $R_{DS(on)}$

R_{DSon}	drain-source on-state resistance	$V_{GS} = 10$ V; $I_D = 25$ A; $T_j = 25$ °C		-	50	60	mΩ
		$V_{GS} = 10$ V; $I_D = 25$ A; $T_j = 175$ °C; Fig. 10		-	120	-	mΩ

Understanding Power GaN FET data sheet parameters

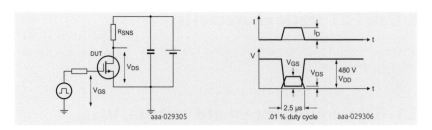

Figure 10 | Test circuit for dynamic R$_{DS(on)}$ **Figure 11** | Dynamic R$_{DS(on)}$ waveform

R$_{DS(on)}$ is the drain-to-source on-state resistance of the GaN FET. This has a dynamic value for GaN FETs. When R$_{DS(on)}$ is measured immediately after turn-on, following period of blocking high-voltage, this value will be slightly higher than normal. This is due to temporary charge trapping in the device structure. Nexperia have optimised the device so that charge trapping and dynamic R$_{DS(on)}$ are minimised.

As can be seen in Figure 12, R$_{DS(on)}$ is shown as a normalised function of junction temperature.

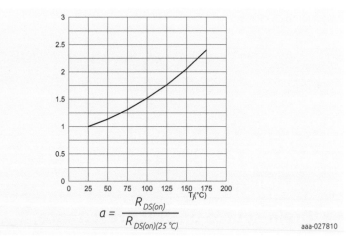

$$a = \frac{R_{DS(on)}}{R_{DS(on)(25\ ^\circ C)}}$$

Figure 12 | Normalised drain-source on-state resistance as a funtion of junction temperature

7 GaN FET dynamic characteristics

These are the device parameters that explain how the GaN FET behaves in its normal operating conditions

7.1 Gate charge $Q_{G(tot)}$, Q_{GS} and Q_{GD}

Dynamic characteristics							
$Q_{G(tot)}$	total gate charge	I_D = 25 A; V_{DS} = 400 V; V_{GS} = 10 V; T_j = 25 °C		-	15	-	nC
Q_{GS}	gate-source charge			-	6	-	nC
Q_{GD}	gate-drain charge			-	4	-	nC

Gate charge for GaN FET is defined in the same way as a normal MOSFET, because the cascode arrangement of a GaN FET means that the gate is in fact the gate of a LV MOSFET. Since the LV MOSFET is a relatively small device it has a small gate charge suited to high speed switching.

7.2 Capacitances C_{iss}, C_{oss} and C_{rss}

C_{iss}	input capacitance	V_{DS} = 400 V; V_{GS} = 0 V; f = 1 MHz; T_j = 25 °C; Fig. 11		-	1000	-	pF
C_{oss}	output capacitance			-	130	-	pF
C_{rss}	reverse transfer capacitance			-	8	-	pF

Traditional small signal capacitance is shown in Figure 13. The discontinuity (step change) in Figure 13 is where GaN HEMT pinches off. Capacitance relates charge to voltage and energy to voltage. For a linear capacitance, the following fundamental equations apply:

$$Q = CV \qquad E = \frac{CV^2}{2}$$

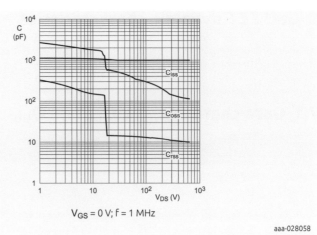

$V_{GS} = 0$ V; $f = 1$ MHz

aaa-028058

Figure 13 | Input, output and reverse transfer capacitance as a funtion of drain-source voltage; typical values

The capacitances $C_{o(er)}$ and $C_{o(tr)}$ attempt to capture these relationships for a nonlinear capacitance.

7.3 Effective output capacitance (energy related), $C_{o(er)}$

$C_{o(er)}$	effective output capacitance, energy related	0 V ≤ V_{DS} ≤ 400 V; $V_{GS} = 0$ V; $T_j = 25$ °C; Fig. 12		-	190	-	pF
$C_{o(tr)}$	effective output capacitance, time related	0 V ≤ V_{DS} ≤ 400 V; $V_{GS} = 0$ V; $T_j = 25$ °C		-	310	-	pF

The GaN FET capacitance parameter $C_{o(er)}$ is the effective output capacitance (energy-related) dependent on the drain voltage

Note that $0 \leq V_{DS} \leq 400$ V shown above, means as the voltage rises from 0 V to 400 V.

$$E_{oss} = \int_{0}^{Q_{oss}} V_{DS} \cdot dq = \int_{0}^{} V_{DS} \cdot C\left(V_{DS}\right) \cdot d V_{DS}$$

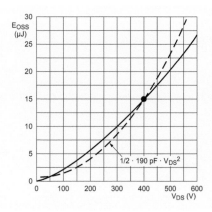

Figure 14 | E_{OSS} as a function of V_{DS}

At a specific V_{DS}, a unique value of C_{oss} satisfies the equation:

$$E_{oss} = 1/2 \cdot Co(er) \cdot V_{DS}^2$$

e.g.

$$E_{oss} = 1/2 \cdot 190\,pF \cdot 400^2 = 15.2\,\mu J$$

By integrating C_{OSS} with respect to V_{DS}, the result will be Q_{OSS}. If we then integrate Q_{OSS} with respect to V_{DS}, we will then arrive at E_{OSS}.

$E_{OSS} *$ switching frequency will give the switching power loss in Watts.

7.4 Effective output capacitance (time related), $C_{o(tr)}$

$C_{o(er)}$	effective output capacitance, energy related	$0\ V \le V_{DS} \le 400\ V; V_{GS} = 0\ V;$ $T_j = 25\ °C;$ Fig. 12		-	190	-	pF
$C_{o(tr)}$	effective output capacitance, time related	$0\ V \le V_{DS} \le 400\ V; V_{GS} = 0\ V;$ $T_j = 25\ °C$		-	310	-	pF

The GaN FET capacitance parameter $C_{o(tr)}$ is the equivalent capacitance to give same charging time, as V_{DS} rises from 0 V to 400 V. This can also be described as a constant current being used to charge the output capacitance, giving a time related effective value.

$$Q_{oss} = \int_0^{Q_{oss}} dq = \int_0^{V} C\left(V_{DS}\right) \cdot d V_{DS}$$

At a specific V_{DS}, a unique value of C_{oss} satisfies the equation:

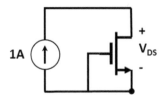

$$V_{DS} = \frac{Q_{OSS}}{C_{(tr)}} = \frac{1}{C_{o(tr)}} \int_0^t i(t) \cdot dt$$

e.g.

$$400\,V = \frac{1}{310\,pF} \cdot \int_0^{120\,ns} 1.0\,A \cdot dt$$

$$Q_{oss} = 124\,nC$$

7.5 Output charge and stored energy, Q_{oss} and E_{oss}

Rather than using the $C_{o(tr)}$ and $C_{o(er)}$ parameters, it is much easier to use the graphs shown below that are also available in the data sheet. The respective Q_{OSS} and E_{OSS} values can be read directly for the required V_{DS}.

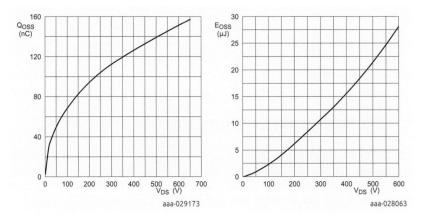

aaa-029173

aaa-028063

Figure 15 | Typical Q_{OSS}

Figure 16 | Typical C_{OSS} stored energy

7.6 GaN FET switching time characteristics

$t_{d(on)}$	turn-on delay time	$V_{DS} = 400$ V; $R_L = 16$ Ω; $V_{GS} = 12$ V; $R_{G(ext)} = 40$ Ω	-	57	-	ns
t_r	rise time		-	10	-	ns
$t_{d(off)}$	turn-off delay time		-	88	-	ns
t_f	fall time		-	11	-	ns
Q_{oss}	output charge	$V_{GS} = 0$ V; $V_{DS} = 400$ V	-	125	-	nC

Nexperia GaN FETs generally require a ferrite bead in series with the gate. This serves to de-"Q" the gate-source loop and improve the switching stability. The ferrite bead effectively provides damping impedance at frequencies > 100 MHz. It also introduces a small propagation delay, however it does not introduce any additional loss.

The GAN063-650WSA in TO247 package has an integral ferrite bead, and so an external bead is not required. Newer GaN FETs may not include the integral ferrite bead, and so one must be included in the external gate drive. **Always refer to the data sheet of specific devices for details.**

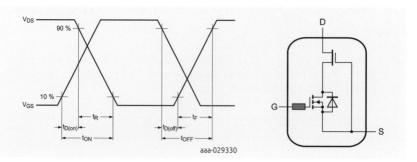

Figure 17 | Switching time waveform

Figure 18 | Internal Ferrite bead

7.7 Source-drain voltage, V_{SD}

Source-drain diode						
V_{SD}	source-drain voltage	I_S = 25 A; V_{GS} = 0 V; T_j = 25 °C; Fig. 13	-	1.9	-	V
		I_S = 12.5 A; V_{GS} = 0 V; T_j = 25 °C	-	1.35	-	V
t_{rr}	reverse recovery time	I_S = 25 A; dI_S/dt = -1000 A/µs;	-	54	-	ns
Q_r	recovered charge	V_{GS} = 0 V; V_{DS} = 400 V; Fig. 14	-	125	-	nC

This device parameter source-drain voltage refers to the GaN FET device when it is acting as a two terminal device when not enhanced with the gate V_{GS} = 0 V.

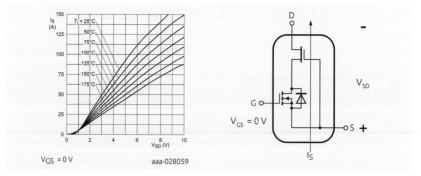

Figure 19 | Source-drain (diode forward) current as a function of source-drain (diode forward) voltage; typical values

Figure 20 | Source-drain (diode forward) voltage

V_{SD} is the voltage developed whilst GaN FET conducts in reverse direction (e.g. acting as a rectifier carrying freewheeling current) Here the voltage V_{SD} comprises the forward voltage of the Silicon MOSFET body diode and the voltage drop across the 2 DEG channel of the GaN HEMT.

8 Q_r for GaN FET switches

Symbol	Parameter	Conditions	Min	Typ	Max	Unit
$t_{d(on)}$	turn-on delay time	$V_{DS} = 400$ V; $R_L = 16\ \Omega$; $V_{GS} = 12$ V; $R_{G(ext)} = 40\ \Omega$	-	57	-	ns
t_r	rise time		-	10	-	ns
$t_{d(off)}$	turn-off delay time		-	88	-	ns
t_f	fall time		-	11	-	ns
Q_{oss}	output charge	$V_{GS} = 0$ V; $V_{DS} = 400$ V	-	125	-	nC
Source-drain diode						
V_{SD}	source-drain voltage	$I_S = 25$ A; $V_{GS} = 0$ V; $T_j = 25$ °C; Fig. 13	-	1.9	-	V
		$I_S = 12.5$ A; $V_{GS} = 0$ V; $T_j = 25$ °C	-	1.35	-	V
t_{rr}	reverse recovery time	$I_S = 25$ A; $dI_S/dt = -1000$ A/μs;	-	84	-	ns
Q_r	recovered charge	$V_{GS} = 0$ V; $V_{DS} = 400$ V; Fig. 14	-	125	-	nC

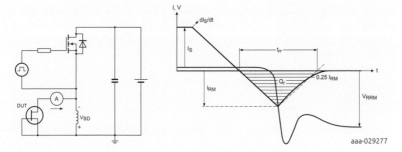

Figure 21 | Recovered charge test circuit and measurement waveforms

The Device Under Test (DUT) is carrying a freewheeling current. The switch in the high side of the test circuit in Figure 21 will then turn on and force a transition at the switching node from low voltage to high voltage. This will cause the current in the DUT to change from freewheeling current to some negative current up until the point that the DUT is blocking the full DC supply voltage. If you integrate the negative current you will get the minority carrier stored change plus any output capacitance charge.

For GaN FETs, the charge on the output capacitance Q_{OSS} is the dominant component of the reverse recovery charge Q_r. Hence the reason that the datasheet for the Nexperia GaN FET specifies the same value for both Q_{OSS} and Q_r.

Some GaN device manufacturers will claim to have zero reverse recovery charge Q_r because they do not have a PN junction body diode. However, they will still have Q_{OSS}.

9 Switching-node snubber

To achieve maximum efficiency and stability when switching high currents, a switching node R_C snubber (R, C_{sn}) is recommended. For $I_L < 14$ A, a switching-node snubber is not required.

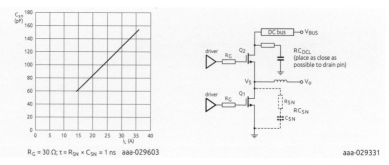

$R_G = 30\ \Omega; \tau = R_{SN} \times C_{SN} = 1$ ns   aaa-029603

aaa-029331

Figure 22 | Snubber capacitance as function of load current

Figure 23 | DC-link snubber circuit

> **Note:** a DC-link snubber is recommended in all cases. Optimal is 20 nF in series with 4 Ω, most easily achieved with parallel combination 10 nF and 8 Ω. This snubber lowers the Q factor of any resonance in the bus. That resonance will act as a load on the high gain amplifier that is the GaN FET and can lead to instability.

For some GaN FETs, like the GAN063-650WSA, an RC snubber is recommended for the switching node. This will increase switching loss, so this is only recommended at high power levels where the losses are a very small percentage of the total power. Other GaN FETs do not require a snubber on the switching node at any power level. **Always refer to the data sheet of specific devices for details.**

How to read a GaN FET
datasheet voltage change

10 Tables

10 Figures

An insight into Nexperia Power GaN technology – Applications, quality, reliability and scalability

Application Note: TN90004

An insight into Nexperia Power GaN technology – Applications, quality, reliability and scalability

1 Introduction

In this chapter we have concentrated on the Power GaN product and technology robustness, quality, reliability and volume manufacturability based on GaN on Si base material. We report here on the product robustness from applications and parametric point of view and qualification testing results of latest generation 650V GaN FETs qualified in accordance with AEC-Q101 standard. Devices offer rated operating temperature of -55°C to +175°C and this family comes with robust gate with high threshold voltage which provides a high safety margin against gate-source transients. Some of the tests are performed beyond AEC-Q101 requirements.

Most efficient power conversion requires best semiconductor devices as the fundamental building block. Power GaN technology offers best possible efficiency. Proving performance is not in question for those closely following the Power GaN technology for its performance demonstration in different applications. Providing robustness of the products in operation, quality, reliability of the technology and the scalability uptake in manufacturing are yet to prove. Power GaN technology is full of challenges. In RF applications they are already successful but in high current high power applications in high voltage, volume manufacturers need to address these challenges to satisfaction. In this paper we'd like to share product robustness for applications, quality and reliability at high voltage and high temperatures, for the Power GaN technology.

Nexperia Power GaN technology focuses on high power applications like AC/DC, PFC, OBC, DC/ DC and Traction Inverters within 650V-900V for Automotive, Telecom, Server, storage, data centres and industrial market sectors.

WBG materials with higher critical electric field and higher mobility together give lowest $R_{DS(on)}$ (source drain on state resistance) for higher voltages and significantly better switching FOM (Figure of Merit). WBG devices as beginning to enter the market shows significant promise and takes away many limitations naturally imposed by Si IGBT and Si SJ devices. Some of the hard switched application topologies where Si SJ FETs cannot be used due to the diode reverse recovery can easily use Power GaN FETs and take full advantage of reduced components count and higher efficiency with simpler control schemes.

GaN HEMT (High Electron Mobility Transistor) works with the formation of 2DEG (2 Dimensional Electron Gas) due to the spontaneous polarisation and piezoelectric polarisation combined at the interface of GaN and Al_xGa1-_xN. Epi is formed on Si substrate via seed layer and a graded layer of GaN and AlGaN layers before the pure GaN layer is grown and thin layer of AlGaN then forms the 2DEG. Electron mobility in this layer is very high hence the name.

Current Power GaN FETs are of two main flavour: E-mode or single die normally off device, and D-mode or two die normally off device. Stability and leakage current of the E-mode gates are of concern but two die normally off or cascode configuration currently gives peace of mind as the driving of these FETs are simple and robust. E-mode device drive is complex, especially for high voltage high power applications. For high voltage and high power applications, to avoid gate bounce and harmful shoot through situation, need to have high gate threshold voltage and stable gate drive without worrying for over drive. This is currently not achievable with existing E-mode technologies. The device in our presentation is two die normally off configuration.

2 Product robustness

The product parameters shared here came from our 50 mΩ (typical at 25 °C) 650 V device but all our products/technology share the same common robustness. Product robustness include parametric assurance like, high reliability gate structure (± 20 V) and high threshold voltage (V_{th} = 4 V) that provides a high safety margin against gate source transients induced due to the high drain source dv/dt, high voltage source-drain transient specification (800 V for 650 V device) capable of handling switching transients up to 800 V reliably, rated operating range of -55 °C to 175°C with $T_{j(max)}$ of 175 °C, body diode characteristics with very low V_F (1.3V @ 12 A) enabling Si- like freewheeling current capability without complex dead time adjustments and along with other parametric performances are part of the product robustness of the GaN product family.

3 Quality / qualification of power GaN technology including failure modes

The latest generation 650 V GaN FETs are qualified in accordance with AEC-Q101 Rev D level qualification tests. Results shared here are done on 50 mΩ (typical at 25 °C) 650 V device that include 650 V, 175 °C High Temperature Reverse Bias (HTRB) tests (1000 hrs) and dynamic $R_{DS(on)}$ shifts. In the following, the term dynamic $R_{DS(on)}$ will be used to emphasize that $R_{DS(on)}$ measurements are made with a dynamic, switch-mode test. Temperature cycling tests (1000 cycles) are performed over the range of -55°C to 150°C. High temperature (175 °C) Gate positive (+20 V) and negative (-20 V) bias tests were performed. Further life tests include high temperature biased and unbiased humidity tests and operating life tests. These are only some of the critical tests performed and passed to show the reliability and high quality of the technology.

3.1 HTRB

High-Temperature Reverse Bias has been performed at full rated voltage and maximum operating temperature: 650 V and 175 °C. The condition for passing is that $R_{DS(on)}$ does not shift by more than 20%. For GaN FETs it is important that $R_{DS(on)}$ be tested dynamically to detect any short-term change due to charge trapping. Figure 1 shows the shift in dynamic $R_{DS(on)}$ for the test population. Note that the maximum shift is less than 15%. An additional HTRB test was performed and passed at 800 V for 10 hours. This voltage is well above the DC rating, but does correspond to the repetitive transient voltage rating.

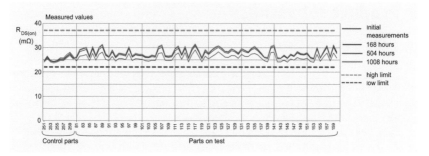

Figure 1 | Dynamic $R_{DS(on)}$ measurement during HTRB

3.2 HTOL

High-Temperature Operating Life tests are not part of the AEC-Q101 standard, but are useful in validating reliability of the parts under actual operating conditions. This is particularly important for new materials, like GaN, to ensure that any new or unfamiliar failure modes are uncovered. A basic half-bridge operating in continuous conduction mode provides the most fundamental exercise of switching behaviour. For this test, a number of identical half-bridge circuits were prepared using two each of the GAN063-650WSA. These were operated continuously as synchronous-boost converters with the following conditions:

- V_{in} = 200 V
- V_{out} = 480 V
- P_{out} = 800 W
- T_j = 175 °C
- Frequency = 300 kHz

The following graph shows efficiency of all samples during the 1,000 hour test. As may be seen, there is no indication of degradation in any of the sample circuits. Following the tests, all devices were tested for shifts in dynamic $R_{DS(on)}$, leakage current, and threshold voltage. All parameters were found to be stable, with any parametric shift within allowed levels.

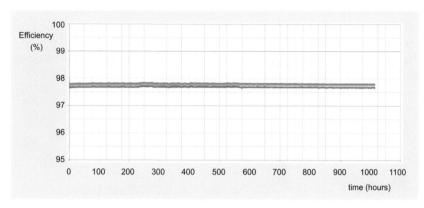

Figure 2 | Efficiency of boost converters (HTOL) over 1000 hours

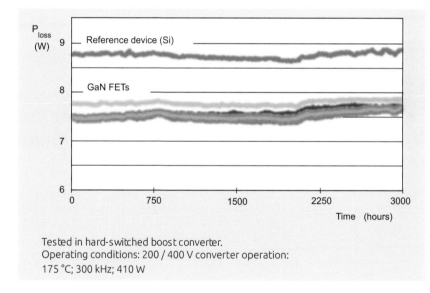

Tested in hard-switched boost converter.
Operating conditions: 200 / 400 V converter operation:
175 °C; 300 kHz; 410 W

Figure 3 | Hard switched boost converter (HTOL) @ 175 °C for 3000 hours

Failure modes addressed by life testing power GaN technology failure modes can be linked back to the life testing and extra testing performed. Like power cycling relates to wire bond heel crack, temperature cycling address the solder degradation, HTGB look at the gate insulator failure, HTRB addresses the field plate insulator failure while high temperature direct current test addresses the trapped charge in gate region and consequently higher $R_{DS(on)}$ (>20% assumes fail).

4 Conclusion

Power GaN technology, though at the early stage of technology maturity offers significant commercial viability with robustness and reliability. For scaling up, tremendous growth potential is better addressed with power GaN technology on Si.

What is CCPAK?

GaN FETs delivering AEC-Q101 level robustness

CCPAK copper clip comes to high voltage applications

Power GaN the need for efficient power conversion

Power GaN FETs a strategic approach to bring the best without compromising robustness and quality

Nexperia copper-clip SMD CCPAK GaN FET package in half-bridge evaluation board

5 References

1. 600 V JEDEC-qualified highly reliable GaN HEMTs on Si substrates
   - T. Kikkawa et al., 2014 IEEE International Electron Devices Meeting,
   San Francisco, CA, 2014, pp. 2.6.1-2.6.4.

2. 650 V Highly Reliable GaN HEMTs on Si substrates over multiple
   generations: matching Silicon CMOS manufacturing metrics and process
   control
   - S. Chowdhury, et al., Compound Semiconductor Integrated Circuit Symposium
   (CSICS), IEEE, 2016.

An insight into Nexperia Power GaN technology – Applications, quality, reliability and scalability

6 Figures

Chapter 20

Power GaN technology: the need for efficient power conversion

Application Note: AN90021

1 Introduction

Power Gallium Nitride(GaN) technology shows the greatest performance benefits against other incumbent technologies including silicon (Si) technology. This chapter details the scalability and growth of the technology as well as the quality and reliability of Nexperia GaN FETs. The performance of GaN FET power switches in various applications is examined.

The biggest motivation and driver for semiconductor power device innovation is improved efficiency in power conversion. Power Gallium Nitride (GaN) technology shows the greatest performance benefits against other incumbent technologies, including silicon (Si) technology. A reduction in power losses is the key challenge industries are facing. Pressure from society and government legislation for reduced CO_2 emission are all trending towards more efficient power conversion and electrification.

Automotive electrification, telecom infrastructure, server storage and industrial automation using power electronics are the biggest trends in the technology sector. GaN field-effect transistors (FETs) can enable us to achieve the best efficiency with lower system costs while making the system lighter, smaller and cooler. Specifically, electrification in the automotive sector can be the biggest beneficiary of this new power GaN FET technology.

To make all-electric vehicles (xEVs) a real replacement for vehicles that have fossil-fuelled internal combustion engines, efficient power conversion is key. There are many challenges, such as range anxiety, harmful emissions, power losses, heat dissipation, cooling systems, system weight and power densities. On this journey, industry is working in many ways to address these major issues to reduce range anxiety and harmful emissions. These are integral parts to make the xEV platforms a commercial and social reality.

Application areas in which there is a drive for significant improvement include:

- Improved more efficient power conversion
    - AC-to-DC onboard charging
    - DC-to-DC power conversion
    - DC-to-AC inverter to drive the traction motors
    - Improved power density
    - Simpler driver and control scheme
- Improved traction motors
    - Improved efficiency
    - Better torque and power
    - Lower losses
    - Higher dV/dt handling
- Improved batteries, storage and battery management systems

Efficient power conversion helps significantly in many ways. An example is a 200 kW inverter with 95% efficiency versus 99% efficiency. A reduction in power loss in full load is from 10 to 2 kW, about one-fifth, which means a significant decrease of the cooling system. Not only that the loss is 8 kW lower (which can be effective for useful traction power), but the smaller cooling also can help with reducing the cooling energy consumption and on size and weight. Hence, a longer range or smaller battery can be achieved.

This highlights the importance of achieving very high efficiencies. Power GaN FETs based on GaN on Si epitaxy (epi) help significantly in this area, not only by offering higher efficiency but also the most desirable scalability for growth to support the xEV growth ambitions. The simple Si fabrication (fab) process steps also allow the best cost roadmap for commercial viability. Power GaN technology currently serves with 650 V products for 400 V battery voltage and can serve up to 800 V battery systems with up to 1,200 V power GaN devices. The power range can be up to 300 kW.

2 Power GaN FET switches

High-voltage (HV) power semiconductor switches are the fundamental building blocks of any power conversion. Si-based insulated-gate bipolar transistors (IGBTs) are currently dominating this market with significant maturity in the absence of any better alternatives. The improvement of Si IGBTs and combining them with silicon carbide (SiC) diodes helps to achieve incremental higher efficiencies, but has a limit on how much further improvement is possible. Si IGBTs are fundamentally limited in frequency of operations, speed and poor high-temperature performance along with poor low- current characteristics. Si super-junction (SJ) technology is dominating the power conversion at higher frequencies like AC-to-DC power factor correction (PFC) and DC-to-DC power conversion. To achieve higher efficiency, these devices are fundamentally limited to size and cost due to their inherent material limitation for high-frequency operation. These limitations can be summarised by switching crossover losses, conduction, and reverse recovery losses.

In contrast however, wide band-gap (WBG) materials like GaN and SiC, as summarized in Table 1 are free from reverse recovery loss and can offer very low switching cross-over losses (due to very fast turn on and off characteristics) and lower conduction losses. WBG materials with a higher critical electric field and higher mobility together give the lowest drain source on-state resistance ($R_{DS(on)}$) for higher voltages and a significantly better switching figure of merit. The WBG devices beginning to enter the market show significant promise and remove many of the limitations naturally imposed by Si IGBT and Si SJ devices. Some of the difficult switched-application topologies where Si SJ FETs cannot be used due to diode reverse recovery can easily use power GaN FETs and take full advantage of the reduced component counts and higher efficiency with simpler control schemes.

The faster switching speeds and higher frequencies of operation enabled by GaN power transistors help improve signal control, higher cutoff frequencies for passive filter designs, and lower ripple currents, allowing for smaller inductors, capacitors, and transformers. Consequently, the compact and smaller system solution offers cost savings.

Table 1. Material properties

Material	Band Gap (eV)	Critical Electric Field E_c (MV/cm)	Electron mobility μ_0 (cm^2/Vs)	Thermal conductivity (W/cmK)	Saturation velocity (cm/s)
GaN	3.4	3.5	2,000	1.3	2.5×10^7
SiC	3.3	2.2	950	3.7	2×10^7
Si	1.12	0.23	1,400	1.5	1×10^7

There are two main options for current power GaN FETs: enhancement mode (E-mode) or single die normally off devices and depletion mode (D-mode) or two-die normally off devices. The stability and leakage currents of the E-mode gates are of concern but the two-die normally off or cascade configuration currently offers peace of mind as driving these FETs is simple and robust. The E-mode device drive is complex, especially for HV, high-power applications. For these applications, to avoid gate bounce and harmful shoot-through situations, it is necessary to have a high gate threshold voltage and stable gate drive without worrying about overdrive,which currently is not achievable with existing E-mode technologies. For operations up to 1 MHz switching frequency, cascode GaN FETs are best suited, although current HV power-conversion frequencies are around only 300 kHz and traction inverter frequencies are still below 40 kHz. The GaN on Si two-die normally off configuration allows significant design flexibility. Nexperia GaN FET offers a ±20 V gate rating with an oxide/insulator gate, 4 V gate threshold voltage with 0 V turn off, and low gate charge. Hence, simple Si drivers are suitable for use with these devices and for 0 – 8, 10, or 12 V, any gate drive can be used. In contrast, the SiC technology generally requires at least 15 V, a very-high-current driver with a negative gate drive capability to turn off the device adds costs for the driver and increased driver and switching losses. Nexperia GaN also brings a very good anti-parallel diode built-in that helps with the robust freewheeling conduction path. The cascode version offers significant freedom to make the gate structure have the same robustness that automotive customers are used to. This is valid for both Si FET and the GaN high electron mobility transistor (HEMT) with insulated gates.

Figure 1 shows the cross-section for the GaN HEMT, which works with the formation of the 2D electron gas (2DEG) due to the spontaneous and piezoelectric polarization combined at the interface of GaN and Al_xGa1-_xN. GaN Epi is formed on the Si substrate via the seed layer and a graded layer of GaN and AlGaN layers before the pure GaN layer grows. A thin layer of AlGaN then forms the 2DEG. Electron mobility in this layer is very high, hence the name.

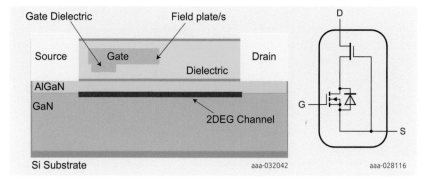

Figure 1 | GaN HEMT cross section

Figure 2 | GaN HEMT graphic symbol

Figure 2 shows how combining a low-voltage (LV; 30 V) robust Si MOSFET with the cascode configuration can eliminate all of the major concerns regarding the poor gate structures of the E- mode devices and make the entire usage very simple. An LV Si-based gate structure is a very mature technology and engineers are accustomed to using them.

The reverse recovery charge (Q_{rr}) for the cascode power GaN is very low as shown in Figure 3 and mostly capacitive and allows the full potential of the power GaN technology. Actual reverse recovery charge (Q_{rr}) for the LV Si FET used here is only ~12 nC. The E-mode device channel mobility is much lower compared to the channel mobility in a D-mode GaN HEMT channel.

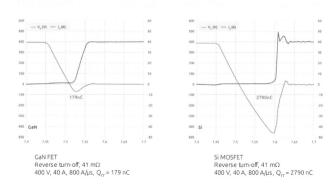

GaN FET
Reverse turn-off, 41 mΩ
400 V, 40 A, 800 A/µs, Q_{rr} = 179 nC

Si MOSFET
Reverse turn-off, 41 mΩ
400 V, 40 A, 800 A/µs, Q_{rr} = 2790 nC

Figure 3 | Q_{rr}, reverse recovery charges for GaN FET vs Si MOSFET

Power GaN technology: the need for efficient power conversion

Driving a cascode device is also very simple. Cascode device operation is shown in Figure 4 and Figure 5 for different bias situations. Power GaN FETs can be used in a bi-directional form and also allow simpler bi-directional power conversion.

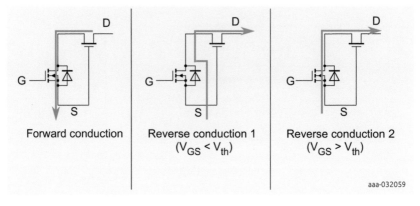

Forward conduction | Reverse conduction 1 $(V_{GS} < V_{th})$ | Reverse conduction 2 $(V_{GS} > V_{th})$

aaa-032059

Figure 4 | GaN FET operation

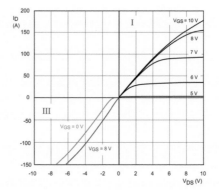

aaa-032043

Figure 5 | Cascode GaN HEMFET forward and reverse output characteristics

Since power GaN transistors were introduced to the market, significant improvements in performance, reliability, cost, and availability have taken place. More capable GaN power transistors are becoming available to drive higher power to be compatible with the EV requirements while being well positioned for applications in data centres, telecom infrastructures and industrial.

3 Scalability and growth

Si wafers are widely available in different sizes. GaN on Si wafers allow us to use 150 mm, 200 mm metal organic chemical vapor deposition (MOCVD) reactors for epi growth and can be processed in mature silicon semiconductor fabs. There are lots of Silicon fab capacity that can be utilised. Processing is similar to standard Si processing, which is not so complex. Tremendous growth potential is better addressed with power GaN technology on Si at a right cost point.

4 Applications and performance

Whether it is AC-to-DC PFC stage, a DC-to-DC converter Figure 6 or traction inverter Figure 7 the basic building block for most topologies is a half-bridge (Figure 9). Hence when GaN FETs are compared against Si FETs in a simple boost converter, GaN FET shows its superior performance due to the differences in material properties (Figure 8). All of these applications can take advantage of these benefits and hence reduce losses. The advantages of power GAN FETs compared to Si IGBTs come from the light load, high temperatures and higher frequencies when the losses are very high.

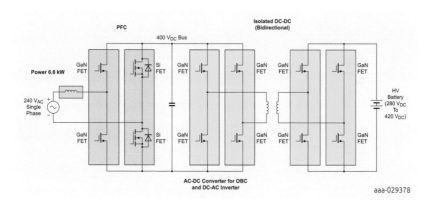

Figure 6 | AC-to-DC PFC stage and isolated DC-DC configuration

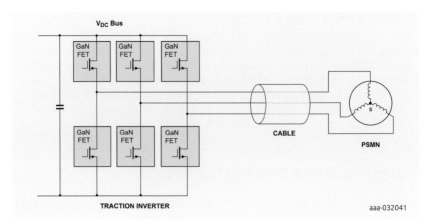

Figure 7 | Traction inverter

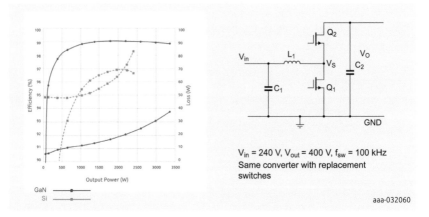

V_{in} = 240 V, V_{out} = 400 V, f_{sw} = 100 kHz
Same converter with replacement
switches

Figure 8 | Half-bridge boost converter
(GaN switch vs Si CoolMOS)

Figure 9 | Half-bridge boost converter

GaN FET losses are significantly lower due to the absence of reverse recovery losses and switching crossover losses. It is possible to achieve near ideal turn on and off losses with dV/dt of approximately 200 V/ns.

GaN switches are extremely fast and routinely used in radio-frequency amplifiers at gigahertz frequencies, although at much lower voltages but show the capability as both use the GaN HEMT structure. Since the GaN devices are very fast and can be used in applications with high dV/dt and high dI/dt, care must be taken to optimize the PCB layouts. To minimize parasitic inductances layout optimization is absolutely fundamental to Power GaN usage. To maximize the performance of surface-mount packages and low inductance, high-current, high-performance modules are essential and being worked on. Currently, using GaN devices in a traction inverter means slowing it down significantly to save the motor windings. They are nearly limited to a dV/dt of 10 V/ns, which holds significant potential to improve the motors and take the frequency up to 40 kHz to improve the power density significantly. The development of new electric motor technology with improved ability is on the way to make the system more efficient.

5 Quality and reliability

Power GaN FET technology currently showing good quality and reliability as multiple vendors demonstrated Joint Electron Device Engineering Council (JEDEC) and Automotive Electronics Council (AEC) Q101 quality standards. To demonstrate the reliability of power GaN technology, these are minimums and must be fulfilled. For GaN, only the existing quality standards are not enough as the material is new and operates differently. Dynamic $R_{DS(on)}$ or current collapse phenomena is well known for power GaN FETs and this method for testing is introduced and devices are verified. Material quality, trapping and appropriate de-trapping that is responsible for the dynamic $R_{DS(on)}$ can be measured and given high-level confidence for its usage as the values getting better and are now around 10%. We need to continuously look at the different failure modes and take the devices to failure and understand the physics of failure.

Beyond AEC-Q101 qualifications, for validating the GaN FETs' reliability in actual operating conditions, several identical half-bridge circuits (with continuous current conduction mode) were prepared using one high and one low side GAN063-650WSA. These were operated continuously for 1000 hours as synchronous-boost converters with the conditions: $V_{in} = 200$ V, $V_{out} = 480$ V, $P_{out} = 800$ W, $T_j = 175$ °C and frequency = 300 KHz. There is no indication of any degradation in the performance of any circuits for all samples for the whole duration of 1000 hours of test.

Following the high temperature switching tests, all devices were tested for shifts in dynamic $R_{DS(on)}$, leakage current, and threshold voltage. All parameters were found to be stable, with any parametric shifts below the allowed levels.

The device specification has 800 V transient voltage capability guaranteed by test to eliminate any concerns for over voltage spikes Similarly many other over stresses like voltage and temperatures are used and different acceleration factors are defined for end of life and Failure in Time (FIT) rates estimated for the application situations. As the volume of products shipped increases, real field failure rates will be determined.

Power GaN technology is ready to take its place for efficient power conversion. We are beginning to see its adoption in the non-auto segments and soon it will be used in automotive applications which can take advantage of lower losses and higher power densities. Si technology is well established in the market but reaching its limit. Power GaN technology will be the norm in the future as fear of unknown is reduced going forward.

6 References

1. AN90005 - Understanding Power GaN FET data sheet parameters

2. AN90006 - Circuit design and PCB layout recommendations for GaN FET half-bridges

7 Tables

8 Figures

Chapter 21

Circuit design and PCB layout recommendations for GaN FET half bridges

Application Note: AN90006

1 Introduction - Diode-free bridges

This chapter explains the recommendations for circuit design and PCB layout when applying GaN FET half bridges.

Power GaN FETs are nearly ideal switches for many applications. A particular advantage in bridge circuits is that they can carry the freewheeling current without the need of an additional anti-parallel diode. The diagrams in Figure 1 compare a traditional high-voltage half bridge to a half bridge made with GaN FET devices. In the traditional half bridge each switch (shown here as an IGBT) is paired with a freewheeling diode. Because the HEMT channel exists in pure, undoped GaN, there is no parasitic p-n junction to provide an unwanted current path, and bidirectional flow of majority carriers can be realized in the channel.

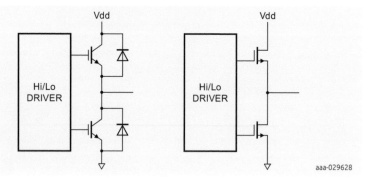

aaa-029628

Figure 1 | Comparison of a traditional high-voltage half bridge to a GaN FET half bridge.

In Nexperia's two-die GaN FET the freewheeling current does indeed flow in the body diode of a silicon MOSFET, but because the silicon MOSFET is a low voltage part, the injected charge is very small. Indicated in Figure 2 are the current paths for three modes of operation. In the reverse conducting mode the conduction loss may be reduced by enhancing the silicon MOSFET (driving $V_{GS} > V_{GS(th)}$). As indicated in Figure 2, the voltage drop from source to drain decreases by about 0.8 V with a 5 A reverse current when the gate is enhanced.

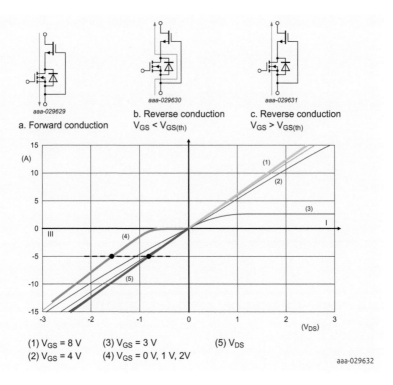

aaa-029629

a. Forward conduction

aaa-029630

b. Reverse conduction
$V_{GS} < V_{GS(th)}$

aaa-029631

c. Reverse conduction
$V_{GS} > V_{GS(th)}$

(1) V_{GS} = 8 V   (3) V_{GS} = 3 V   (5) V_{DS}
(2) V_{GS} = 4 V   (4) V_{GS} = 0 V, 1 V, 2V

aaa-029632

Figure 2 | Current paths in the GaN FET switch for three operating modes, and the corresponding I-V characteristic.

Some transistor technologies include junctions which could, if permitted, serve the function of the freewheeling diode, the body diode of a MOSFET being one example. The reverse recovery charge for these devices will be much larger than for a GaN FET with similar ratings. The graphs shown in Figure 3 compare the total reverse-recovery charge for a Nexperia GaN FET to a low-Q_{rr} (CFD series) superjunction silicon MOSFET. The Q_{rr} ratio, Si/GaN, varies with exact part numbers.

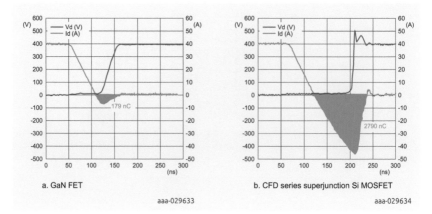

a. GaN FET

aaa-029633

b. CFD series superjunction Si MOSFET

aaa-029634

Figure 3 | Reverse recovery charge test result for a GaN FET (left) and a CFD series superjunction Si MOSFET (right).

2 Circuit-design recommendations

The high switching speed of GaN FET devices necessitates observation of a few specific circuit-design guidelines. Before explaining these requirements, however, one simplification may be mentioned: negative gate drive is neither necessary nor recommended. Due to the high threshold voltage (V_{th} = 4 V typical) and extremely low Miller capacitance (Q_{GD} = 6 nC typical), there is adequate turn-off margin with a simple 0 V to 10-12 V drive.

While high-speed switching brings the benefit of reduced power loss, the inherent transients can create stability problems. Specifically, the high $\frac{di}{dt}$ transient during switching, combined with parasitic inductances, leads to transient voltages in the circuit. These voltage transients can interfere with the gate and the driver of the device, and, in the worst case, creates sustained oscillation that must be prevented for safe operation of the circuit. The following section provides guidance on how to eliminate oscillation and how to achieve high switching current with a controlled $\frac{di}{dt}$.

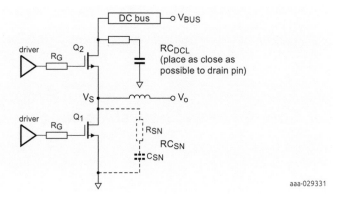

Figure 4 | Half-bridge switching circuit

2.1 Solutions to suppress oscillation

To avoid sustained oscillation, it is important to minimize noise generation, to minimize noise feedback, and to damp the ringing energy resulting from the high current and voltage transients. This can be achieved with the recommendations outlined below using a half-bridge switching circuit in Figure 4 as an example.

1. Optimize the PCB layout to minimize external parasitic inductances and associated feedback. Details follow in Section 3 of this chapter.

2. Use a DC-link RC snubber [RC_{DCL} in Figure 4]. The DC rail or DC-link, when decoupled with a low-ESR fast capacitor, can be considered a high-Q C-L network at high frequencies (with "L" being the feed inductance of the DC bus). This can interact with the devices during transients and lead to ringing. Adding an RC snubber across the DC-link close to the drain pin of the high- side device can effectively absorb the ringing energy, suppressing potential oscillation. This effect can be seen where the high-frequency ringing at 25 A turn-off is substantially damped with the RC_{DCL}. Since this snubber is not inserted at the switching node, it does not add switching loss to the circuit.

   Note: This is recommended even for single-ended non-half-bridge designs. The practical values of the RC_{DCL} can be two sets of 6 - 10 Ω / 0.5 W SMD resistors in series with a 10 nF / 600 - 1000 V ceramic SMD capacitor, or one 3 - 4 Ω / 1 W resistors in series with a 10 - 20 nF / 600 - 1000 V capacitor if space is limited.

3. Adding a switching-node RC snubber [RCSN in Figure 4] can further reduce high-frequency ringing and help control $\frac{di}{dt}$ transients at high operating

currents. The effect of the RC_{SN} on the switching waveform can be seen at a switching current > I_{SWL}, see Table 1. Unlike the RC_{DCL}, the capacitance of the RC_{SN} does increase switching loss. The degradation in efficiency is minimal however, when using the recommended snubber parameters given in the data sheet, and summarized in Table 1.

2.2 Gate drive and bootstrap supply

Since high slew rates of the order of 50 - 100 V/ns are normal, the high-side gate-driver must have good common-mode transient immunity. Apart from that consideration, there are no special requirements for the Hi/Lo gate driver used with Nexperia's GaN FET switches. As with any insulated-gate power transistor, the gate-drive current should be consistent with the desired turn-on time and total gate charge. As mentioned in the opening paragraph of Section 2, use of a negative gate voltage in the off state is not recommended. Selecting a gate driver with a lower drive current can be appropriate for reducing $\frac{di}{dt}$. Drivers with 0.5 A output current have been used with good results, for example. Nexperia GaN FETs in the TO-247 package include an integrated ferrite bead in series with the gate.

The bootstrap, or floating, supply for the high-side gate drive comprises components R4, D1, C12, and C13 in Figure 8. The junction capacitance of D1 contributes directly to switching loss, and so a fast, low capacitance diode should be used. Resistor R4 is critical for limiting the inrush charging current; a value of 10 - 15 Ω works well. If an isolated DC-DC converter is used for the high-side supply, the isolation capacitance plays the same role as the junction capacitance of D1 in the bootstrap supply. Inductance in series with this capacitance will create an additional resonance which will be excited with each switching transient, so careful layout applies here. Use of a common-mode choke in the floating supply can be helpful.

2.3 Summary of circuit-design recommendations

- SMD mounting is recommended for all snubber components.
- A gate resistor (RG) is required for all devices.
- The RC_{DCL} snubber reduces voltage ringing due to interaction of the GaN FET with the bypass network.
- The RC_{SN} snubber enables increased output power while slightly reducing light and medium load efficiency.
- The RC_{SN} implementation in a half-bridge has the advantage of allowing a higher peak turn-off switching current due to the reduction of the $\frac{di}{dt}$ seen by the freewheeling device as the main active switch turns off.

- Gate ferrite beads (FB1) may be required for future devices in other package types; TO-247 devices have built-in ferrite beads hence no external FB1 is needed.
- Refer to Nexperia Application Note AN90005 (chapter 18 in this book) - Understanding Power GaN FET data sheet parameters for an explanation of data-sheet limitations and relevant recommendations for when to use a switching-node snubber.

2.4 Required and recommended external components

The recommended components of the half-bridge circuit in Figure 4 are summarized in Table 1.

They have been tested and verified to prevent oscillation for safe, reliable operation with the recommended gate drive voltage ranges shown. Using a higher "on" voltage is not recommended and may increase the propensity for oscillation and will require a larger gate resistor. Using a lower "on" voltage may increase switching and conduction losses due to increased $R_{DS(on)}$.

Table 1. Recommended components for half-bridge circuit

Parameters \ Part Number	GaN041-650WSA	GaN063-650WSA
Package	TO-247	TO-247
Recommended Gate-Drive Voltage	0 V, 10 - 12 V	0 V, 10 - 12 V
Recommended Gate Resistor (R_g)	30 Ω	30 - 45 Ω
Gate Ferrite Bead (FB1)	Not required	Not required
Recommended RC_{SN}	200 pF + 5 Ω	100 pF + 10 Ω
Recommended RC_{DCL}	(10 nF + 8 Ω) x 2	(10 nF + 8 Ω) x 2
ISWL	17 A	14 A

2.5 To verify GaN FET stable operation

To verify adequate operational margin without oscillation, as a minimum observe the V_{DS} waveforms at the turn-on and turn-off switching edges at the application's maximum drain current. This may occur during start-up or at the application's maximum load step. A double-pulse or multi-pulse test is highly recommended utilizing the actual layout, with current levels at or greater than 120 % of the application's anticipated peak current. Verify that the ringing on the V_{DS} waveform at the transition edges is adequately damped.

3 PCB layout

The parasitic inductances of the input (gate) and output (power) loops contribute significantly to overshoot, ringing, and stability in general.

3.1 Pin assignment

Nexperia GaN FETs in the TO-247 package use a Gate-Source-Drain pin assignment, which differs from that used for older transistors in the same package. The reason for centering the source rather than the drain is that the source is the common node to both gate and power loops. This minimizes coupling of the two loops, as illustrated in Figure 5.

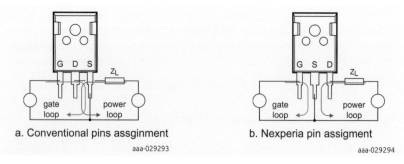

a. Conventional pins assgnment

aaa-029293

b. Nexperia pin assigment

aaa-029294

Figure 5 | Illustration of the de-coupling achieved with a centered-source pin assignment

3.2 Power loop

Although the various charges are low with GaN FET switches, they are not zero, and there will be a very fast transient current during switching as these charges are redistributed. This current will flow from the positive supply node, through both transistors to the negative supply node. To minimize ringing due to this transient, inductances in this path should be minimized. Referring to Figure 6, these inductances are indicated as LS1, LD1, LS2, and LD2. To minimize these, low impedance power and ground traces, or planes, should be used and bypass capacitance and DC-link snubber should be placed as close as possible to the transistors. It is not critical to minimize inductance L_{out} since it is in series with the load inductance, and to a first approximation simply adds to it. The connection between the high-side (Q1) source pin and the low-side (Q2) drain pin should also be very short. Placing the two transistors back-to-back on a common heat sink helps accomplish this. Shown in Figure 7 to Figure 10, is a portion of the layout of a Nexperia half-bridge evaluation board, indicating the placement of the power transistors

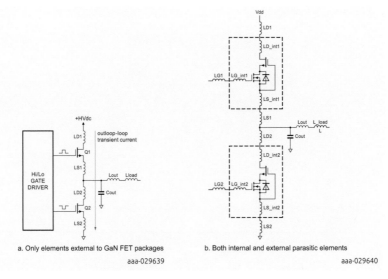

a. Only elements external to GaN FET packages

aaa-029639

b. Both internal and external parasitic elements

aaa-029640

Figure 6 | Parasitic elements in the power loop

Details of the power loop layout are highlighted in Figure 9. To minimize inductance, the drain of Q1 is connected directly to the power plane; the source of Q2 is connected directly to the ground plane.

The power and ground planes are on internal layers of the PCB, not visible in the figure. The switching node is formed by the wide trace connecting the source of Q1 to the drain of Q2.

Circuit design and PCB layout recommendations for GaN FET half bridges

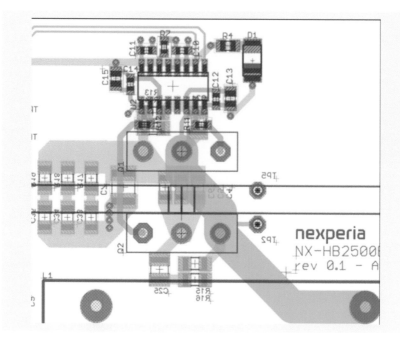

Figure 7 | PCB layout - Power-stage

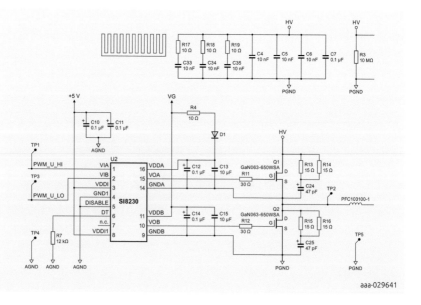

aaa-029641

Figure 8 | PCB layout - Corresponding schematic section

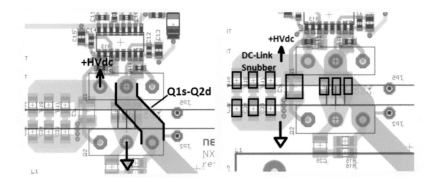

Figure 9 | PCB layout - Detail of power connections   Figure 10 | PCB layout - Detail of bypassing: SMD capacitors on PCB backside

Illustrated in Figure 11 is an alternative placement where the GaN FETs are side-by-side, rather than back-to-back, as in Figure 7 to Figure 10. Inductances are higher with this arrangement, but it is sometimes preferable for manufacturing reasons.

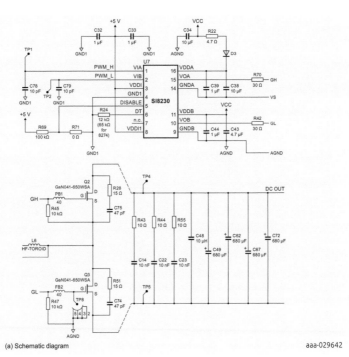

(a) Schematic diagram

aaa-029642

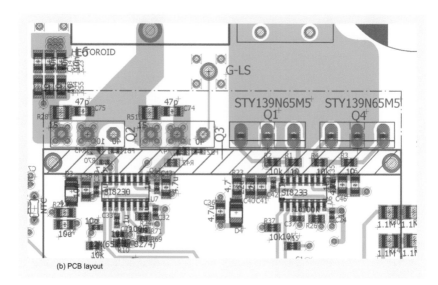

(b) PCB layout

Figure 11 | Totem pole PFC PCB

Capacitance on the switching node, indicated as C_{out} in Figure 6, adds directly to switching loss, and so the total area of copper which forms the switching node should be kept low, but not so low that inductance becomes significant. A typical 4-layer board with 12 mils (0.3 mm) between outer trace and internal ground plane adds about 15 pF / cm². At 100 kHz switching, each 1 cm² would add $P = 1/2\ CV^2\ f_s = 120$ mW switching loss, for example.

4 Heat Sink connection

The heat sink should be connected to an AC ground. In the evaluation board of Figure 7 to Figure 10 the heat sink is electrically connected to the negative supply, or ground plane. Both low-side and high-side transistors are insulated from the heat sink. For the low-side transistor the capacitance between tab and heat sink is not critical, since the tab of the TO-247 is connected to the source. This transistor could be mounted directly to the heat sink, but the possibility that load current could flow in the heat sink must be allowed for. If a reliable connection between tab and heat sink is either not possible or not desirable, use of an insulator is necessary. For the high-side transistor, capacitance between the TO-247 mounting base and the heat sink will add to switching loss, and so a thick and/or low permittivity insulator should be used.

4.1 Gate-drive loop

As with the output loop, minimizing inductance in the input, or gate-drive loop is critical. Particularly important is the source inductance (LS2 in Figure 6, for example), which is common to both loops.

Any voltage developed across this inductance due to a change in the output current, $\frac{diD}{dt}$, will appear in the input loop. The gate–source loop should be made as compact as possible to minimise the gate loop inductance. The gate-source loop inductance and GaN FET input capacitance form a resonant tank and will have a corresponding resonant frequency. The resonant circuit will be excited into oscillation by the back EMF produced by the $\frac{di}{dt}$ in the source inductance. Figure 12 Usually the resonant frequency of the gate-source loop will be less than 200 MHz. A ferrite bead fitted in series with the gate can have a beneficial effect by "de-Qing" the gate-source resonant circuit. For this reason, a small ferrite bead is integrated inside the TO-247 package.

For future Nexperia GaN FETs where it is not integrated, the ferrite bead should be located as close as possible to the gate pin of the GaN FET so that the damping is applied to the device gate where it is needed. A gate ferrite bead is needed for both single-ended non half-bridges as well as half-bridge designs.

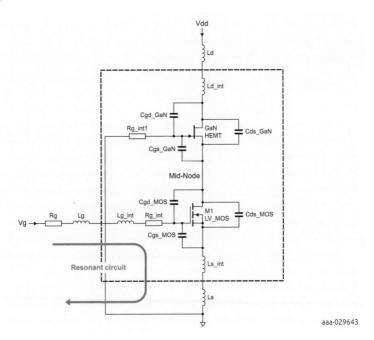

Figure 12 | Input loop for a cascode GaN FET

aaa-029643

4.2 Summary of PCB layout recommendations

- Place the RC$_{DCL}$ as close as possible to the drain pin of the high-side GaN FET and ground it to the large ground plane.
- Use a large area ground plane for an overall low-noise base potential.
- Arrange the gate drive circuit on one side and the output circuit on the other side of the PCB to minimize noise feedback from the output loop to the input loop.
- Place the driver circuit close to the gate of the device.
- Shorten the power loop by arranging the high-side and low-side devices close-by.

Nexperia copper-clip
SMD CCPAK GaN FET
package in half-bridge
evaluation board

5 Tables

Circuit design and PCB layout recommendations for GaN FET half bridges

6 Figures

Chapter 22

Probing considerations for fast switching applications

Application Note: AN90004

Probing considerations for fast switching applications

1 Introduction

Accurate voltage waveform measurements of fast switching circuits require special care and attention in the use of the oscilloscope probe. This chapter details the use of a probe ground spring to achieve the best results.

The latest GaN FET devices from Nexperia are capable of very fast switching of high voltages and currents. This requires special care to be taken in the measurement of the switching waveforms.

In order to accurately measure voltages on fast switching nodes, best measurement practices should be followed. It should be noted that unless efforts are made to follow best practice as closely as possible, then the voltages seen on the oscilloscope may be an artefact of the measurement rather than a true representation of the real voltage on the node.

An example of a fast switching waveform is shown in Figure 1 below. Note the difference between measurements results with a) the oscilloscope probe ground connection made using a standard probe ground wire and b) the same measurement with the ground connection made using a probe ground spring.

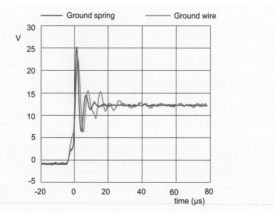

Figure 1 | Switching waveform; probe grounding method comparison

2 Oscilloscope probe ground spring

The ground lead length of the oscilloscope probe can have a very detrimental effect on the measurements taken. If you use the standard 10 cm loop supplied with the scope probe, the measurements that you make will be prone to noise and pickup, as the loop acts as an aerial and picks up noise in proportion to the loop area.

In order to make switching node measurements that are less prone to noise and pickup, the following type of oscilloscope probe connections should be made:

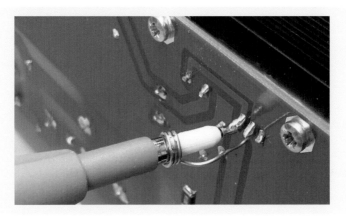

Figure 2 | Probing a fast switching node

Note that the oscilloscope probe ground connection is made via a test probe ground spring, see Figure 3. It is important that the ground wire is kept in parallel with the probe tip and the loop area is kept to an absolute minimum.

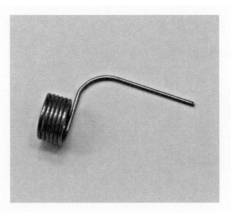

Figure 3 | Probe ground spring

These oscilloscope probe accessories are available from electronic test equipment distributors and retailers - e.g. Mouser Electronics Part No: 940-PK1-5MM-118 (Mfr. Part No: PK1-5MM-118).

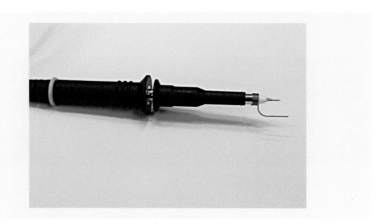

Figure 4 | Oscilloscope probe with ground spring attached

It is possible to make your own probe ground spring using TCW25 tinned copper wire, see (Figure 2). Form the spring around the probe, remove and apply a little flux and solder to hold it in place. Trim the ends and use appropriately.

3 Oscilloscope and probes

When measuring fast switching nodes always use a high-quality oscilloscope that does not introduce unwanted parasitic capacitance, especially in the sensing loop.

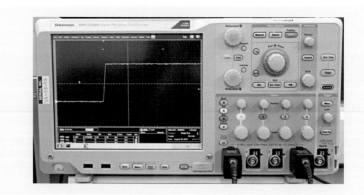

Figure 5 | Typical oscilloscope used in a Nexperia measurement lab

To make accurate measurements, the best quality scope probes should be used. These should have high input impedance: preferably 100 MΩ or greater, and very low capacitance: less than 4 pF. Also, the greatest bandwidth scope probes should be used in line with the switching edges that are being measured.

The impedance and capacitance of the scope probe can have an effect on the voltage that is being measured. By using high input impedance and very low capacitance the effect of the probe on the node being measured is minimised.

Always check that the oscilloscope probe you are using has the correct maximum voltage rating for the signal being measured. Do not exceed the manufacturer's recommendations - voltages close to a probe's maximum rating should be avoided.

Detailed information about probes and advice on measurement best practice is often available from probe manufacturers. As an example, Tektronix publish a comprehensive guide - ABCs of Probes Primer, (http://info.tek.com/www-abcs-of-probes-primer.html).

4 Probe positioner

When measuring high voltages extreme caution should be taken and best practices adhered to.

With this in mind, the use of a probe positioner is highly recommended. The oscilloscope probes can be adjusted to make contact with the required measurement points, leaving the test setup to be operated "hands free".

The following probe positioner is recommended: Type : MSA100 3D PROBE POSITIONER Farnell part number 1552771.

Figure 6 | Probe positioner

Probing considerations for fast switching applications

Figures

Abbreviations

Abbreviations

2DEG	2-Dimensional Electron Gas
AC	Alternating current
AEC-Q101	Automotive Electronics Council Quality System
AN	Application Note
BJT	Bipolar Junction Transistor
BW	Bandwidth
C	Capacitor
C_{add}	Additional external capacitance fitted drain to source
C_{GD}	Gate-drain capacitance
C_{GS}	Gate-source capacitance
Ci	Constituent thermal capacitance element
CISPR	International Special Committee on Radio Interference
C_{ISS}	Input capacitance
C_{LK}	Parasitic capacitance
C_{OSS}	Output capacitance
C_p	Specific heat capacity
CSP	Chip Scale Package
C_{th}	Thermal capacitance
DC	Direct current
de-Q	Reduce the quality factor of a resonance; damp
dIs/dt	Time rate of change of source current
DUT	Device Under Test
$E_{DS(AL)R}$	Non-repetitive drain-source avalanche energy
EMC	Electro-magnetic compatibility
EMI	Electro-magnetic interference
E_{OS}	Electrical Overstress
E_{oss}	Energy stored on output capacitance
E_{OX}	Oxide electric field strength
ESD	ElectroStatic Discharge
ESL	Equivalent series inductance
ESR	Equivalent series resistance
FET	Field Effect Transistor
FIT	Failure In Time
FR4	Flame Retardant epoxy glass laminate (see NEMA LI 1-1998)
F_{RING}	Oscillation (ringing) frequency
GaN	Gallium Nitride
HEMT	High Electron Mobility Transistor
HS	High side MOSFET
I/O	Input/Output
I^2C-bus	Inter-Integrated Circuit bus
I_D	MOSFET drain current

I_{DM}	Pulsed drain current
$I_{DS(AL)S}$	Non-repetitive drainsource avalanche current
I_{DSS}	Drain current source shorted (drain leakage current)
IEC	International Electrotechnical Commission
I_{GSS}	Gate current source shorted (gate leakage current)
IPC	Institute of Printed Circuits
I_S	Source current
I_{SM}	Peak source current
JEDEC	Joint Electron Device Engineering Council
KGD	Known Good Die
L	Inductor
LFPAK	Loss Free Package (Nexperia package naming)
L_{LK}	Stray (leakage) inductance
LS	Low side MOSFET
LV	Low Voltage
MOSFET	Metal-Oxide Semiconductor Field-Effect Transistor
NTC	Negative Temperature Coefficient
OEM	Original Equipment Manufacturer
$P_{(t)}$	Power as a function of time
PCB	Printed Circuit Board
PSMN	Power Silicon Max N-Channel
PTC	Positive Temperature Coefficient
P_{tot}	Maximum continuous power the device can dissipate with the mounting base held continuously at 25 °C
PWM	Pulse Width Modulation
Q_G	Gate Charge
Q_{GD}	Gate-Drain Charge
Q_{OSS}	Charge stored in the output capacitance
R	Resistor
$R_{BDD(on)}$	On-state bulk-drain-drain resistance
$R_{BDS(on)}$	On-state bulk-drain-source resistance
RC	Resistor-Capacitor
RCDCL	DC Link RC snubber
RCSN	Switching Node RC snubber
$R_{DS(on)}$	Drain-source on-state resistance
RG(ext)	Gate resistance external to the package
R_i	Constituent thermal resistance element
RL	Load resistance
RPP	Reverse polarity protection
$R_{SS(on)}$	On-state source-source resistance
R_{th}	Thermal resistance
$R_{th(j-amb)}$ / $R_{th(j-a)}$	Thermal resitance (junction to ambient)

$R_{th(j-mb)}$	Thermal resistance (junction to mounting base)
SN	Switch node
SOA	Safe Operating Area
SPICE	Simulation Program with Integrated Circuit Emphasis
T	Total time of heating pulse
τ	RC time constant
T_{amb}	Ambient temperature
T_c	Case temperature (plastic housing)
TDDB	Time Dependant Dielectric Breakdown
τ_i	Thermal time constant
T_j	Junction temperature
$T_{j(rise)}$	Junction temperature rise in the MOSFET
T_{mb}	Mounting base temperature of the MOSFET
T_{OX}	Oxide thickness
tp	Pulse width, pulse duration
T_s	Surface temperature
T_{stg}	Storage Temperature
UIS	Unclamped Inductive Switching
V_{BR}	Breakdown voltage
V_D	Drain to ground voltage
V_{DD}	Application supply voltage
V_{DGR}	Gate-source voltage
V_{drop}	Voltage drop
V_{DS}	Drain-source voltage
V_G	Gate to ground voltage
V_{GS}	Gate-source voltage
$V_{GS(th)}$	Gate-source threshold voltage
V_{in}	Input voltage
V_S	Source to ground voltage
WLCSP	Wafer Level Chip Scale Package
ZTC	Zero temperature coefficient
$Z_{th(j-mb)}$	Thermal impedance (junction to mounting base)
$Z_{th(t)}$	Transient thermal impedance
δ_{factor}	Duty factor, duty cycle
ΔT	Change in temperature
ΔT_j	Average temperature rise from average
$\Delta T_{j(max)}$	Maximum junction temperature variation
ΔT_{on}	On-state temperature difference
ζ	Zeta, damping factor

Index

Index

Page numbers in **bold** denote tables, *italics* denote figures, and those <u>underlined</u> denote QR code links.

Page numbers in **bold** denote tables, *italics* denote figures, and those <u>underlined</u> denote QR code links.

Page numbers in **bold** denote tables, *italics* denote figures, and those <u>underlined</u> denote QR code links.

Page numbers in **bold** denote tables, *italics* denote figures, and those <u>underlined</u> denote QR code links.

Page numbers in **bold** denote tables, *italics* denote figures, and those <u>underlined</u> denote QR code links.

Page numbers in **bold** denote tables, *italics* denote figures, and those <u>underlined</u> denote QR code links.

Page numbers in **bold** denote tables, *italics* denote figures, and those <u>underlined</u> denote QR code links.

Page numbers in **bold** denote tables, *italics* denote figures, and those <u>underlined</u> denote QR code links.

Index

Page numbers in **bold** denote tables, *italics* denote figures, and those <u>underlined</u> denote QR code links.

Page numbers in **bold** denote tables, *italics* denote figures, and those <u>underlined</u> denote QR code links.

Page numbers in **bold** denote tables, *italics* denote figures, and those <u>underlined</u> denote QR code links.

Page numbers in **bold** denote tables, *italics* denote figures, and those <u>underlined</u> denote QR code links.

Page numbers in **bold** denote tables, *italics* denote figures, and those <u>underlined</u> denote QR code links.

Page numbers in **bold** denote tables, *italics* denote figures, and those <u>underlined</u> denote QR code links.

Page numbers in **bold** denote tables, *italics* denote figures, and those <u>underlined</u> denote QR code links.

Page numbers in **bold** denote tables, *italics* denote figures, and those <u>underlined</u> denote QR code links.

Page numbers in **bold** denote tables, *italics* denote figures, and those <u>underlined</u> denote QR code links.

Page numbers in **bold** denote tables, *italics* denote figures, and those <u>underlined</u> denote QR code links.

Legal information

Definitions

Draft — The document is a draft version only. The content is still under internal review and subject to formal approval, which may result in modifications or additions. Nexperia does not give any representations or warranties as to the accuracy or completeness of information included herein and shall have no liability for the consequences of use of such information.

Disclaimers

Limited warranty and liability — Information in this document is believed to be accurate and reliable. However, Nexperia does not give any representations or warranties, expressed or implied, as to the accuracy or completeness of such information and shall have no liability for the consequences of use of such information. Nexperia takes no responsibility for the content in this document if provided by an information source outside of Nexperia.

In no event shall Nexperia be liable for any indirect, incidental, punitive, special or consequential damages (including - without limitation - lost profits, lost savings, business interruption, costs related to the removal or replacement of any products or rework charges) whether or not such damages are based on tort (including negligence), warranty, breach of contract or any other legal theory.

Notwithstanding any damages that customer might incur for any reason whatsoever, Nexperia's aggregate and cumulative liability towards customer for the products described herein shall be limited in accordance with the Terms and conditions of commercial sale of Nexperia.

Right to make changes — Nexperia reserves the right to make changes to information published in this document, including without limitation specifications and product descriptions, at any time and without notice. This document supersedes and replaces all information supplied prior to the publication hereof.

Suitability for use — Nexperia products are not designed, authorized or warranted to be suitable for use in life support, life-critical or safety-critical systems or equipment, nor in applications where failure or malfunction of an Nexperia product can reasonably be expected to result in personal injury, death or severe property or environmental damage. Nexperia and its suppliers accept no liability for inclusion and/or use of Nexperia products in such equipment or applications and therefore such inclusion and/or use is at the customer's own risk.

Applications — Applications that are described herein for any of these products are for illustrative purposes only. Nexperia makes no representation or warranty that such applications will be suitable for the specified use without further testing or modification.

Customers are responsible for the design and operation of their applications and products using Nexperia products, and Nexperia accepts no liability for any assistance with applications or customer product design. It is customer's sole responsibility to determine whether the Nexperia product is suitable and fit for the customer's applications and products planned, as well as for the planned application and use of customer's third party customer(s). Customers should provide appropriate design and operating safeguards to minimize the risks associated with their applications and products.

Nexperia does not accept any liability related to any default, damage, costs or problem which is based on any weakness or default in the customer's applications or products, or the application or use by customer's third party customer(s). Customer is responsible for doing all necessary testing for the customer's applications and products using Nexperia products in order to avoid a default of the applications and the products or of the application or use by customer's third party customer(s). Nexperia does not accept any liability in this respect.

Export control — This document as well as the item(s) described herein may be subject to export control regulations. Export might require a prior authorization from competent authorities.

Translations — A non-English (translated) version of a document is for reference only. The English version shall prevail in case of any discrepancy between the translated and English versions.

Trademarks

Notice: All referenced brands, product names, service names and trademarks are the property of their respective owners.